CERTIFICATE PHYSICAL AND HUMAN GEOGRAPHY

Goh Cheng Leong

B. A. (Hons.), Lond., F.R.G.S.

Second Edition

OXFORD
UNIVERSITY PRESS

OXFORD
UNIVERSITY PRESS

Oxford University Press is a department of the University of Oxford. It furthers the University's objective of excellence in research, scholarship, and education by publishing worldwide. Oxford is a registered trade mark of Oxford University Press in the UK and in certain other countries.

Published in India by
Oxford University Press
22 Workspace, 2nd Floor, 1/22 Asaf Ali Road, New Delhi 110002

The moral rights of the author/s have been asserted.

First Edition published 1974
Second Edition published 2024

ISBN-13: 978-93-5497-566-0
ISBN-10: 93-5497-566-6

Typeset in ITC Franklin Gothic Std Book and Cronos Pro
by B2K-BYTES 2 KNOWLEDGE, Tamil Nadu
Printed in India by Nutech Print Services India

Acknowledgements

The author and publishers are grateful to the following for permission to reproduce copyright photographs: G.C. Morgan (p17: Minor faulting in sedimentary rocks of the Kenny Hill Series; p32: When corestones are exposed to tropical weather conditions they are subject to repeated wetting and drying which cause the outer layers to peel off), and Swiss National Tourist Office (p51: A glacial landscape in Switzerland).

Acknowledgements are credited with their respective reproductions in the book. Every effort has been made to contact the holders of copyright to the reproductions, but in some cases without success. To these, the author and publishers offer their apologies, trusting that they will accept the will for the deed.

The publisher would also like to thank the following for permission to use photographs and other copyright material:

Getty images:

p5: Earth viewed from the moon: Heritage Images; **p26:** Sunrise over Mayon Volcano and Legazpi City: Quynh Anh Nguyen; **p117:** Typhoon Haiyan in the South China Sea approaching Vietnam: Stocktrek Images; **p124:** Kinabalu mountain massif in a morning sunrise, Boneo Island, Malaysia: Punnawit Suwuttananun; **p168:** Large-scale fabric spool used in an Indian factory to assist in the meticulous process of dyeing textiles: xavierarnau

Shutterstock images:

p15: Prehistoric limestone range rings Kuala Lumpur: Gwoeii; **p23:** Phillippines Mt. Mayon Eruption 2018: Gabriel Alagaban Jr; **p29:** Banda Aceh, Aceh, Indonesia – December 31, 2004: Frans Delian; **p31:** Corestones created by spheroidal weathering, Kazakhstan: Moehring; **p34:** View of the after effects of extreme landslides and flood, Pahang: hudzaqwan; **p35:** Engineering protection from landslides: Nordroden; Large boulders tied with wire mesh to prevent landslides: MTPk MAX; **p36:** Aerial view of flooding in Penampang town: Yusnizam Yusof; **p42:** Passage of famous Samaria Gorge, Crete, Greece: proslgn; **p44:** Spring sunrise along the Arda river, Bulgaria: Flaviya; **p52:** Landscape of Zermatt: Florist Kuniko; **p54:** A drumlin field: YueStock; **p58:** Sand dunes against mountains, Death Valley: Wirestock Creators; **p65:** Scout Scar, Cumbria. Limestone escarpment: George green; **p66:** Newbiggin Crags limestone pavement: Philip Brookes; **p70:** Blea Water, A Glacially Excavated Tarn or Corrie: Peter Turner Photography; **p73:** Aerial top view of blue lakes with islands and green forests in Finland: nblx; **p78:** Sea cliff and wave cut platform details: EDP Photography; **p79:** Natural arch above ocean: Michal Balada; **p84:** Rarotonga stunning breathtaking views from a plane of beautiful beaches: Svetype26; **p85:** Aerial Tupai Bora Bora Tahaa Society Islands Atoll: Spotmatik Ltd; Coral reefs fringe convoluted, tropical islands found in a remote part of the Solomon Islands: Ethan Daniels; **p89:** Underwater diver in deep sea dive: Lillac; **p105:** Cloud in Cirrocumulus state in the blue sky: MG2018; Cirrostratus clouds on a sultry summer day: martin.dlugo; **p106:** White clouds cumulus floating on blue sky: Muk Photo; Altocumulus floccus white fluffy clouds covering the blue sky: KHUNNINE; Large cumulonimbus calvus clouds: Ninevija; **p118:** Damage caused by Super Typhoon Mangkut: KingRobert; **p125:** Senior traditional Asian palm oil farmer pruning palm oil fronds and harvesting palm oil fruit: Heru Anggara; **p126:** Farmer at work: Nazri Yaakub; **p132:** Two women collect tea in Sri Lanka: La Bella Studio; **p136:** Kenya Safari Mara: Ketan shah; **p138:** Two male shepherds of the Masai tribe drive their herd of cattle towards new pastures: Robin Nieuwenkamp; **p144:** Saguaro and Four Peaks near Phoenix, Arizona: LHBLLC; **p146:** Amazing place to visit, Algeria: mounir sila; **p153:** Large cultivated fields of olive trees in Andalusia (Spain): Miguel Angel RM; **p154:** Grape garden and making molasses: Toroslarinsesi; **p159**: Grain elevator in Bracken in Saskatchewan, Canada: Bennekom; **p161:** Cargo ship approaching port on north shore of Lake Erie in Southern Ontario, Canada: Marc Kirouac; **p167:** Rice terraces at sunset in Maruyama-senmaida, Kumano, Japan: Sean Pavone; **p173:** Tree collection: VRVIRUS; **p175:** Combine harvester harvesting in a field: David Calvert; **p176:** Sheep eating grass on the mountains of the north island of New Zealand: Shay Yacobinski; **p181:** View on coniferous woods and Rocky mountains of Canada: Protasov AN; **p183:** Lumberjack speed-sawing competition at Grouse Mountain, Vancouver, Canada : Anton Bielousov; Loading of timber on railroad cars: Scharfsinn; **p190:** Petty Harbour, Newfoundland and Labrador, Canada: Claude Huot; **p191:** Pear aqua farming cultivation, Shima, Japan: Nataliia Maksymenko

Others:

p61: Ayers Rock, Australia: eo Tang; **p68:** Burren Region, Clare, Ireland: Bjoern Alberts; **p105:** Cirrus Clouds: C_Eng-Wong Photography; **p132**: Close-up of sugar cane harvesting in Queensland, Australia: Johan Larson; **p194:** Reindeer in natural environment, Tromso Region, Northern Norway: Dmitry Chulov

Cover:

Abstract white spiral background: © 3d_kot/Shutterstock

Preface

In this **second edition** of *Certificate Physical and Human Geography*, we present a comprehensive resource tailored to the latest syllabus, specifically designed to meet the needs of students preparing for competitive examinations conducted by the UPSC, State Public Service Commissions, and other examining bodies in India. The book is thoughtfully enriched with maps, schematic diagrams, graphs, and photographs, all carefully crafted to enhance the reader's understanding of the subject matter. The maps, meteorological graphs, illustrations and pictures have undergone meticulous revision to aid students in their interpretation of geographical concepts presented within these pages, and relevant examples have been thoughtfully included wherever possible.

Part 1, devoted to **Physical Geography**, lays the foundation for geographical knowledge by delving into the fundamental principles and components of this subject. It provides students with a comprehensive discussion that aids their understanding of the concepts.

Part 2, focusing on **Weather, Climate, and Vegetation**, extends its scope to encompass the economic development of natural regions. This section provides in-depth coverage of the significant agricultural and other economic activities in each region, offering a nuanced understanding of the subject matter.

To facilitate student learning, key terms, essential facts, and headings have been thoughtfully highlighted in colour. Maps and illustrations have also been updated and rendered in colour for enhanced clarity and reference. Additionally, each chapter includes practice questions to aid in reinforcing the concepts presented.

This second edition also features a fully updated and meticulously revised index, making it easier for students to locate and understand key terms and terminologies with their respective page references.

What's new in this edition:

- **Holistic Approach:**

  This edition seamlessly integrates the key components of physical geography, global climatic and vegetational regions, and human geography. It brings these vital aspects together, facilitating a comprehensive understanding of their association.

- **Up-to-date, Comprehensive and Authoritative:**

  The book contains the latest available socio-economic data and climatological graphs, as well as the latest known place names. The book covers a wide range of topics in physical and human geography, and the information is sourced from authoritative sources.

- **Rich Visual, Engaging and Informative Content:**

  The book includes new, attractive, and informative maps, images, graphs and illustrations. These visuals help in visualizing geographical concepts and trends, making study experience interesting, engaging and effective.

- **Redrawn Climate Graphs (1991-2021):**

  Climate patterns are evolving, and this edition acknowledges this fact by redrawing climate graphs based on data spanning the years 1991 to 2021. These updated graphs offer a comprehensive understanding of climate trends and variations, equipping you with the latest insights into the world's climatic dynamics (Data source: https://en.climate-data.org/).

- **Relevance and Timeliness:** With its commitment to up-to-date information, the book remains relevant and timely, reflecting the ever-changing landscape of geography and socio-economic trends.

- **Valuable Digital Resource:** In today's digital age, learning extends beyond the printed page. To augment your studies, this edition includes a valuable digital resource packed with additional online materials for reading and reference. This digital component further enriches your learning experience, providing access to a wealth of supplementary information.

Contents

Conversion Scales for Temperature and Rainfall

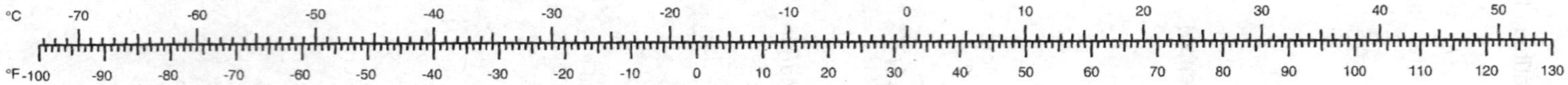

$°C = \frac{5}{9}(°F-32)$ $°F = \frac{9}{5}C+32$

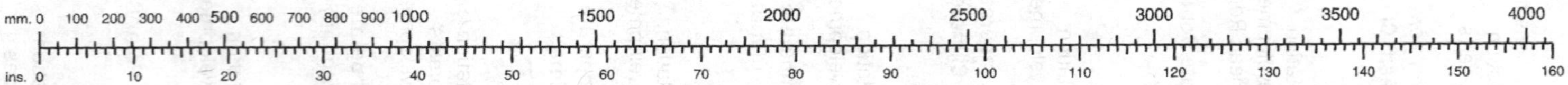

1 mm. = 0.0394 ins. 1 inch = 25.4000 mm.

Other Conversion Factors

1 cm.	=	0.3937 ins.
1 m.	=	3.2808 feet
1 km.	=	0.6214 miles
1 foot	=	0.3048 m.
1 mile	=	1.6093 km.
1 hectare	=	2.4711 acres
1 sq. km. = 100 hectares	=	247.1054 acres = 0.3861 sq. mile
1 acre	=	0.4047 hectares
1 sq. mile. = 640 acres	=	2.5900 sq. km. = 258.9988 hectares
32° fahrenheit (°F)	=	0° centigrade (°C)
1° centigrade (°C)	=	33.8° fahrenheit (°F)
1 metric ton = 1000 kg.	=	1.1023 short tons = 0.9842 long tons
1 short ton = 2000 lbs.	=	0.9072 metric tons
1 long ton = 2240 lbs.	=	1.0161 metric tons

1 The Earth and the Universe

Exploring the Universe

On a fine bright night when you look up at the sky, it seems to be studded with stars. Little do you realize that each of the stars is far bigger than the earth on which we live. Some of the larger ones have been estimated to be many millions of times the size of the earth. These stars are not scattered regularly in space; they occur in clusters, better described as *galaxies* or *nebulas*. Each galaxy may contain as many as 100 million stars. It is believed that the earth's own galaxy (the *Milky Way*) alone contains as many as 100,000 million stars.

The stars appear small to us even through a telescope because they are so far away. The light from the nearest star travelling at the speed of light (i.e. 186,000 miles per second or 299,792 kilometres per second) takes something like four years to reach us. A ray of light from the sun takes about eight minutes to reach the earth. Light takes only a second to reach us from the moon.

The Solar System

The solar system comprises the Sun and its eight planets (Fig. 1) which are believed to have been developed from the condensation of gases and other lesser bodies. All the planets revolve round the Sun in *elliptical orbits*. Like the earth, they shine only by the reflected light of the sun. The Sun has a surface temperature of 6,000°C (10,800°F) and increases to 20 million°C (36 million°F) in the interior. All over its surface are fiery gases that leap up in whirls of glowing flames like a volcano in eruption. In size, the Sun is almost unimaginable. It is about 300,000 times as big as the earth!

Amongst the eight planets, Mercury is the smallest and closest to the sun, only 36 million miles (57.9 million km) miles away. It thus completes its orbit in a much shorter space of time than does Earth. A year in Mercury is only 88 days. Venus, twice the distance away from the sun, is the next closest planet. It is often considered as *'Earth's twin'* because of their close proximity in size, mass (weight) and density. But no other planet is in any way comparable to Earth which has life and all the living things we see around us. Like many other planets, the Earth has a natural *satellite*, the Moon, 238,900 miles (384,000 km) away, that revolves eastward around the Earth once in every 27 days.

Fig. 1 The Solar System—the Sun and the eight Planets

The fourth planet from the sun is Mars which has dark patches on its surface and is believed by most professional astronomers to be the next planet after Earth to have the possibility of some plant life. Much attention has been focused on Mars to explore the possibilities of extending man's influence to it. Mars has two tiny natural satellites. Next comes Jupiter, the largest planet in the solar system. Its surface is made up of many gases like hydrogen, helium, and methane. It is distinguished from other planets by its circular light and dark bands, and the 79 satellites that circle round it. As it is more than 485 million miles (778 million km) from the Sun, its surface is very cold, probably about –200°F. (–130°C.).

Another unique planet is Saturn which has three rings and 53 satellites around it. In size, it is the second largest after Jupiter. It is so far from the Sun that it takes 29½ years to complete its orbit. The seventh planet, Uranus, was not known to astronomers until the late eighteenth century when it was first seen as a faint bluish-green disc through a very powerful telescope. It is another giant planet, 50 times larger than Earth and 15 times as heavy. Unlike other planets, Uranus orbits around the sun in a clockwise direction from east to west with 27 satellites revolving round it.

The outermost planet in the solar system, Neptune is just visible with telescopes. Discovery of Neptune was the result of mathematical calculations on its irregular gravitational effects on neighbouring planetary bodies. Neptune closely resembles Uranus, except that it has only 14 known satellites and is probably much colder.

Dwarf Planets and Plutoids

Pluto, which was considered to be a planet since its discovery in 1930, was reclassified as a 'dwarf planet' on 24 August, 2006 by the International Astronomical Union (IAU).

According to the IAU, a dwarf planet fulfils the following criteria:

- It is in orbit around the Sun.
- It has sufficient mass for its self-gravity to overcome rigid body forces so that it assumes a hydrostatic equilibrium (nearly round) shape.
- It has not 'cleared the neighbourhood' around its orbit.
- It is not a satellite of a planet, or other non-stellar body.

Two years after coining the term 'dwarf planets', the IAU has decided to call trans-Neptunian dwarf planets similar to Pluto, 'plutoids'. While all plutoids are dwarf planets, all dwarf planets are not plutoids. Currently, there are five celestial bodies that have been redefined by the IAU as dwarf planets, of which four belong to the subset plutoids. Eris, Pluto, and most recently, MakeMake and Haumea have been classified as plutoids and dwarf planets, while Ceres remains in the category dwarf planet.

The Shape of the Earth

In the olden days, sailors feared to venture far into the distant ocean because they thought the earth was as flat as a table. They thought that when they reached the edge of the earth, they would slip down and perish in the bottomless ocean. This is, of course, not true. From years of accumulated knowledge, experience and observations in different parts of the world, we know that the earth is round. Its spherical shape is an established fact, proved, and accepted by all. There has been so much research done on earth science that its various dimensions have been accurately found. It has an equatorial circumference of 24,874 miles (40,030 km) and its polar circumference is less by 83 miles. Its equatorial diameter is 7,918 miles (12,742 km) and its polar diameter is shorter by 26 miles (42 km). This simply shows that the earth is not a perfect sphere. It is a little flattened at both ends like an orange. It can, in fact, be called a *geoid* ('earth-shaped'). The spherical shape of the earth is also masked by the intervening highlands and oceans on its surface.

Evidence of the Earth's Sphericity

There are many ways to prove that the earth is spherical. The following are some of them.

1. **Circum-navigation of the earth.** The first voyage around the world by Ferdinand Magellan and his crew, from 1519 to 1522 proved beyond doubt that the earth is spherical. No traveller going round the world by land or sea has ever encountered an abrupt edge, over which he would fall. Modern air routes and ocean navigation are based on the assumption that the earth is round (Fig. 2).

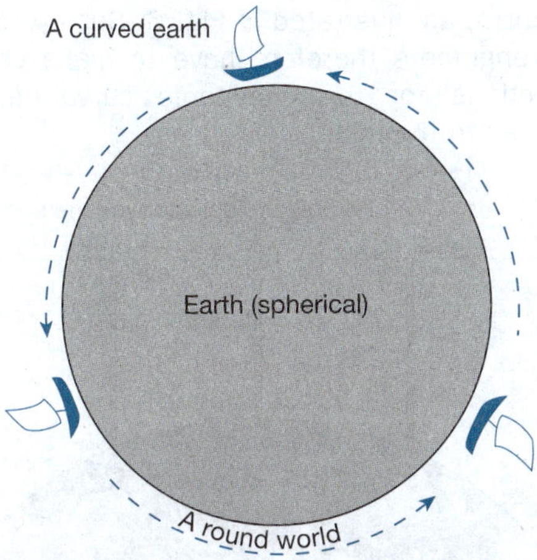

Fig. 2 (a) Circumnavigation of the earth

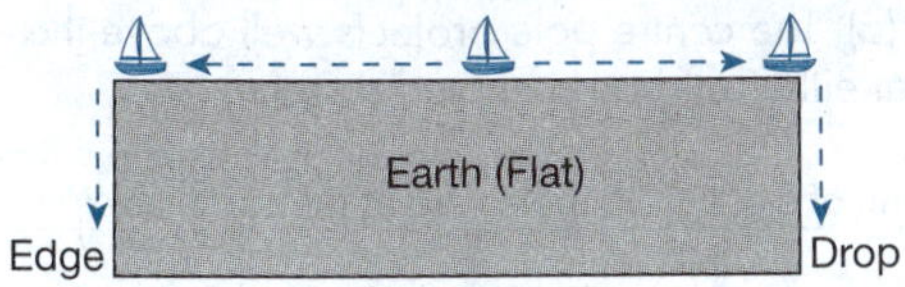

(b) Abrupt drop at the edge of a table-like earth

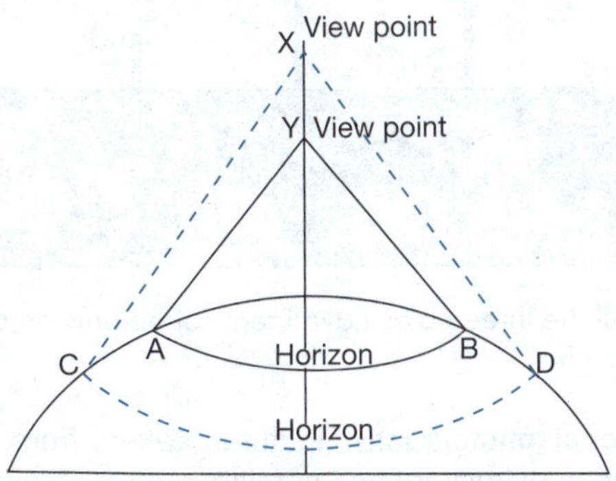

Fig. 3 (a) Increasing altitude widens the circular horizon. Viewed from Y the horizon would be AB but from a higher viewpoint (X) a wider horizon (C, D) would be seen

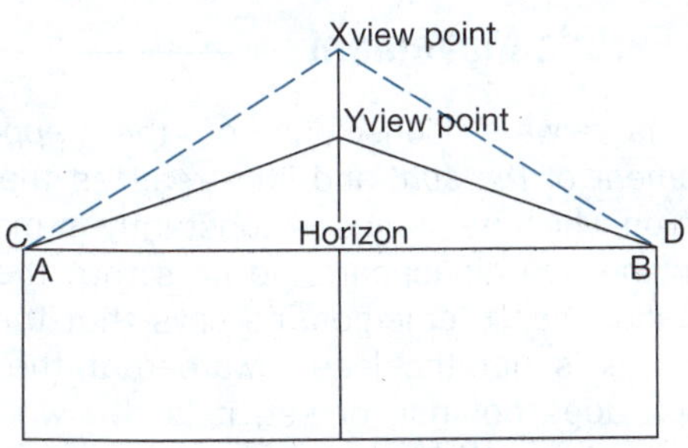

(b) Visible horizon remains the same regardless of altitude. If the earth were flat the horizon seen from either Y or X would be the same

2. **The circular horizon.** The distant horizon viewed from the deck of a ship at sea, or from a cliff on land is always and everywhere circular in shape. This circular horizon widens with increasing altitude and could only be seen on a spherical body. This is illustrated in Fig. 3.

3. **Ship's visibility.** When a ship appears over the distant horizon, the top of the mast is seen first before the hull. In the same way, when it leaves harbour, its disappearance over the curved surface is equally gradual. If the earth were flat, the entire ship would be seen or obscured all at once. This is apparent from Fig. 4.

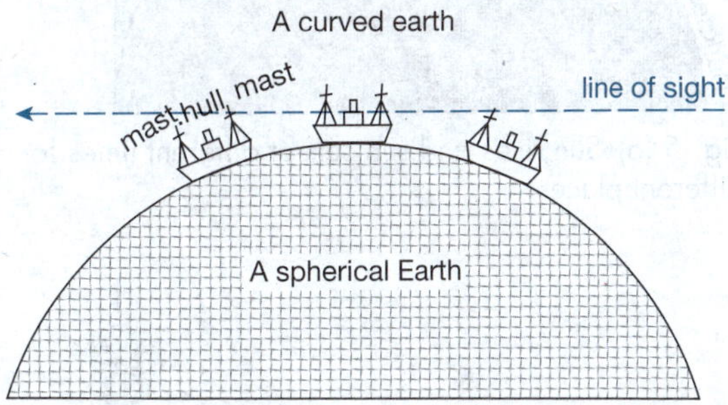

Fig. 4 (a) The mast of a ship is seen before the hull on curved horizon

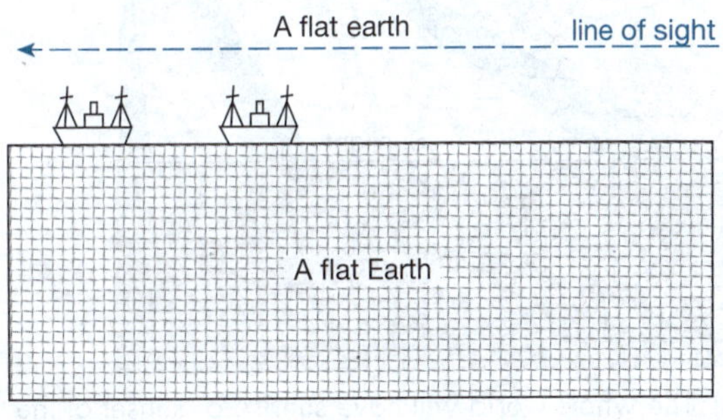

(b) A flat earth, the entire ship is seen at once on a flat surface

4. **Sunrise and sunset.** The sun rises and sets at different times in different places. As the earth rotates from west to east, places in the east see the sun earlier than those in the west. If the earth were flat, the whole world would have sunrise and sunset at the same time. But we know this is not so. Fig. 5 illustrates this.

5. **The lunar eclipse.** The shadow cast by the earth on the moon during the lunar eclipse is always circular. It takes the outline of an arc of a circle. Only a sphere can cast such a circular shadow.

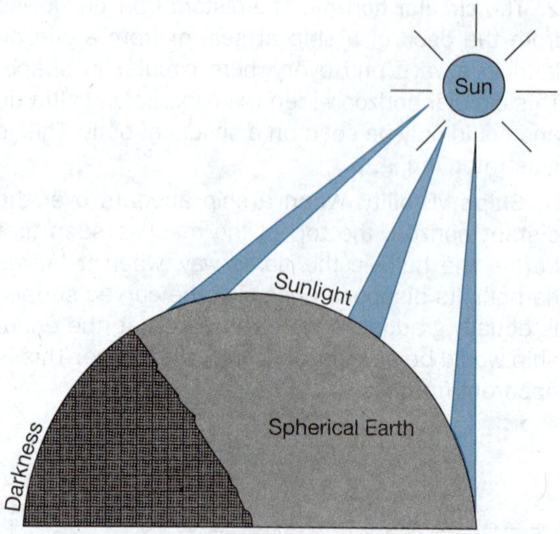

Fig. 5 (a) Sun rises and sun sets at different times for different places

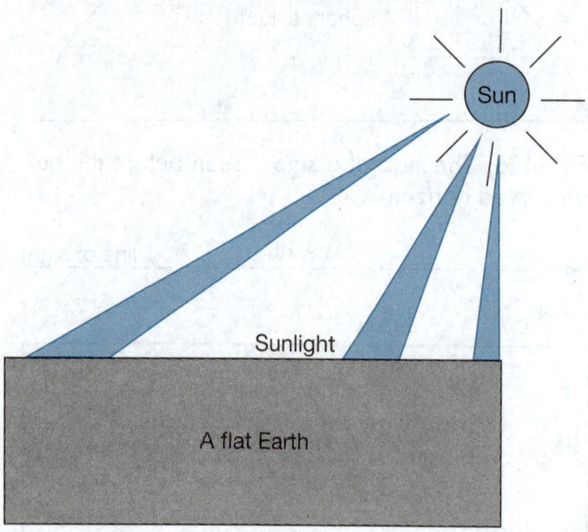

(b) The whole world will have sunrise or sunset at the same time

6. **Planetary bodies are spherical.** All observations from telescopes reveal that the planetary bodies, the Sun, Moon, satellites and stars have circular outlines from whichever angle you see them. They are strictly spheres. Earth, by analogy, cannot be the only exception.

7. **Driving poles on level ground on a curved earth.** Engineers when driving poles of equal length at regular intervals on the ground have found that they do not give a perfect horizontal level. The centre pole normally projects slightly above the poles at either end because of the curvature of the earth, as illustrated in Fig. 6. Surveyors and field engineers therefore have to make certain corrections for this inevitable curvature, i.e. 8 inches to the mile.

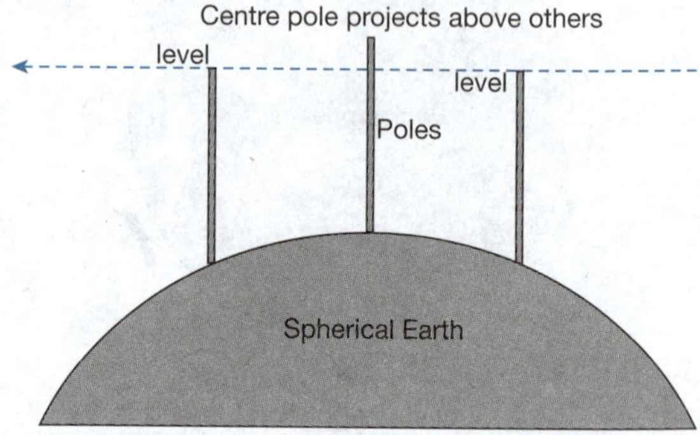

Fig. 6 (a) The centre pole projects well above the poles at either end on a curved surface

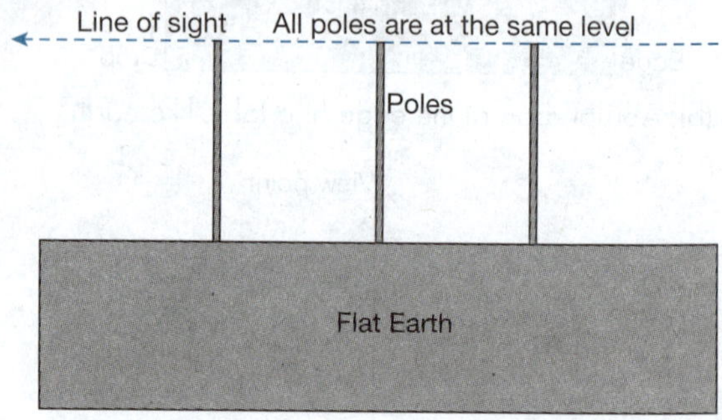

(b) All the three poles have identical heights on a flat surface

8. **Aerial photographs.** Pictures taken from high altitudes by rockets and satellites show clearly the curved edge of the earth. This is perhaps the most convincing and the most up-to-date proof of the earth's sphericity.

The Earth's Movement

Man is always conscious of the *'apparent movement of the sun'* and little realizes that the earth on which he stands is constantly in motion. When the sun disappears, he says that the sun sets and when it emerges, he says that the sun rises. He is not the least aware that the sun, in fact, does not rise or set, it is 'we who rise and we who set'! The earth moves in space in two distinct ways: it *rotates* on its own axis from west to east once in every 24 hours, causing

The earth viewed from the moon. The picture was taken on the Apollo 8 mission of 1968 which prepared the way for the moon landing

day and night; it also revolves round the sun in an orbit once in every 365¼ days. causing the *seasons* and the *year*.

Day and Night

When the earth *rotates* on its own axis, only one portion of the earth's surface comes into the rays of the sun and experiences daylight. The other portion which is away from the sun's rays will be in darkness. As the earth rotates from west to east, every part of the earth's surface will be brought under the sun at some time or other. A part of the earth's surface that emerges from darkness into the sun's rays experiences sunrise. Later, when it is gradually obscured from the sun's beams it experiences sunset. The sun is, in fact, stationary and it is the earth which rotates. The illusion is exactly the same as when we travel in a fast-moving train. The trees and houses around us appear

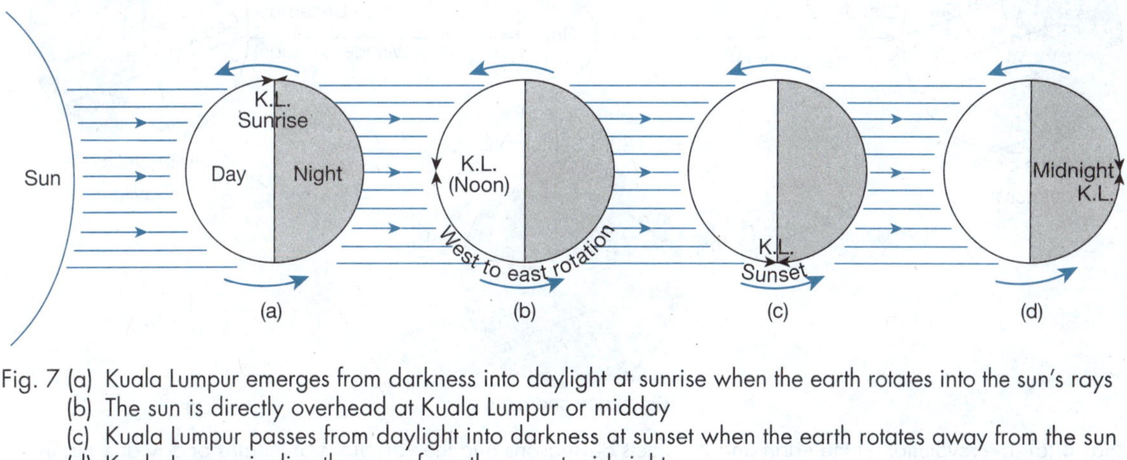

Fig. 7 (a) Kuala Lumpur emerges from darkness into daylight at sunrise when the earth rotates into the sun's rays
(b) The sun is directly overhead at Kuala Lumpur or midday
(c) Kuala Lumpur passes from daylight into darkness at sunset when the earth rotates away from the sun
(d) Kuala Lumpur is directly away from the sun at mid-night

to move and we feel that the train is stationary. Fig. 7 explains the earth's rotation and the causes of day and night.

The Earth's Revolution

When the earth *revolves* round the sun, it spins on an elliptical orbit at a speed of 18.5 miles (29.77 km) per second or 66,600 miles (107,182 km) per hour. One complete revolution takes 365¼ days or a year. As it is not possible to show a quarter of a day in the calendar, a normal year is taken to be 365 days, and an extra day is added every four years as a *Leap Year*.

1. Varying Lengths of Day and Night

The axis of the earth is *inclined* to the plane of the ecliptic (the plane in which the earth orbits round the sun) at an angle of 66½°, giving rise to different seasons and varying lengths of day and night (Fig. 8). If the axis were perpendicular to this plane, all parts of the globe would have equal days and nights at all times of the year, but we know this is not so. In the northern hemisphere in winter (December) as we go *northwards*, the hours of darkness steadily increase. At the Arctic Circle (66½°N.), the sun never 'rises' and there is darkness for the whole day in mid-winter on 22 December. Beyond the Arctic Circle the number of days with complete darkness increases, until we reach the North Pole (90°N.) when half the year will have darkness. In the summer (June) conditions are exactly reversed. Daylight increases as we go polewards. At the Arctic Circle, the sun never 'sets' at mid-summer (21 June) and there is a complete 24-hour period of continuous daylight. In summer the region north of the Arctic Circle is popularly referred to as *'Land of the Mid-night Sun'*. At the North Pole, there will be six months of continuous daylight. Fig. 8 (a) illustrates the revolution of the earth and its inclination to the plane of the ecliptic which cause the variation in the length of day and night at different times of the year.

In the southern hemisphere, the same process takes place, except that the *conditions are reversed*. When it is summer in the northern hemisphere, the southern continents will experience winter.

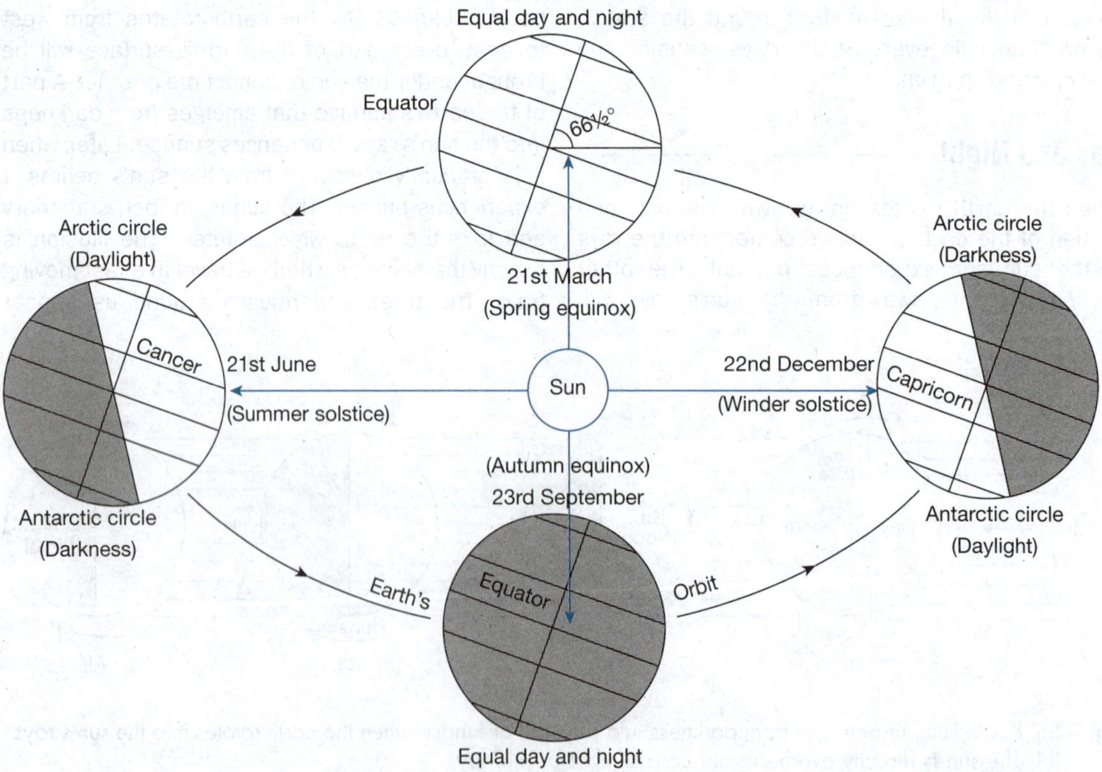

Fig. 8 (a) The revolution of the earth and its effects on seasons and the variations of lengths of day and night

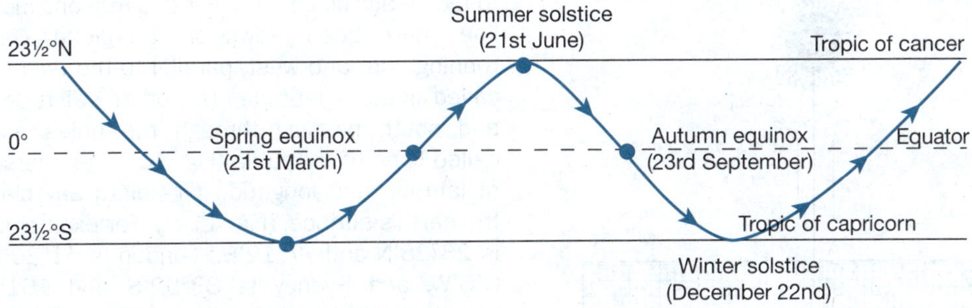

(b) A simplified diagram showing the annual movement of the sun and the causes of the seasons

Mid-summer at the North Pole will be mid-winter at the South Pole.

2. The Altitude of the Midday Sun

In the course of a year, the earth's revolution round the sun with its axis inclined at 66½° to the plane of the ecliptic changes the apparent altitude of the midday sun. The sun is *vertically overhead at the equator* on two days each year. These are usually 21 March and 21 September though the date changes because a year is not exactly 365 days. These two days are termed equinoxes meaning 'equal nights' because on these two days all parts of the world have equal days and nights. After the March equinox the sun appears to move north and is vertically overhead at the *Tropic of Cancer* (23½°N.) on about 21 June. This is known as the *June or summer solstice*, when the northern hemisphere will have its longest day and shortest night. By about 22 December, the sun will be overhead at the *Tropic of Capricorn* (23½°S.). This is the *winter solstice* when the southern hemisphere will have its longest day and shortest night. The Tropics thus mark the limits of the overhead sun, for beyond these, the sun is *never overhead* at any time of the year. Such regions are marked by distinct seasonal changes – spring, summer, autumn and winter. Beyond the Arctic Circle (66½°N.) and the Antarctic Circle (66½°S.) where darkness lasts for six months and daylight is continuous for the remaining half of the year, it is always cold; for even during the short summer the sun is never high in the sky. Within the tropics, as the midday sun varies very little from its vertical position at noon daily, the four seasons are almost indistinguishable. Days and nights are almost equal all the year round Fig. 8 (b).

3. Seasonal Changes and their Effects on Temperature Summer is usually associated with much heat and brightness and winter with cold and darkness. Why should this be so? In *summer,* the sun is higher in the sky than in winter. When the sun is overhead its rays fall almost vertically on the earth, concentrating its heat on a small area; temperature therefore rises and summers are always warm. In winter the oblique rays of the sun, come through the atmosphere less directly and have much of their heat absorbed by atmospheric impurities and water vapour. The sun's rays fall faintly and spread over a great area. There is thus little heat, and temperatures remain low.

In addition, days are longer than nights in summer and more heat is received over the *longer daylight* duration. Nights are shorter and less heat is lost. There is a net gain in total heat received and temperature rises in summer. *Shorter days* and *longer nights* in winter account for the reverse effects.

Dawn and Twilight

The brief period between sunrise and full daylight is called dawn, and that between sunset and complete darkness is termed twilight. This is caused by the fact that during the periods of dawn and twilight the earth receives diffused or refracted light from the sun whilst it is still below the horizon. Since the sun rises and sets in a vertical path at the equator the period during which refracted light is received is short. But in temperate latitudes, the sun rises and sets in an oblique path and the period of refracted light is longer. It is much longer still at the poles, so that the winter darkness is really only twilight most of the time. (Fig. 9).

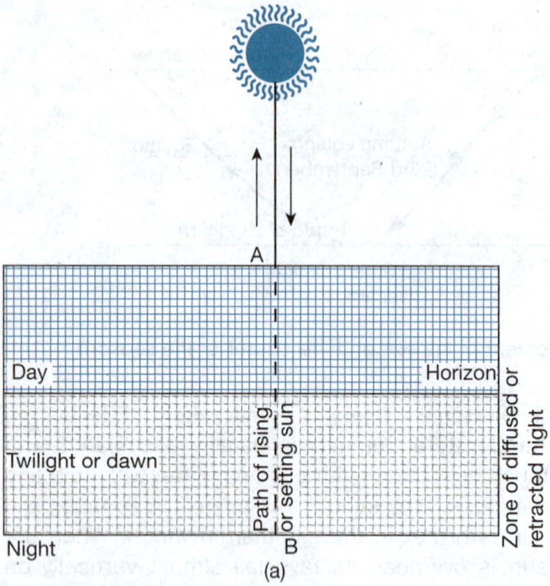

Fig. 9 Dawn and Twilight (a) at the equator (b) in temperate latitude

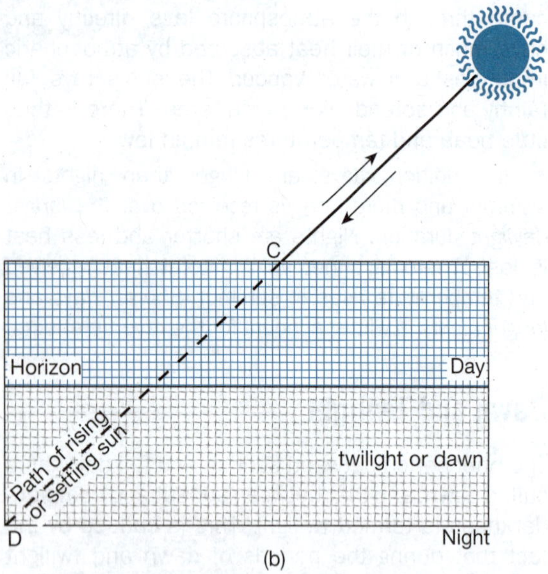

At the equator the sun rises and sets almost vertically so the time it takes to pass through the 'twilight zone' (A, B) will be shorter than for temperate latitudes where the sun rises and sets obliquely. Here the time taken to pass through the twilight zone (C, D) is longer

Mathematical Location of Places on the Globe

The earth's surface is so vast that unless a mathematical method can be used, it is impossible to locate any place on it. For this reason, imaginary lines have been drawn on the globe. One set running east and west, parallel to the equator, are called lines of latitude. The other set runs north and south passing through the poles and are called lines of longitude (Fig. 10). The intersection of latitude and longitude pin-points any place on the earth's surface, (Fig. 11 c.). For example, Delhi is 28°38'N and 77°12'E.; London is 51°30'N and 0°5'W, and Sydney is 33°52'S and 151°12'E. We shall examine more closely how latitude and longitude are determined and the role they play in mathematical geography.

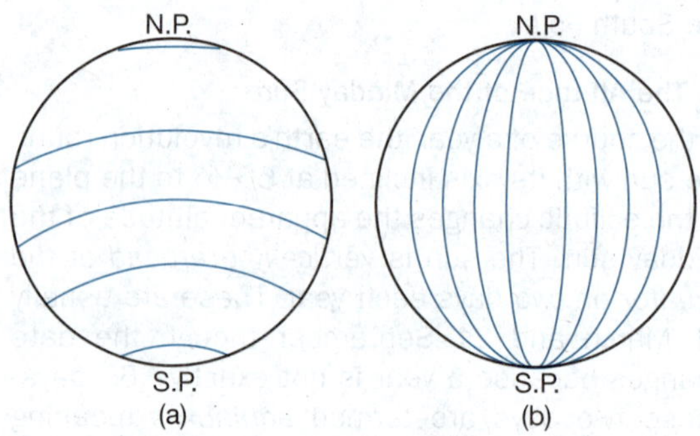

Fig. 10 (a) Parallels of latitude
(b) Meridians of longitude

Latitude

Latitude is the angular distance of a point on the earth's surface, measured in degrees from the centre of the earth as shown in Fig. 10 (a). It is parallel to a line, the *equator,* which lies midway between the poles. These lines are therefore called *parallels of latitude,* and on a globe are actually circles, becoming smaller polewards. The equator represents 0° and the North and South Poles are 90°N and 90°S. Between these points lines of latitude are drawn at intervals of 1°. For precise location on a map, each degree is sub-divided into 60 minutes and each minute into 60 seconds. The most important lines of latitude are the equator, the Tropic of Cancer (23½°N), the Tropic of Capricorn (23½°S), the Arctic Circle (66½°N) and the Antarctic Circle (66½°S). As the earth is slightly flattened at the poles, the linear distance of a degree of latitude at the pole is a little longer than that at the equator. For example, at the equator (0°) it is 68.704 miles (110.57 km), at 45° it is 69.054 miles (111.13 km) and at the poles it is 69.407 miles

(111.70 km). The average is taken as 69 miles (111 km). This is a useful figure and can be used for calculating distances to any place. Mumbai is 18°55'N; it is therefore 18.55 × 69 or 1,280 miles (18.55 × 111 or 2,059 km) from the equator. With the aid of your atlas find the approximate distance of the following places from the equator: Singapore, Kolkata, Paris, New York, Buenos Aires, and Auckland.

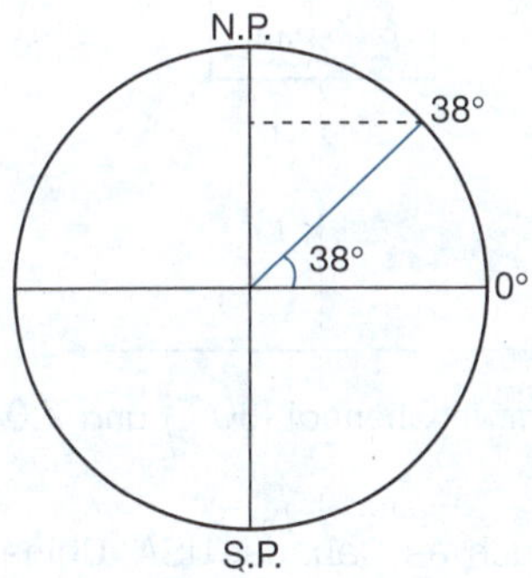

Fig. 11 (a) The latitude of 38°N is the angular distance of a point on the earth's surface north of the centre of the earth

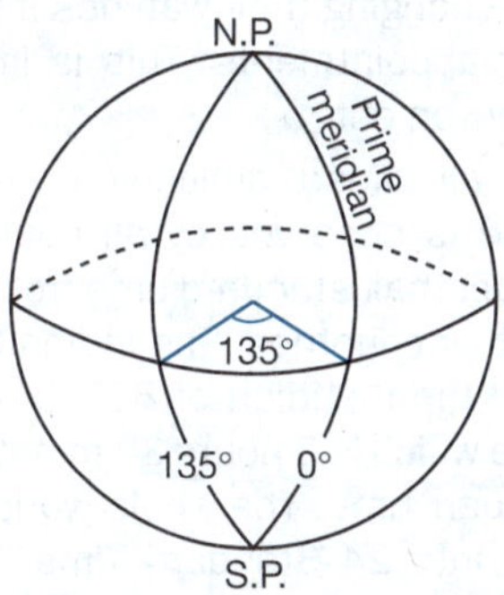

(b) The longitude of 135°W is the angular distance west of the Prime Meridian

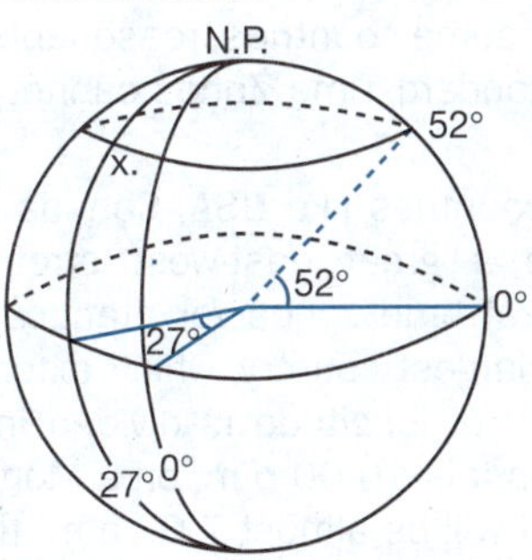

(c) The precise location of place X is latitude 52°N and longitude 27°W where they intersect

Longtitude

Longitude is an angular distance, measured in *degrees* along the equator east or west of the *Prime* (or First) *Meridian,* as indicated in Fig. 11 (b). On the globe longitude is shown as a series of semi-circles that run from pole to pole passing through the equator. Such lines are also called meridians. Unlike the equator, which is centrally placed between the poles, any meridian could have been taken to begin the numbering of longitude. It was finally decided in 1884, by international agreement, to choose as the zero meridian, the one which passes through the Royal Astronomical Observatory at *Greenwich,* near London. This is the Prime Meridian (0°) from which all other meridians radiate eastwards and westwards up to 180°. Since the earth is *spherical* and has a circumference calculated at 24,901 miles (40,075 km), in linear distance each of the 360 degrees of longitude is 24,901 ÷ 360 or 69.17 miles (40,075 ÷ 360 or 111.32 km). As the parallels of latitude become shorter polewards, so the meridians of longitude, which converge at the poles, enclose a narrower space. The degree of longitude therefore decreases in length. It is longest at the equator where it measures 69.17 miles (111.32 km). At 25° it is 62.73 miles (100.95 km), at 45° it is 49 miles (78.86 km), at 75° it is 18 miles (28.97 km) and at the poles, it is 0 mile (0 km). There is so much difference in the length of degrees of longitude outside the tropics, that they are not used for calculating distances as in the case of latitude. But they have one very important function, they determine local time in relation to G.M.T. or *Greenwich Mean Time,* which is sometimes referred to as World Time.

Longitude and Time

Local Time. Since the earth makes one complete revolution of 360° in one day or 24 hours, it passes through 15° *in one hour* or 1° in 4 minutes. The earth rotates from *west to east,* so every 15° we go *eastwards,* local time is advanced by 1 hour. Conversely, if we go *westwards,* local time is retarded by 1 hour. We may thus conclude that places east of Greenwich see the sun earlier and gain time, whereas places west of Greenwich see the sun later and lose time. If we know G.M.T., to find local time, we merely have to add or subtract the difference in the number of hours from the

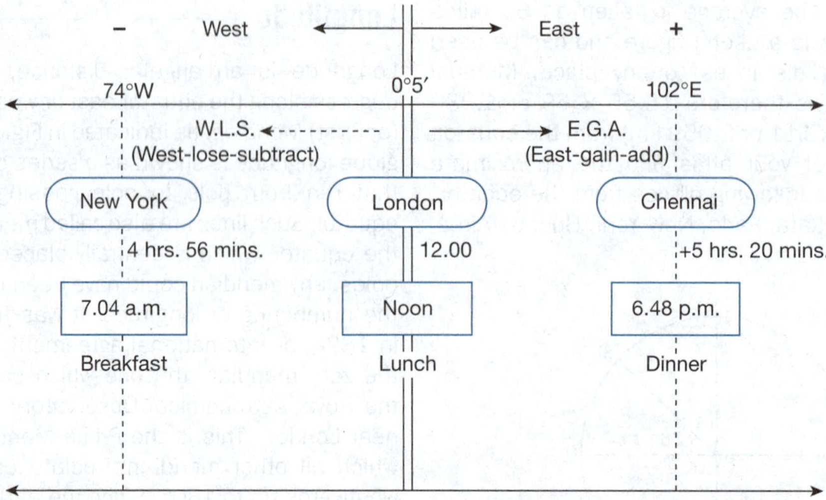

Fig. 12 Longitude and time—when it is noon in London, it is 5.20 p.m. in Chennai (80°E) and 7.04 a.m. in New York (74°W).

given longitude, as illustrated below. A simple memory aid for this will be *East-Gain-Add (E.G.A.)* and *West-Lose-Subtract (W.L.S.)*. You could coin your own rhymes for the abbreviations. Hence when it is noon, in London (Longitude 0°5'W), the local time for Chennai (80°E) will be 5 hours 20 minutes ahead of London or 5.20 p.m. But the local time for New York (74°W) will be 4 hours 56 minutes behind London or 7.04 a.m. We can put it in another way, when Londoners are having lunch, Indians will have dinner and New Yorkers will have breakfast. (Fig. 12). This is difficult to believe, but it is true. The rotation of the earth round the sun means that at any point in time different places will experience a different time of day.

There are many ways of determining the longitude of a place. The simplest way is to compare the local time with G.M.T.. For example: the captain of a ship in the midst of the ocean wants to find out in which longitude his ship lies. If G.M.T. is 8.00 a.m. and it is noon in the local region, it means that he is four hours ahead of Greenwich, and must be east of Greenwich. His longitude is 4 × 15° or 60°E.

Standard Time and Time Zones

If each town were to keep the time of its own meridian, there would be much difference in local time between one town and the other. 10 a.m. in Georgetown, Penang would be 10.10 in Kota Bharu (a difference of 2½° in longitude). In larger countries such as Canada, USA, China, India and Russia the confusion arising from the differences alone would drive the people mad. Travellers going from one end of the country to the other would have to keep changing their watches if they wanted to keep their appointments. This is impracticable and very inconvenient.

To avoid all these difficulties, a system of standard time is observed by all countries. Most countries adopt their standard time from the central meridian of their countries. The Indian Government has accepted the meridian of 82°30' east for the standard time which is 5 hours 30 minutes ahead of Greenwich Mean Time. The whole world has in fact been divided into 24 Standard Time Zones, each of which differs from the next by 15° in longitude or one hour in time. Most countries adhere to this division but due to the peculiar shapes and locations of some countries, reasonable deviations from the Standard Time Zones cannot be avoided (Fig. 13).

Larger countries like USA, Canada and Russia which have a great east-west stretch have to adopt several time zones for practical purposes. Russia the largest country, which extends through almost 165° of longitude is divided into 11 time zones. When it is 10.00 p.m. on a Monday night in Leningrad, it will be almost 7.00 a.m. the following Tuesday morning in Vladivostok. Travellers along the Trans-Siberian Railway have to adjust their watches almost a dozen times before they reach their destination. Both Canada and USA have

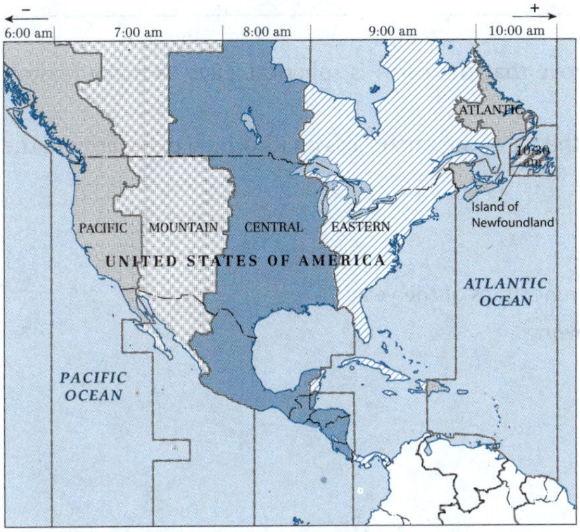

Fig. 13 The five time zones of North America

five time zones – the Atlantic, Eastern, Central, Mountain and Pacific Time Zones. The difference between the local time of the Atlantic and Pacific coasts is nearly five hours (Fig. 13).

The International Date Line

A traveller going eastwards gains time from Greenwich until he reaches the meridian 180°E. when he will be 12 hours ahead of G.M.T. Similarly, in going westwards, he loses 12 hours when he reaches 180°W. There is thus a total difference of 24 hours or a whole day between the two sides of the 180° meridian. This is the *International Date Line* where the date changes by exactly one day when it is crossed. A traveller crossing the date line from *east to west loses* a day (because of the loss in time he has made); and while crossing the dateline from *west to east* he gains a day (because of the gain in time he encountered). Thus when it is midnight, Friday on the Asiatic side, by crossing the line eastwards, he gains a day; it will be midnight Thursday on the American side, i.e. he experiences the same calendar date twice! When Magellan's ship eventually arrived home in Spain in 1522 after circumnavigating the world from the Atlantic Ocean to the Pacific Ocean and westwards across the International Date Line, the crew knew nothing about adding a day for the one they had missed. They thought they had arrived on the 5th of September. They were shocked to be told that the date was 6th September. A modern aircraft leaving Wellington at 5.00 p.m. on Friday reaches Hawaii 4,100 miles (6,598 km) away at 2.00 p.m. the same Friday. The same aircraft on its return journey from Hawaii leaves at 6.00 p.m. on Friday but arrives at Wellington at 11.00 a.m. on Sunday. Can you explain this?

The International Date Line in the mid-Pacific curves from the normal 180° meridian at the Bering Strait, Fiji, Tonga and other islands to prevent confusion of day and date in some of the island groups that are cut through by the meridian. Some of them keep Asiatic or New Zealand standard time, others follow the American date and time. The International Date Line is shown in Fig. 14.

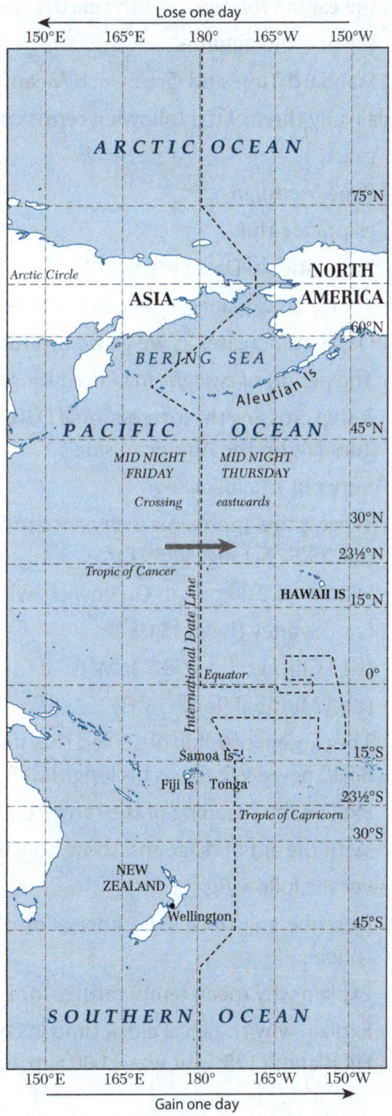

Fig. 14 The International Date Line

QUESTIONS AND EXERCISES

1. With the aid of annotated diagrams, attempt to prove that the earth is spherical. Give as many reasons as you can.
2. Explain with the aid of fairly accurate diagrams, how the tilt of the earth's axis on its orbital plane around the sun causes:
   (a) the seasons
   (b) the variations in the length of day and night
   (c) the altitude of the midday sun to change at different times of the year.
3. Explain the differences between any *three* of the following:
   (a) perihelion and aphelion
   (b) parallels of latitude and meridians of longitude
   (c) the earth's rotation and the earth's revolution
   (d) solstice and equinox
   (e) Standard Time and Greenwich Mean Time
4. Explain any *three* of the following terms connected with the earth and its planetary relations:
   i. galaxy
   ii. Pime Meridian
   iii. elliptical orbit
   iv. International Date Line
5. *Either:* Give an explanatory account of the following.
   (a) Daylight increases as we go polewards in summer in the northern hemisphere.
   (b) The period of twilight in United Kingdom is longer than in Malaysia.
   (c) A ship crossing the International Date Line at midnight on Wednesday eastwards finds that it is midnight, Tuesday, on the American side.

   Or: Work out the following.
   i. What is the approximate distance in a straight line between Cairo (lat. 30°0'N, long. 31°5'E) and Durban (lat. 29°57'S, long. 30°59'E)?
   ii. When it is 2.00 p.m. in Greenwich, what is the local time of
      (a) Sydney (long. 151°E.)
      (b) Chicago (long. 87°30'W.)
      (c) Mumbai (long. 73°E.)
   iii. The captain of a ship observed that it was local noon. He turned on the radio and listened to the 7.00 a.m. B.B.C. news. What was his longitude?
6. (a) Explain the meaning of the terms 'Equinox' and 'Solstice'.
   (b) With the aid of diagrams, show how they are related to the movements of the earth.
7. Answer the following:
   (a) Describe any *three* experiments or observations which support the belief that the earth is roughly a sphere.
   (b) Explain why mean temperatures for London are lowest in winter.
   (c) Explain why the local clock time in the Samoa Islands (171°W) was noon on 1st November when in the Fiji Islands (178°E), it was 11.00 a.m. on 2nd November.

2 The Earth's Crust

The Structure of the Earth

In order to understand the geography of the external landforms of the earth, it is essential that we have some idea of what lies within the earth's crust. It is not possible to know exactly how the earth was formed about 4,500 million years ago, but from the evidence of volcanic eruptions, earthquake waves, deep-mine operations and crustal borings the following facts are quite clear.

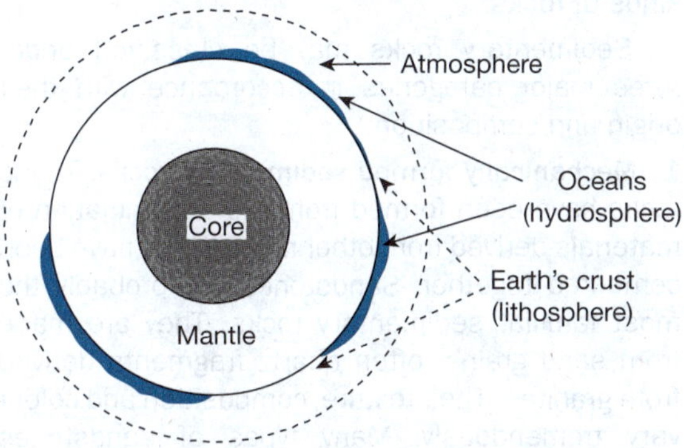

Fig. 15 A section showing the structure and composition of the earth

The earth is made up of several concentric layers (Fig. 15). The outer layer is the earth's crust – the lithosphere – which comprises two distinct parts. The upper part consists of granitic rocks and forms the continents. Its main mineral constituents are *si*lica and *al*umina so it is collectively referred to as the *sial*. It has an average density of 2.7. The lower part is a continuous zone of denser basaltic rocks forming the ocean floors, comprising mainly silica, *i*ron and *ma*gnesium. It is therefore called *sima* and has an average density of 3.0. The sial and the sima together form the earth's crust which varies in thickness from only 3–4 miles beneath the oceans to as much as 30 miles under some parts of the continents. Since the sial is lighter than the sima, the continents can be said to be 'floating' on a sea of denser sima. This is illustrated in Fig. 16.

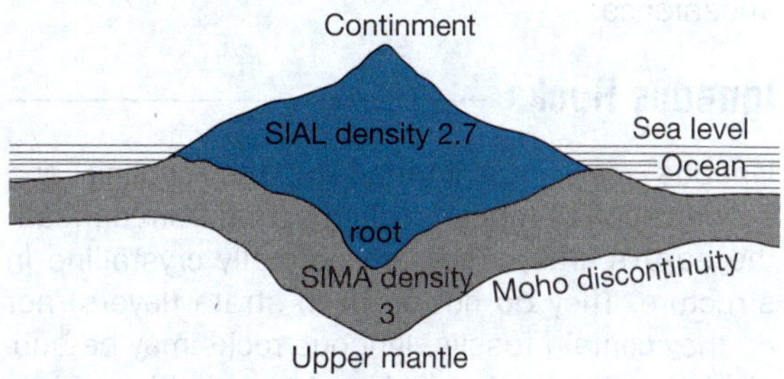

Fig. 16 A section showing how the continent (SIAL) floats on the denser SIMA

Immediately beneath the crust or lithosphere is the mantle (or *mesosphere*) about 1,800 miles thick, composed mainly of very dense rocks rich in *olivine*. The interior layer is the *core*, (or *barysphere*) 2,160 miles (3,476 km) in radius, and is made up mainly of iron (*Fe*) with some *nickel* and is called *nife*. The temperature here is estimated to be as high as 3,500°F (1,927°C), and the core is subject to extremely high pressure. Under such conditions, the core could be expected to be in a liquid state. But recent studies through earthquake waves have suggested that the innermost part of the core is probably a crystalline or solid mass.

Parts of the earth's crust are immersed by oceans and seas. These oceans and seas form the hydrosphere. Extending skywards for over fifteen miles from the surface of the earth, there is an envelope of gases which make up the atmosphere.

The Classification of Rocks

The earth's crust is made up of various types of rocks, differing from one another in texture, structure, colour, permeability, mode of occurrence and degree of resistance to denudation. A knowledge of these rocks is of paramount importance to geologists, who study the composition and physical history of the earth, but the geographer, too, needs a basic knowledge of the most common rocks and their relationship with landforms. Rocks also form the basis for soil, and determine to some extent the type of natural vegetation and land use, so we must have a fair acquaintance with the rocks around us.

Generally speaking, all rocks may be classified into *three* major groups – *igneous, sedimentary and metamorphic,* according to their origin and appearance.

Igneous Rocks

Igneous rocks are formed by the cooling and solidification of molten rock (magma) from beneath the earth's crust. They are normally crystalline in structure. They do not occur in strata (layers) nor do they contain fossils. Igneous rocks may be subdivided on the basis of mineral composition. When they contain a high proportion of silica they are said to be acid. Acid igneous rocks, such as granite, are less dense and are lighter in colour than basic rocks. These contain a greater proportion of basic oxides, e.g. of iron, aluminium or magnesium, and are thus denser and darker in colour.

In terms of origin there are *two* main classes of igneous rocks.

1. **Plutonic rocks.** These are igneous rocks, formed at some depth in the earth's crust. They have cooled and solidified slowly so that large, easily-recognized crystals have been able to form. These intrusive rocks, such as granite, diorite and gabbro, are exposed at the surface by the processes of denudation and erosion.

2. **Volcanic rocks.** These are molten rocks poured out of volcanoes as lavas. They *solidify rapidly* on the earth's surface and the crystals are small.

Basalt is a common volcanic or extrusive rock and forms lava flows, lava sheets and lava plateaux, e.g. those of Antrim in Northern Ireland, the Deccan Plateau in India and the Columbia-Snake Plateau in USA. Some kinds of basalt solidify in a very peculiar manner to form long *polygonal columns*. A well-known example is the columnar basalt of the Giant's Causeway in Antrim. Some of the molten lava may push its way to the surface through clefts and passages, solidifying as *vertical* dykes or *horizontal* sills. Their origin and occurrence will be discussed in greater detail in Chapter 3.

Most igneous rocks are extremely hard and resistant. For this reason, they are quarried for road-making and polished as monuments and gravestones.

Sedimentary Rocks

Sedimentary rocks are formed from sediment accumulated over long periods, usually under water. They are distinguished from the other rock types in their characteristic layer formation and are termed stratified rocks. The strata may vary in thickness from a few inches to many feet. The rocks may be coarse or fine-grained, soft or hard. The materials that form sedimentary rocks may be brought by streams, glaciers, winds or even animals. They are non-crystalline and often contain fossils of animals, plants and other microorganisms. Sedimentary rocks are thus the most varied in their formation of all rocks. These rocks are classified according to their age and different kinds of rocks formed during the same period are grouped together. It is more useful to know the characteristics of the various kinds of rocks.

Sedimentary rocks may be classified under *three* major categories in accordance with their origin and composition.

1. **Mechanically formed sedimentary rocks.** These rocks have been formed from the accumulation of materials derived from other rocks which have been cemented together. Sandstones are probably the most familiar sedimentary rocks. They are made from sand grains, often quartz fragments derived from granites. Their texture, composition and colour vary tremendously. Many types of sandstones have been quarried for building purposes or for making grindstones. A coarser type of sandstone is known as *grit*. When larger pebbles are firmly cemented to form a rock it is called conglomerate when the pebbles are rounded, or breccia when the fragments are angular. The finer sedimentary materials form clay, widely used for brick-making, shale or mudstone. Sand and gravel may occur in uncemented form.

2. **Organically formed sedimentary rocks.** These rocks are formed from the remains of living organisms such as corals or shellfish, whose fleshy parts have been decomposed, leaving behind the hard shells. The most common rocks formed in this way are of the calcareous type. They include limestones and chalk.

The carbonaceous rocks are also organically formed but from vegetative matter – swamps and forests. The pressure of overlying sediments has compressed the plant remains into compact masses of *carbon* which eventually become peat, lignite or coal, all of which bear great economic value.

3. **Chemically formed sedimentary rocks.** Such rocks are precipitated chemically from solutions of one kind or another. Rock salts are derived from strata which once formed the beds of seas or lakes. *Gypsum* or calcium sulphate is obtained from the evaporation of salt lakes, such as the Dead Sea, which have a very high salinity. In similar ways, *potash* and *nitrates* may be formed.

A prehistoric limestone hill near Kuala Lumpur. Compare this hill with the limestone features shown in Chapter 7

Metamorphic Rocks

All rocks whether igneous or sedimentary may become metamorphic or changed rocks under great heat and pressure. Their original character and appearance may be greatly altered by such forces, particularly during intense earth movements. In this manner, clay may be metamorphosed into slate, limestone into marble, sandstone into quartzite. granite into gneiss, shale into schist and coal into graphite.

The Influence of Rock Types on Landscape

The appearance and characteristic features of landforms are greatly influenced by the underlying rock type. Softer rocks like clay and shale are worn down much faster than harder rocks like granite.

Within West Malaysia the resistant granites form the high ground of the Main Range and the Eastern Range, where several peaks rise to over 2,000 feet. The landscape is one of smooth slopes and rounded hill-tops. The highest peak in West Malaysia, Gunong Tahan (7,186 feet) is composed of even more resistant quartzite. Shales, schists and sandstones, being less resistant, form the much lower, rounded hills. Recent river sediments form flat plains. The limestones, resistant because of their permeability, form prominent steep-sided hills such as those near Ipoh and in Perlis.

Earth Movements and the Major Landforms

The face of the earth is constantly being reshaped by the agents of denudation – running water, rain, frost, sun, wind, glaciers and waves, so that our present landforms are very varied and diverse. But these agents only modify the pattern of mountains, plateaux and plains which have been modelled by movements of the earth's crust.

Since the dawn of geological time, no less than nine orogenic or mountain building movements have taken place, folding and fracturing the earth's crust. Some of them occurred in Pre-Cambrian times between 600–3,500 million years ago. The three more recent orogenies are the Caledonian, Hercynian and Alpine. The Caledonian about 320 million years ago raised the mountains of Scandinavia and Scotland, and is represented in North America. These ancient mountains have been worn down and no longer exhibit the striking forms that they must once have had. In a later period, during the Hercynian earth movements about 240 million years ago, were formed such ranges as the Ural Mountains, the Pennines and Welsh Highlands in United Kingdom, the Harz Mountains in Germany, the Appalachians in North America as well as the high plateaux of Siberia and China. These mountains have also been reduced in size by the various sculpturing forces.

We are now living in an era very close to the last of the major orogenic movements of the earth, the Alpine, about 30 million years ago. Young fold mountain ranges were buckled up and overthrust on a gigantic scale. Being the most recently formed, these ranges, such as the Alps, Himalayas, Andes and Rockies (shown in Fig. 17) are the loftiest and the most imposing. Their peaks are sometimes several miles high. But the time will come when these lofty ranges will be lowered like those that existed before them. From the eroded materials, new rocks will be formed, later to be uplifted to form the next generation of mountains.

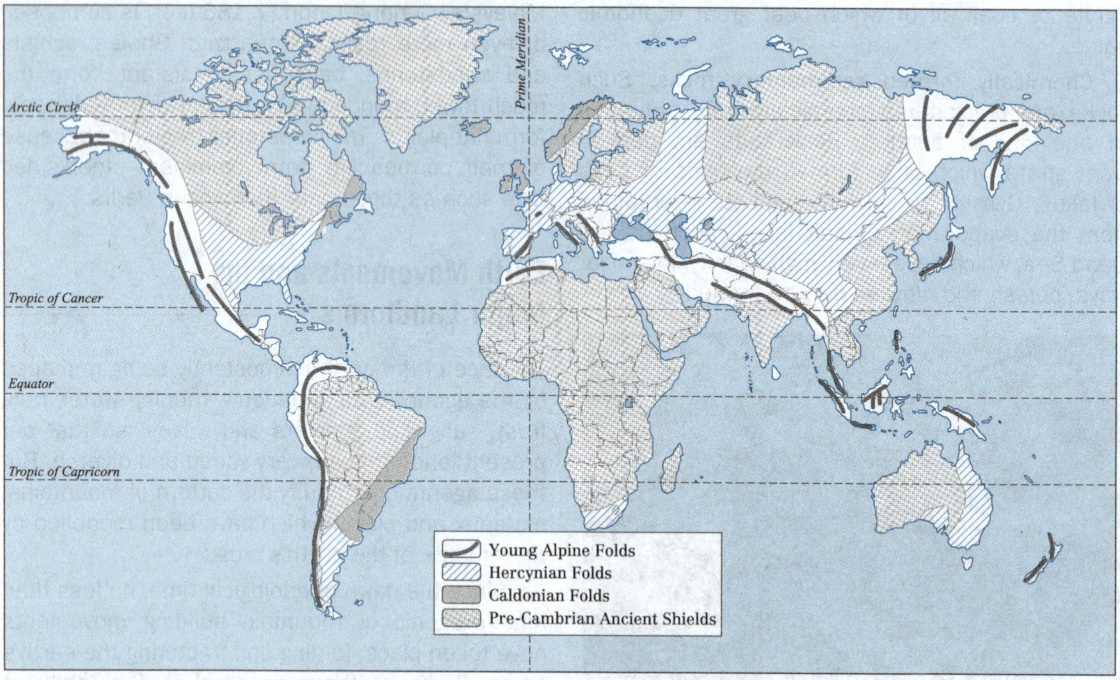

Fig. 17 Structural divisions of the earth

Types of Mountains

Mountains make up a large proportion of the earth's surface. Based on their mode of formation, *four* main types of mountains can be distinguished.

1. **Fold mountains.** These mountains are by far the most widespread and also the most important. They are caused by large-scale earth movements, when stresses are set up in the earth's crust. Such stresses may be due to the increased load of the overlying rocks, flow movements in the mantle, magmatic intrusions into the crust, or the expansion or contraction of some part of the earth. When such stresses are initiated, the rocks are subjected to compressive forces that produce wrinkling or folding along the lines of weakness. As illustrated in Figs. 18 (a) and (b) folding effectively shortens the earth's crust, creating from the original level surface a series of 'waves'. The upfolded waves are called anticlines and the troughs or downfolds are synclines. The formation of up- and downfolds closely resembles that of the wrinkles of a table-cloth when it is pushed from either one or both sides of the table.

In the great fold mountains of the world such as the Himalayas, Rockies, Andes and Alps, due

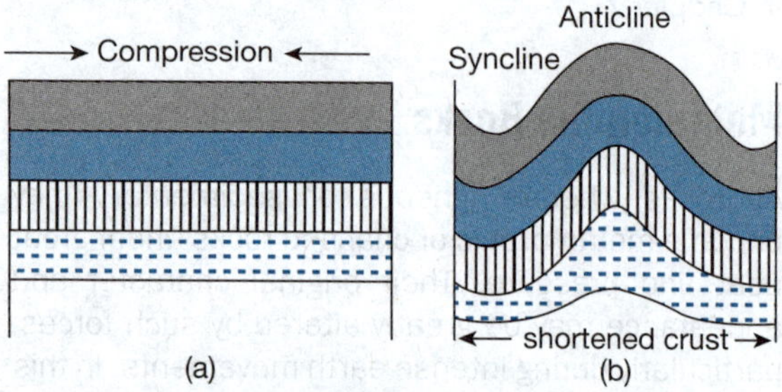

Fig. 18 (a) The horizontal strata of the earth's crust before folding
(b) Compression shortens the crust forming fold mountains

to the complexity of the compressional forces, the folds developed much more complicated forms. When the crest of a fold is pushed too far, an overfold is formed (Fig. 19). If it is pushed still further, it becomes a recumbent fold (Fig. 19). In extreme cases, fractures may occur in the crust, so that the upper part of the recumbent fold slides forward over the lower part along a thrust plane, forming an overthrust fold. The overriding portion of the thrust fold is termed a nappe (Fig. 19). Since the rock strata have been elevated to great

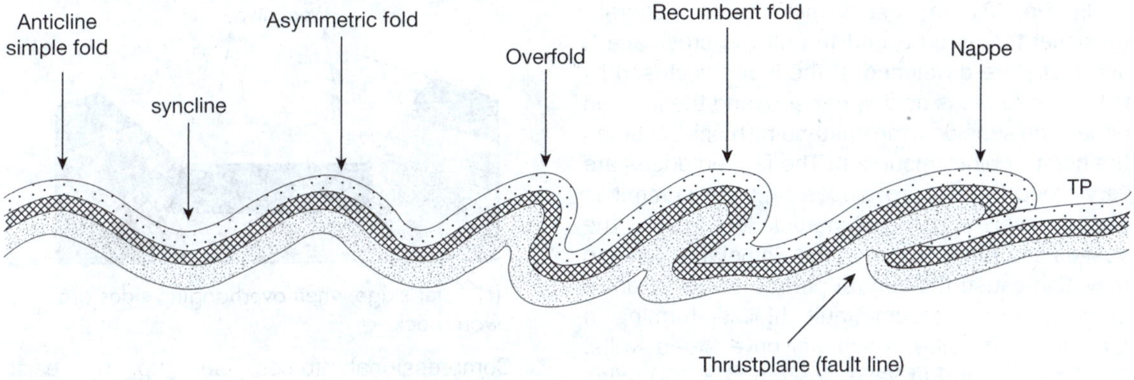

Fig. 19 Types of folding

heights, sometimes measurable in miles, fold mountains may be called mountains of elevation. The fold mountains are also closely associated with volcanic activity. They contain many active volcanoes, especially in the Circum-Pacific fold mountain system. They also contain rich mineral resources such as tin, copper, gold and petroleum.

2. **Block mountains.** When the earth's crust bends folding occurs, but when it cracks, faulting takes place (Fig. 20). Faulting may be caused by tension or compression, forces which lengthen or shorten the earth's crust, causing a section of it to subside or to rise above the surrounding level. Figs. 21 (a) and (b) explain how faulting causes horsts or block mountains and their counterparts graben or rift valleys.

Minor faulting in sedimentary rocks of the Kenny Hill Series. Two small faults have distorted the strata *G.C. Morgan*

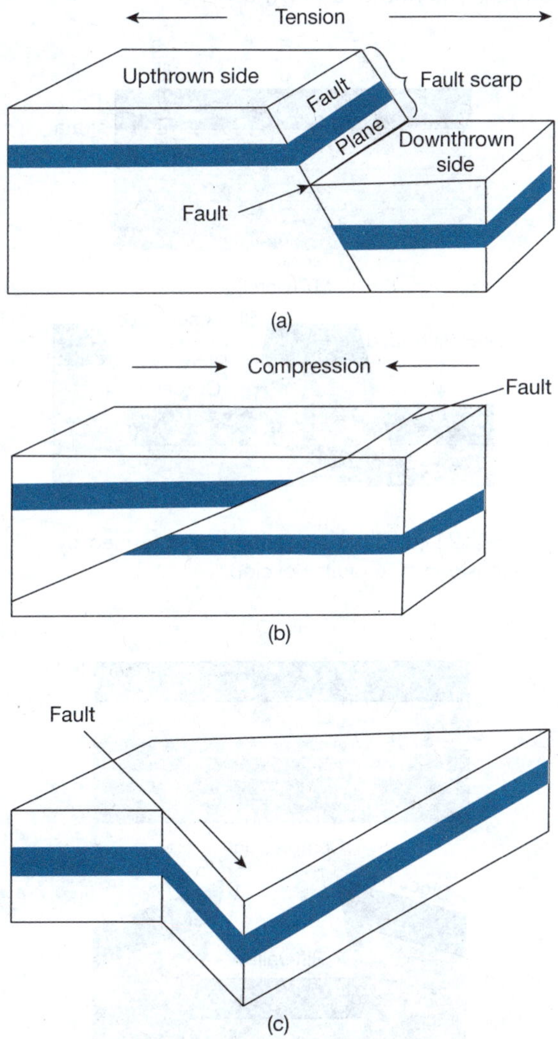

Fig. 20 Normal, reverse and transcurrent faults

In Fig. 21 (a) earth movements generate tensional forces that tend to pull the crust apart, and *faults* are developed. If the block enclosed by the faults remains as it is or rises, and the land on either side subsides, the upstanding block becomes the horst or block mountain. The faulted edges are very steep, with scarp slopes and the summit is almost level, e.g. the Hunsruck Mountains, the Vosges and Black Forest of the Rhineland. Tension may also cause the central portion to be let down between two adjacent fault blocks forming a graben or rift valley, which will have steep walls. The East African Rift Valley system is 3,000 miles (4,828 km) long, stretching from East Africa through the Red Sea to Syria.

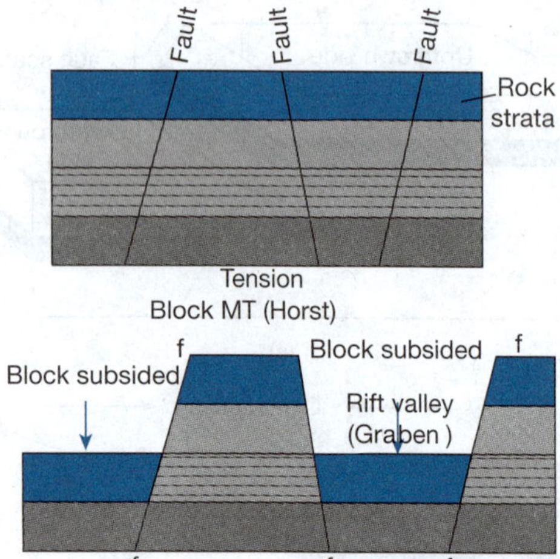

Fig. 21 (a) Block mountain (horst) formed by tension when faults develop

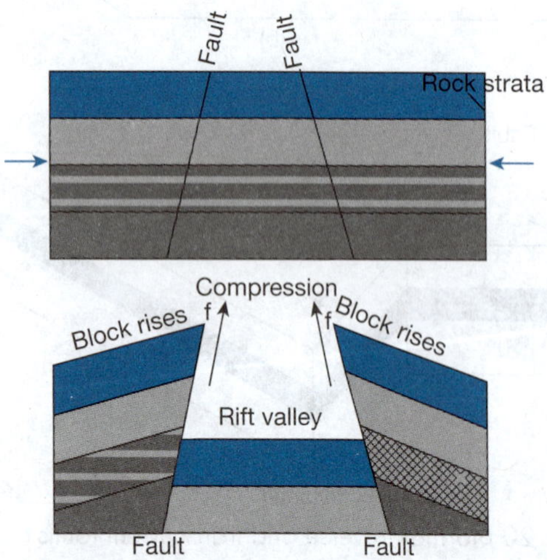

(b) Rift valley formed by compression when faults develop

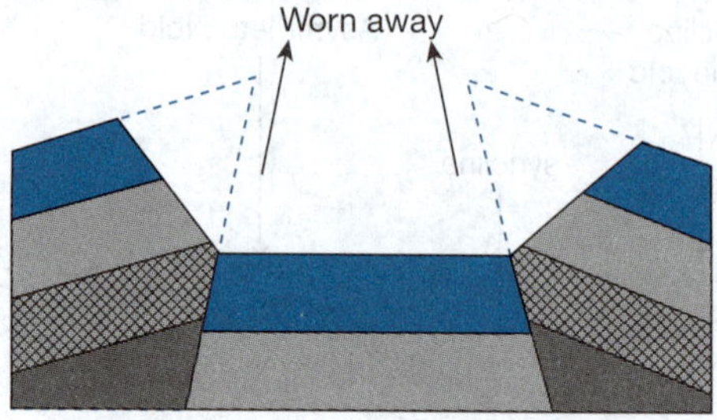

(c) Later stage when overhanging sides are worn back

Compressional forces set up by earth movements may produce a thrust or reverse fault and shorten the crust. A block may be raised or lowered in relation to surrounding areas. Fig. 21 (b) illustrates a rift valley formed in this way. In general large-scale block mountains and rift valleys are due to tension rather than compression. The faults may occur in series and be further complicated by tilting and other irregularities. Denudation through the ages modifies faulted landforms.

3. **Volcanic mountains.** These are, in fact, volcanoes which are built up from material ejected from fissures in the earth's crust. The materials include molten lava, volcanic bombs, cinders, ashes, dust and liquid mud. They fall around the vent in successive layers, building up a characteristic volcanic cone (Fig. 22). Volcanic mountains are often called mountains of accumulation. They are common in the Circum-Pacific belt and include such volcanic peaks as Mt. Fuji (Japan) Mt. Mayon (Philippines), Mt. Merapi (Central Java), Mt. Agung (Bali) and Mt. Catopaxi (Ecuador). Further details are given in Chapter 3.

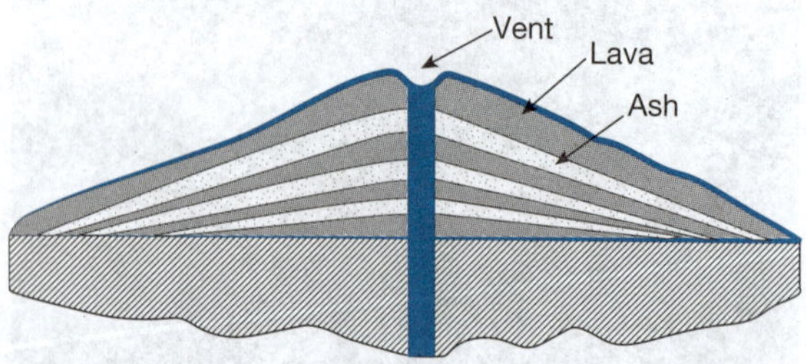

Fig. 22 A volcano or 'mountain of accumulation' with successive layers of lava

4. **Residual mountains.** These are mountains evolved by denudation. Where the general level of the land has been lowered by the agents of denudation some very resistant areas may remain and these form residual mountains, e.g. Mt. Monadnock in USA. Residual mountains may

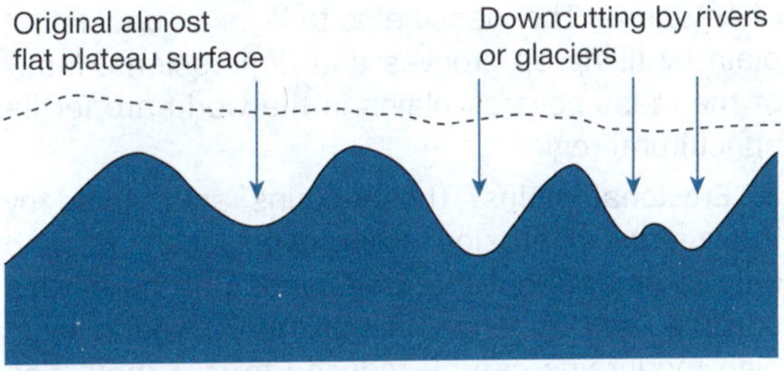

Fig. 23 Residual mountains or mountains of denudation.

also evolve from plateaux which have been dissected by rivers into hills and valleys like the ones illustrated in Fig. 23. Here the ridges and peaks are all very similar in height. Examples of *dissected plateaux,* where the down-cutting streams have eroded the uplands into mountains of denudation, are the Highlands of Scotland, Scandinavia and the Deccan Plateau.

Types of Plateaux

Plateaux are elevated uplands with extensive level surfaces, and usually descend steeply to the surrounding lowland. They are sometimes referred to as tablelands. Like all highlands, plateaux are subjected to erosional processes. As a result, their original characteristics may be greatly altered. According to their mode of formation and their physical appearance, plateaux may be grouped into the following types.

1. **Tectonic plateaux.** These are formed by earth movements which cause uplift, and are normally of a considerable size, and fairly uniform altitude. They include continental blocks like the Deccan Plateau in India. Some of the tectonic plateaux may be *tilted* like the Meseta of central Iberia, or *faulted* like the Harz of Germany.

When plateaux are enclosed by fold mountains, they are known as intermont plateaux. Examples are the Tibetan Plateau between the Himalayas and the Kunlun, and the Bolivian Plateau between two ranges of the Andes. Intermont plateaux are some of the highest and the most extensive plateaux in the world.

2. **Volcanic plateaux.** Molten lava may issue from the earth's crust and spread over its surface to form successive sheets of *basaltic lava*. These solidify to form a lava plateau. Some of the better known volcanic plateaux are the Antrim Plateau of Northern Ireland and the north-western part of the Deccan Plateau. The most remarkable plateau built by lava is the Columbia-Snake Plateau which covers an area almost twice as big as Malaysia. Each layer of the lava flow is over 100 feet or about 30 metres thick, and the entire depth of successive lava layers is estimated to be almost a mile.

3. **Dissected plateaux.** Through the continual process of weathering and erosion by running water, ice and winds, high and extensive plateaux are gradually worn down, and their surfaces made irregular. In the humid highlands, stream action and sometimes glaciation cut deep, narrow valleys in the plateaux, which are then described as dissected plateaux. An example is the Scottish Highlands. In drier countries, vertical corrasion by rivers and abrasion by winds will dissect the plateau into steep-sided tabular masses termed mesas and buttes, intersected by deep canyons. This is a common feature of arid and semi-arid areas, e.g. in the south-western USA.

Many of the world's plateaux have *rich mineral resources* and have been actively mined. The African Plateau yields gold, diamonds, copper, manganese and chromium. In the Brazilian Plateau, there are huge resources of iron and manganese, particularly in the Minas Gerais area. The Deccan Plateau has deposits of manganese, coal and iron and the plateau of Western Australia is rich in gold and iron.

Types of Plains

A plain is an area of lowland, either level or undulating. It seldom rises more than a few hundred feet above sea level. There may be low hills which will give a typical rolling topography. The plains usually form the best land of a country and are often intensively cultivated. Population and settlements are normally concentrated here, and when plains are traversed by rivers, as most of them are, their economic importance may be even greater, e.g. the Indo-Gangetic plain, the Mississippi plain and the Yang-tze plain. Some of the most extensive temperate plains are *grasslands* like the Russian Steppes, the North American Prairies, and the Argentinian Pampas. Plains may be grouped into *three* major types based on their mode of formation.

1. **Structural plains.** These are the structurally depressed areas of the world, that make up some of the most extensive natural lowlands on the earth's surface. They are formed by horizontally bedded rocks, relatively undisturbed by the crustal movements of the earth. They include such great plains as the Russian Platform, the Great Plains of USA and the central lowlands of Australia.

2. **Depositional plains.** These are plains formed by the deposition of materials brought by various agents of transportation. They are comparatively level but rise gently towards adjacent highlands. Their fertility and economic development depend greatly on the types of sediments that are laid down.

Some of the largest depositional plains are due to deposition by large rivers. Active erosion in the upper course results in large quantities of alluvium being brought down to the lower course and deposited to form extensive alluvial plains, flood plains and deltaic plains. They form the most productive agricultural plains of the world, intensively tilled and very densely populated. The Nile delta of Egypt is noted for rice and cotton cultivation, the Ganga delta for rice and jute growing, while the plain of North China, where the Hwang Ho (Yellow river) has spread out a thick mantle of alluvium, supports a wide range of crops.

Glaciers and ice-sheets may deposit a widespread mantle of unsorted fluvio-glacial sands and gravels in the outwash plain or may drop *boulder clay*, a mixture of various sizes of boulders and clay, to form a till plain or drift plain. Outwash plains are usually barren lands, e.g. some parts of the Netherlands and northern Germany, but boulder clay may be very valuable farming land, e.g. the Mid-West of USA and East Anglia in England.

In coastal regions, *waves* and *winds* often drive beach materials, mud, sand or shingle, landwards and deposit them on the coastal plain to form marine swamps, mud-flats, tidal and estuarine lowlands. An appreciable portion of the coastal lowlands of Belgium, the Netherlands and the Gulf Coast of USA were formed in this way. Uplift may raise the coastal lowlands slightly and they then form an emergent coastal plain, e.g. the coastal margins from Florida to Texas.

Winds may blow *aeolian deposits* – very fine particles known as loess – from interior deserts or barren surfaces and deposit them upon hills, valleys or plains forming a *loess plateau,* as in north-west China, or a *loess plain,* as in the Pampas of Argentina. The loess helps to level an undulating plain by filling up grooves and depressions. Many of the loess covered plains in the world are fertile agricultural regions.

3. **Erosional plains.** These plains are carved by the agents of erosion. Rain, rivers, ice and wind help to smooth out the irregularities of the earth's surface, and in terms of millions of years, even high mountains can be reduced to low undulating plains. Such *plains of denudation* are described as peneplains a word meaning 'almost-plains'.

Rivers, in their course from source to sea, deepen their valleys and widen their banks. The projecting spurs are cut back so that the level ground bordering the river is constantly widened. At the same time the higher land between the rivers is gradually lowered (Fig. 24).

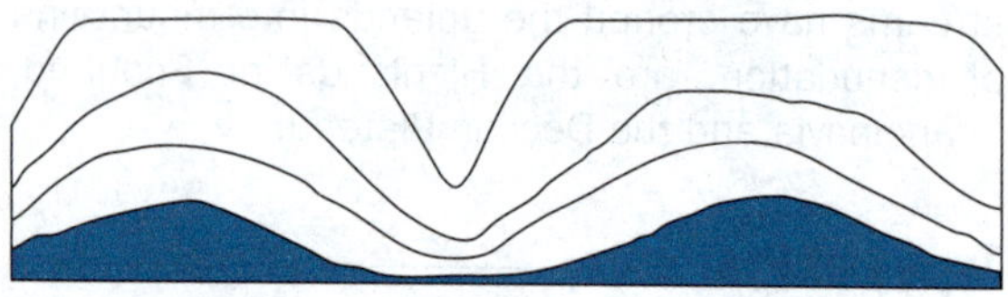

Fig. 24 Peneplain
In the formation of a peneplain in humid conditions the hills are both lowered and worn back to give an undulating lowland

In *glaciated regions,* glaciers and ice-sheets scoured and levelled the land forming ice-scoured plains. Hollows scooped out by the ice are now filled by lakes. There are extensive ice-scoured plains in northern Europe and northern Canada. Finland is estimated to have over 180,000 lakes, occupying 10% of the total land surface of the country.

In arid and semi-arid regions, wind deflation sweeps away much of the eroded desert materials, lowering the level of land and forming extensive plains, e.g. the gravelly or stony desert plains called reg in Africa. *Mechanical weathering* in arid and semi-arid areas *wears back* the mountain slopes to leave a gently sloping pediments or pediplains (Fig. 25).

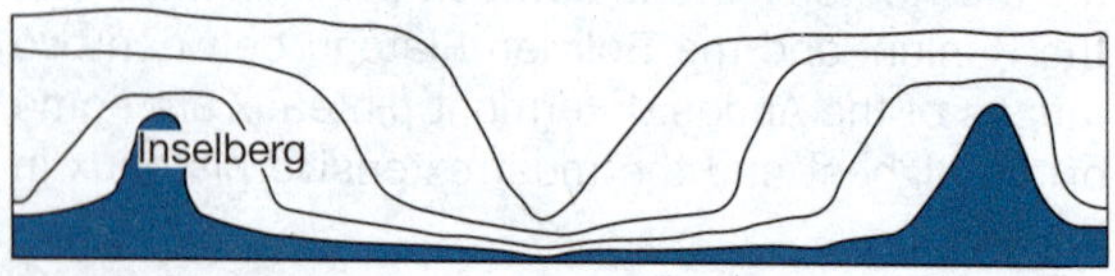

Fig. 25 Pediplain
In the formation of a pediplain in arid or semi-arid conditions the hills are worn back to form a gently sloping plain but some steep hills remain. These are called inselbergs

QUESTIONS AND EXERCISES

1. *Either*: Attempt a classification of mountains according to their mode of formation.

   Or: Explain why a knowledge of rocks and their structures is essential in the interpretation of landforms.
2. With the aid of diagrams, explain the difference in appearance and formation of any *three* of the following:
   (a) folds and faults
   (b) dissected plateau and intermont plateau
   (c) alluvial plain and peneplain
   (d) sima and sial
   (e) lithosphere and mantle
3. What is a sedimentary rock? In what way is it different from igneous rocks? Describe the various sources from which sedimentary rocks may be derived. (Quote actual examples of sedimentary rocks to support your answer.)
4. For each of the following:

   a young fold mountain
   a rift valley
   a loess plain

   (a) Draw a simple diagram to show its characteristic relief.
   (b) Explain its origin.
   (c) Name and locate a region where such a feature may be found.
5. *Either*: Describe and explain the following selected landforms
   (a) Antrim Plateau
   (b) Russian Platform
   (c) Scottish Highlands

   Or: Explain the meaning of any *four* of the following terms connected with the study of landforms and the earth's crust.

   basalt, orogenesis, recumbent fold, fossiliferous rocks, horst, syncline.

3 Volcanism and Earthquakes

Landforms Associated with Volcanic Activities

Volcanic activities have a profound influence on the earth's landforms. Solid, liquid or gaseous materials may find their way to the surface from some deep-seated reservoir beneath. Molten magma is mobile rock that forces its way into the planes of weakness of the crust to escape quietly or explosively to the surface. The resultant landforms depend on the strength and fluidity of the magma, the types of cracks, faults and joints that it penetrates, and the manner in which it escapes to the surface. Magma while thrusting its way up to the surface may cool and solidify within the crust as plutonic rocks resulting in intrusive landforms. Magmas that reach the surface and solidify, form extrusive landforms. Rocks formed by either plutonic or volcanic activity are called igneous rocks.

Landforms of Igneous Intrusions

Perhaps the commonest intrusive landforms are *sills* and *dykes*. When an intrusion of molten magma is made horizontally along the bedding planes of sedimentary rocks, the resultant intrusion is called a sill. Denudation of the overlying sedimentary strata will expose the intrusion which will resemble a lava flow, or form a bold escarpment like the Great Whin Sill of N.E. England. Similar intrusions when injected vertically as narrow walls of igneous rocks within the sedimentary layers are termed as dykes.

Because of their narrowness, dykes seldom dominate the landscape. When exposed to denudation they may appear as upstanding walls or shallow trenches, depending on whether they are more or less resistant than the rocks in which they are emplaced. Examples of dykes are the Cleveland Dyke (or Armathwaite Dyke) of

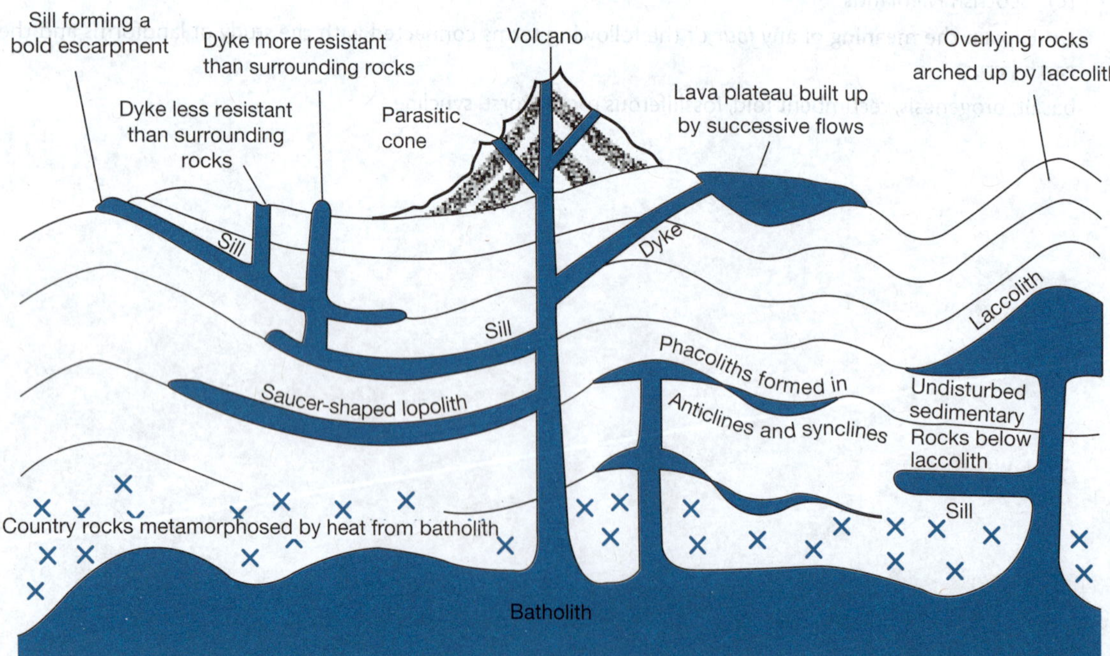

Fig. 26 Intrusive landforms of igneous intrusions in volcanic regions (showing sill, dyke, laccolith, lopolith phacolith and batholith)

North Yorkshire, England and hundreds of others in the Isles of Mull and Arran in Scotland. A large, very resistant dyke of quartzite forms a long ridge to the north of Kuala Lumpur.

Igneous intrusions on a larger scale are the various types of '—liths': *laccoliths, lopoliths, phacoliths* and *batholiths* (Fig. 26). The names may sound difficult; they are, in fact, all variations of igneous intrusions placed differently in the earth's crust, and solidifying within the upper layers of the crust. A laccolith is a large blister or igneous mound with a *dome-shaped* upper surface and a level base fed by a pipe-like conduit from below. It arches up the overlying strata of sedimentary rocks, e.g. the laccoliths of the Henry Mountains, in Utah, USA.

A lopolith is another variety of igneous intrusion with a *saucer shape*. A shallow basin is formed in the midst of the country rocks. The Bushveld lopoliths of Transvaal system, South Africa are good examples.

A phacolith is a lens-shaped mass of igneous rocks occupying the crest of an *anticline* or the bottom of a *syncline* and being fed by a conduit from beneath. An example of a phacolith is Corndon Hill in Shropshire, United Kingdom.

A batholith is a huge mass of igneous rocks, usually *granite*, which after removal of the overlying rocks forms a massive and resistant upland region such as the Wicklow Mountains of Ireland, the uplands of Britanny, France and the Main Range of West Malaysia. Their precise mode of origin is still a matter of controversy. It is generally believed that large masses of magma rising upwards *metamorphosed* the country rocks with which they came into contact. These metamorphosed rocks together with the solidified magma give rise to extensive batholiths, sometimes hundreds of miles in extent. They are the most spectacular of the intrusive landforms.

The Origin of Volcanoes

The ancient Greeks believed that volcanic eruptions occurred when Vulcan, the God of the Underworld, stoked his subterranean furnace beneath Vulcano, a small volcanic island off Sicily, from which the present word volcano is derived. Of course, we no longer believe this is true. Geologists and volcanologists have ascertained that volcanic activity is closely connected with *crustal disturbances*,

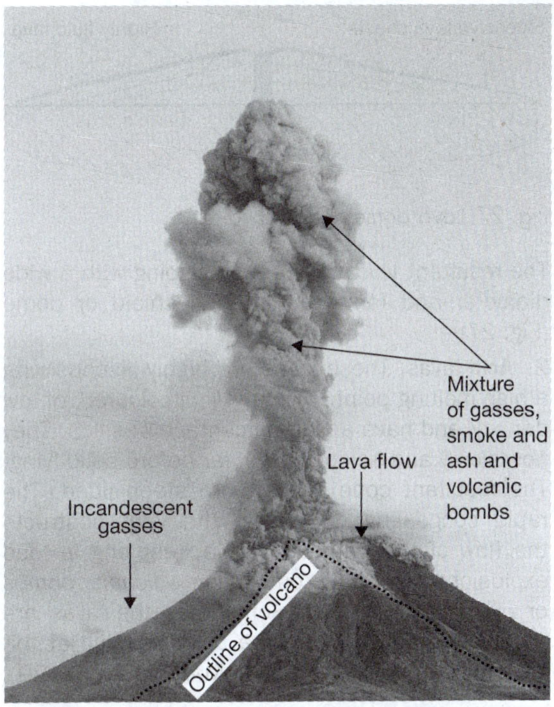

Mt. Mayon, Philippines, in eruption

particularly where there are zones of weakness due to deep faulting or mountain folding. As temperature increases with increasing depth below the earth's crust, at an average rate of about 1°F. for every 65 feet of descent, the interior of the earth can be expected to be in a semi-molten state, comprising solid, liquid and gaseous materials, collectively termed *magma*.

The magma is heavily charged with gases such as carbon dioxide, sulphurated hydrogen, and small proportions of nitrogen, chlorine and other volatile substances. The gases and vapour increase the mobility and explosiveness of the *lavas* which are emitted through the orifice or vent of a volcano during a volcanic eruption. There are two main types of *lavas*.

1. **Basic lavas.** These are the hottest lavas, about 1,000°C (1,832°F) and are highly fluid. They are dark coloured like *basalt*, rich in iron and magnesium but poor in silica. As they are poured out of the volcano, they flow *quietly* and are not very explosive. Due to their high fluidity, they *flow readily* with a speed of 10 to 30 miles (16 to 48 km) per hour. They affect *extensive* areas, spreading out as *thin sheets* over great distances before they solidify.

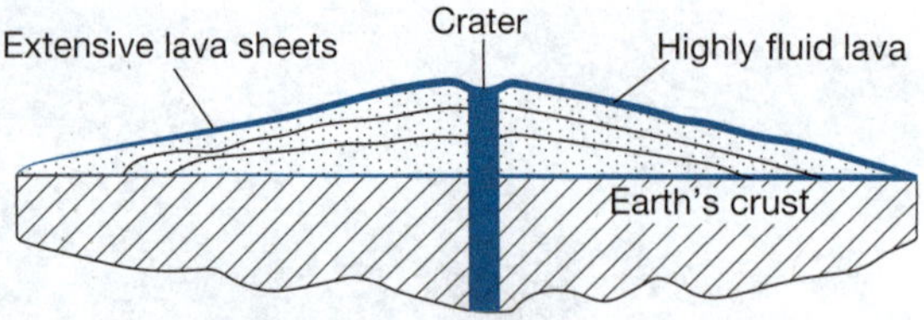

Fig. 27 Lava dome or shield volcano

The resultant *volcano* is gently sloping with a wide diameter and forms a flattened shield or dome (Fig. 27).

2. **Acid lavas.** These lavas are highly viscous with a high melting point. They are *light-coloured,* of low density, and have a high percentage of silica. They *flow slowly* and seldom travel far before solidifying. The resultant cone is therefore steep-sided. The rapid congealing of lava in the vent obstructs the flow of the outpouring lava, resulting in loud explosions, throwing out many *volcanic bombs* or *pyroclasts* (Fig. 28). Sometimes the lavas are so viscous that they form a spine or plug at the crater like that of Mt. Pelee in Martinique (Fig. 29).

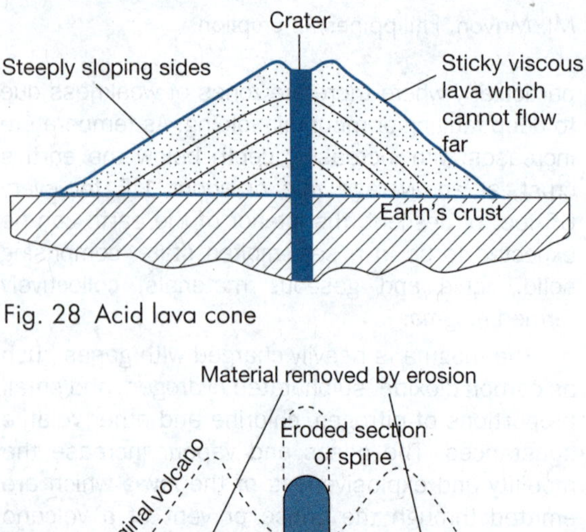

Fig. 28 Acid lava cone

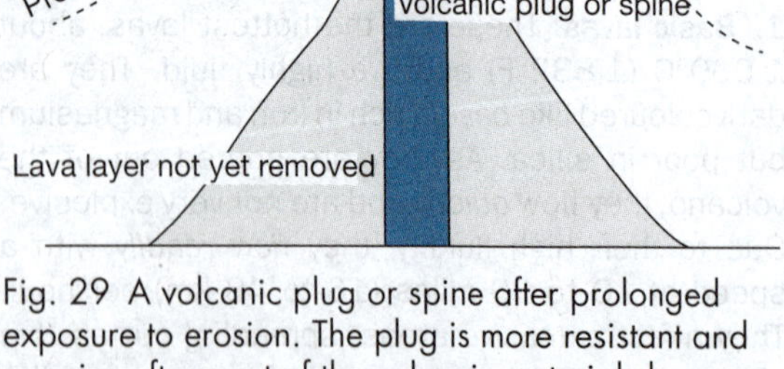

Fig. 29 A volcanic plug or spine after prolonged exposure to erosion. The plug is more resistant and remains after most of the volcanic materials have been worn away.

Some spines are very resistant and while most of the material of very old volcanoes is removed by erosion the spine may remain, e.g. Puy-de-Dôme, France.

Types of Volcanoes

There are three types of volcanoes: *active*, *dormant* and *extinct*. Volcanoes are said to be active when they frequently erupt or at least when they have erupted within recent time. Those that have been known to erupt and show signs of possible eruption in the future are described as dormant. Volcanoes that have not erupted at all in historic times but retain the features of volcanoes are termed extinct. All volcanoes pass through active, dormant and extinct stages but we can never be thoroughly sure when they are extinct. Mt. Vesuvius (Italy) and Mt. Krakatau (Indonesia) were once thought by people to be extinct and yet both erupted most violently.

Extrusive Landforms

Extrusive landforms are determined by the nature and composition of the lava and other ejected materials that reach the surface of the earth. The fluid *basic lava,* flowing for long distances produces extensive lava plains and basalt plateaux, such as the great lava plains of the Snake River Basin, USA. The basalt plateaux are found in many continents, e.g. the north- western part of the Deccan Plateau in India (Asia) and in Iceland (Europe).

Volcanic cones are most typical of the extrusive features. The highly fluid lavas build up lava domes or shield volcanoes with gently rising slopes and broad, flattened tops. The volcanoes of Hawaii have the best developed lava domes. The spectacular Mauna Loa and Kilauea are so accessible that they have been closely studied. Kilauea has a very steep-walled caldera into which the active vent pours red hot lava forming the *lava-pit* of Halemaumau (also Halema`uma`u). Thousands of lava fountains rise and fall in the dazzling pit.

The less fluid lavas that explode more violently form ash and cinder cones with large central craters and steep slopes. They are typical of small volcanoes, occurring in groups and seldom exceeding 1,000 feet or 300 metres in height, such as Mt. Nuovo, near Naples (Italy) and Mt. Paricutin in Mexico. The lava flows are so viscous that they solidify after a short distance. When they are confined in valleys, they form lava tongues and *lava-dammed lakes* when they dam a river valley. Other minor features that may be associated with lava obstructions include lava bridges and lava tunnels.

A volcanic region may be strewn with solid materials that were hurled from the vent of the volcano. The very fine particles are the volcanic dust which may be shot so high into the sky that it travels round the world several times before it eventually comes to rest. The dust or ash falls as 'black snow' and can bury houses and people. The coarser fragmental rocks are collectively called pyroclasts and include cinders or *lapilli, scoria, pumice* and *volcanic bombs*.

The highest and most common volcanoes have composite cones. They are often called strato-volcanoes. The cones are built up by several eruptions of lava, ashes and other volcanic materials from the main conduit which leads down a reservoir of magma. Each new eruption adds new layers of ashes or lava to the sides of the volcano, which grows steadily in height. From the main conduit, subsidiary dykes or pipes may reach the surface as feeders to parasitic cones. Lava escapes through them to the sides of the main cones (Fig. 30). Mt. Etna in Sicily (Italy) has hundreds of such parasitic cones. Another interesting composite volcano is Mt. Stromboli (Italy) whose frequent eruptions that make the summit glow have earned for it the name *'Lighthouse of the Mediterranean'*. Other well-known composite volcanoes include Mt. Vesuvius (Italy), Mt. Fuji (Japan), Mt. Popocatépetl (Mexico) and Mt. Chimborazo (Ecuador).

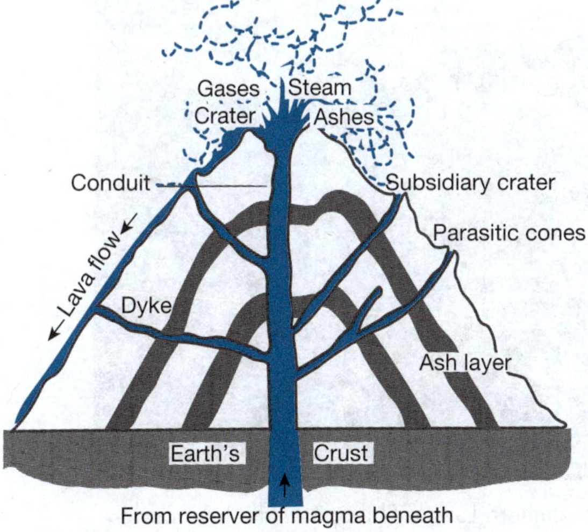

Fig. 30 A composite cone

During an eruption material from the top of the cone is blown off or collapses into the vent widening the orifice into a large crater. Some volcanoes may have greatly enlarged depressions called calderas, which may be several miles across. These are the result of violent eruptions accompanied by the subsidence of much of the volcano into the magma beneath (Fig. 31). Water may collect in the crater or the caldera forming crater or caldera lakes, e.g. Lake Toba in Sumatra.

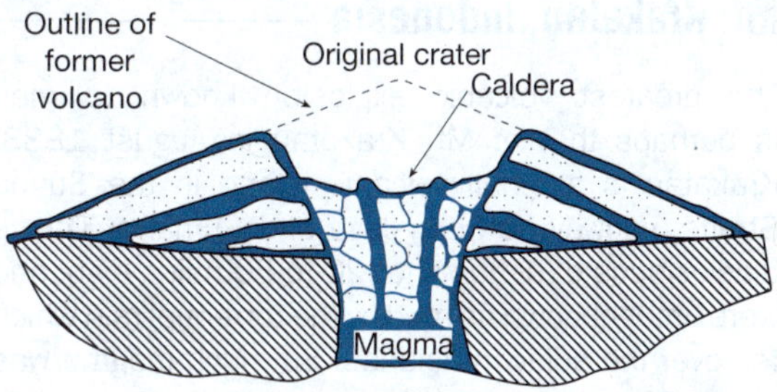

Fig. 31 A caldera. A violent eruption weakens the structure of the volcano and after eruption has ceased much of the volcano subsides into the magma reservoir beneath. The depression may later be filled with water to form a lake.

Some Volcanic Eruptions

In the history of mankind perhaps the most disastrous eruptions were those of Mt. Vesuvius, Mt. Krakatau and Mt. Pelee.

Mt. Vesuvius, Italy

Mt. Vesuvius, standing about 4,000 feet or 1,220 metres above the Bay of Naples, erupted violently on 24 August CE 79 taking the people who lived around it by complete surprise. White-hot lava flowed from parasitic cones. In the midst of a thundering explosion, the highly gaseous magma escaped as gigantic luminous clouds in cauliflower form and shot up to great heights before it fell to earth as pyroclasts and ashes. The city of Pompeii, located to the south-west, was buried beneath 20 feet of volcanic ashes which were later cemented by the torrential downpours of heavy rain that accompanied the violent eruption. In a similar way, the city of Herculaneum on the west was completely overwhelmed by a mudflow of ashes and cinders almost 50 feet thick, washed down by torrential rain from the slopes of Vesuvius. Almost the entire population of the two cities was buried alive.

After this, minor eruptions occurred from time to time, but the fertility of the solidified volcanic ashes tempted many farmers to begin anew on the slopes of Vesuvius. Then came the catastrophic eruption of December 1631 when an avalanche comprising red hot volcanic debris, pasty lava and highly energized gases ruined fifteen towns and killed about 4,000 inhabitants. The ashes that descended on Naples were estimated to be a foot thick.

Mt. Krakatau, Indonesia

The greatest volcanic explosion known to men is perhaps that of Mt. Krakatau in August 1883. Krakatau is a small volcanic island in the Sunda Straits, midway between Java and Sumatra. Dense black clouds of ashes shot 20 to 50 miles high, and were brought down as mud by the torrential rain which fell over the adjacent islands. So much magma was ejected from the underlying reservoir that two-thirds of the island collapsed and disappeared forming a huge submarine caldera. The explosion could be heard in Australia, almost 3,000 miles (4,828 km) away. The fine dust that was thrown into the upper part of the atmosphere travelled several times around the world, causing brilliant sunsets and glowing sky in many parts of the globe. Though Krakatau itself was not inhabited and nobody was killed by the lava flows, the vibration set up enormous waves over 100 feet high which drowned 36,000 people in the coastal districts of Indonesia.

After remaining dormant for almost half a century, an eruption in 1927 pushed up a cinder cone from the submarine floor, culminating in a summit of 220 feet above sea level by 1952. This new volcanic island was named Anak Krakatau, meaning 'the child of Mt. Krakatau'.

Mt. Pelee, (Martinique)

The eruption of Mt. Pelee of the West Indies in May 1902 was the most catastrophic of modern times. The volcano erupted white-hot lava and super-heated steam which swept down the slope at an amazing speed as a *nuee ardente* (glowing avalanche). St. Pierre, the capital of Martinique, lying on the path of the lava, was completely destroyed within minutes. Its entire population of 30,000, except two of them, was killed almost instantly. Even the sea was boiling and all the ships in the harbour were wrecked.

The ejection of volcanic materials continued for several months until a vertical spine rose from the crater, almost a thousand feet high by the middle of 1903. The spine was formed by the pasty lava, partially solidified in the neck of the volcano. Part of the spine, however, crumbled under continual weathering as well as internal forces.

Mt. Mayon as viewed from the town of Legazpi, southern Luzon, Philippine. Hot lava and steam violently erupted from the crater of Mayon volcano during the eruption on the morning of July 16, 2006.

The Distribution of Volcanoes in the World

Volcanoes are located in a fairly clearly-defined pattern around the world, closely related to regions that have been intensely folded or faulted. There are well over 500 active volcanoes and thousands of dormant and extinct ones. They occur along coastal mountain ranges, as offshore islands and in the midst of oceans, but there are few in the interiors of continents. The greatest concentration is probably that in the Circum-Pacific region, popularly termed the *'Pacific Ring of Fire'*, which has been estimated to include two-thirds of the world's volcanoes (Fig. 32). The chain of volcanoes extends for almost 2,000 miles (about 3,200 km) from the Aleutian Islands into Kamchatka, Japan, the Philippines, and Indonesia (Java and Sumatra in particular), southwards into the Pacific islands of Solomon, New Hebrides, Tonga and North Island, New Zealand. On the other side of the Pacific, the chain continues from the Andes to Central America (particularly Guatemala, Costa Rica and Nicaragua), Mexico and right up to Alaska. It is said that there are almost 24 active volcanoes in the Philippines (out of around 300 volvanoes), 44 in the Andes, 110 in Japan, and more than 70 in Indonesia.

In contrast, the *Atlantic coasts* have comparatively few active volcanoes but many dormant or extinct volcanoes, e.g. Madeira, Ascension, St. Helena, Cape Verde Islands and Canary Islands, but those of Iceland and the Azores are active. Volcanoes of the Mediterranean region are mainly associated with the Alpine folds, e.g. Vesuvius, Etna, Stromboli, Vulcano and those of the Aegean islands. A few continue into Asia Minor (Mt. Ararat, Mt. Elbruz). **The Himalayas have, surprisingly, no active volcano at all.**

In *Africa* some volcanoes are found along the East African Rift Valley, e.g. Mt. Kilimanjaro and Mt. Kenya, both probably extinct. The only active volcano of West Africa is Mt. Cameroon. There are some volcanic cones in Madagascar, but active eruption has not been known so far. The *West Indian islands*

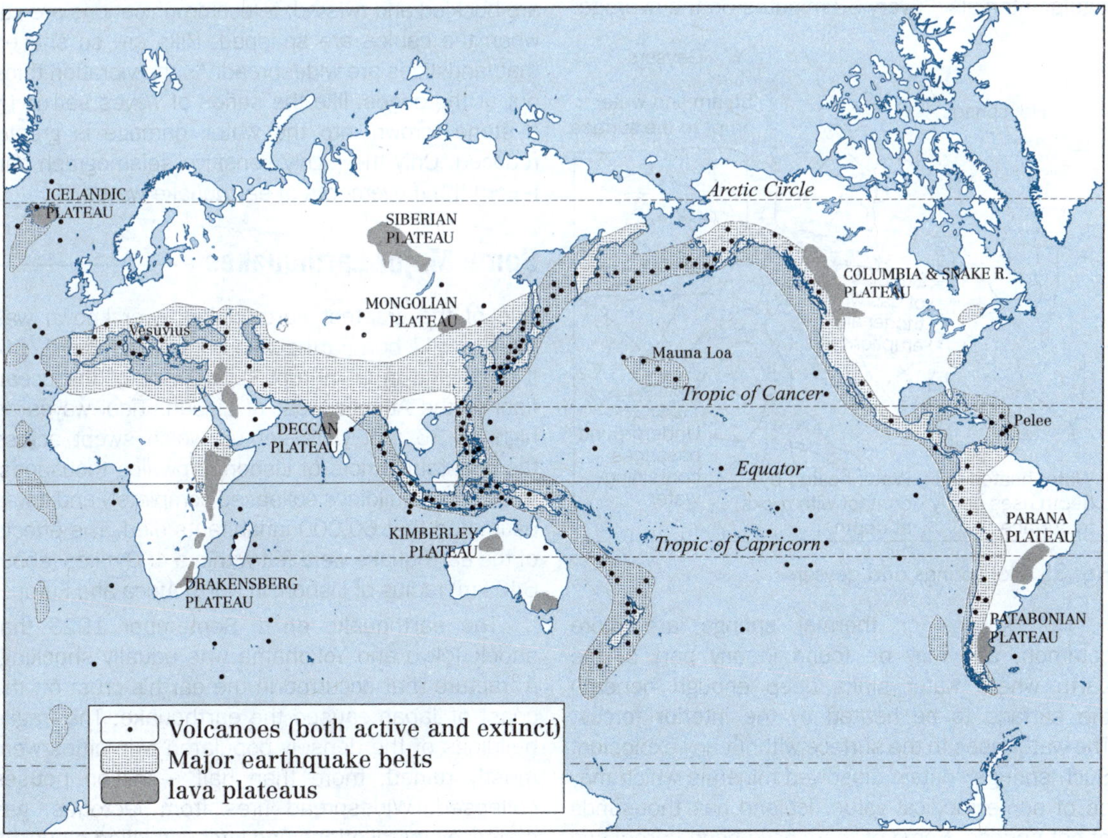

Fig. 32 World distribution of volcanoes, lava plateaux and earthquakes

have experienced some violent explosions in recent times, e.g. Mt. Pelee in Martinique, and in St. Vincent further south. The Lesser Antilles are made up mainly of volcanic islands and some of them still bear signs of volcanic liveliness. Elsewhere in the interiors of continents – Asia, North America, Europe and Australia, active volcanoes are rare.

Geysers and Hot Springs

Geysers are fountains of hot water and superheated steam that may spout up to a height of 150 feet from the earth beneath. The phenomena are associated with a thermal or volcanic region in which the water below is being heated beyond boiling-point (100°C. or 212°F.). The jet of water is usually emitted with an explosion, and is often triggered off by gases seeping out of the heated rocks (Fig. 33). Almost all the world's geysers are confined to three major areas: Iceland, the Rotorua district of North Island, New Zealand and Yellowstone Park of USA. The world's best known geyser is perhaps 'Old Faithful' in Yellowstone National Park, Wyoming which erupts at regular intervals – every 63 minutes on the average.

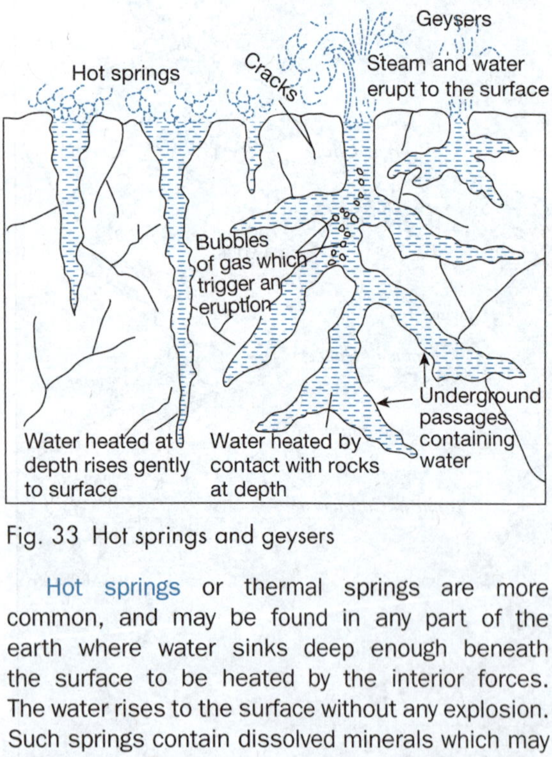

Fig. 33 Hot springs and geysers

Hot springs or thermal springs are more common, and may be found in any part of the earth where water sinks deep enough beneath the surface to be heated by the interior forces. The water rises to the surface without any explosion. Such springs contain dissolved minerals which may be of some medical value. Iceland has thousands of hot springs. Some of them have been harnessed to heat houses, swimming pools and for other domestic purposes. Hot springs and geysers have become tourist attractions, e.g. in Japan and Hawaii.

Earthquakes

The earth is never free from earthquakes for long and more than 50,000 of them are recorded annually. Minor earth tremors caused by gentle waves of vibration within the earth's crust occur every few minutes. Major earthquakes, usually caused by movement along faults, can be very disastrous particularly in densely populated areas. Earthquakes themselves may cause only restricted damage in the regions of occurrence, but their after-effects can be very catastrophic. They produce gigantic tidal waves, called tsunamis by the Japanese, which flood towns and drown thousands of people. Fires break out beyond control as gas mains are shattered and buildings collapse. In severe earthquakes, fissures gape open, and the ground writhes and undulates in the passage of the 'surface waves'. A wave height of a quarter of an inch in the upheaval is sufficient to bring down most ordinary buildings. Roads, railways and bridges are buckled and twisted; telecommunications are cut when the cables are snapped. Hills are so shaken that landslides are widespread. As the vibration thins out at the edges, like the series of waves set up by a stone thrown into the water, damage is greatly reduced. Only the highly sensitive seismograph can record the movements of earthquake waves.

Some Major Earthquakes

One of the greatest earthquakes ever known was the Great Lisbon Earthquake on 1 November 1755. It originated in an abrupt subsidence of the ocean floor in the Atlantic west of Lisbon. Tidal waves as high as 35 feet were set up which swept across the coastal districts of Lisbon, drowning thousands. Most of the buildings collapsed completely and it was estimated that 60,000 inhabitants died. The effects of the earthquake were felt within a 400 miles (about 640 km) radius of Lisbon, in North Africa and Europe.

The earthquake on 1 September 1923 that shook Tokyo and Yokohama was equally shocking. A fracture that occurred in the earth's crust off the coast of Japan caused the earthquake. The fragile buildings of the densely populated twin cities were mostly ruined; more than half a million houses collapsed. Widespread fires from factories, gas mains, oil installations and kitchens killed a quarter of a million people and many more were injured.

Other disastrous earthquakes include that of *San Francisco* in 1906 which ruined the greater part of the heart of San Francisco. In the loess region of *Kansu* in China, the 1920 earthquake claimed 200,000 lives, and again in 1927 when 100,000 cave-dwellers were buried alive. In 1960, the earthquake at *Agadir,* Morocco sealed the fate of 10,000 inhabitants, besides causing untold damage, and in 1968 there was a disastrous earthquake in eastern Iran, with its epicentre at *Kakh*.

The 2004 Indian Ocean tsunami was one of the deadliest disasters in modern history, causing widespread destruction and a significant loss of life. It resulted in the deaths of approximately 230,000 people and left millions displaced in countries such as Indonesia, Sri Lanka, India, Maldives, and Thailand. This catastrophic event occurred on December 26, 2004, at 7:59 AM local time when a powerful earthquake measuring 9.1 magnitude struck off the coast of Sumatra, Indonesia. The ensuing tsunami, a series of massive ocean waves, spread across the Indian Ocean over the next seven hours, causing extensive damage even as far as East Africa. In some areas, the waves reached heights of 30 feet (9 metres) or more upon reaching the shore.

Post-tsunami debris in Banda Aceh, Indonesia, 2004

The Distribution of Earthquakes

The world's distribution of earthquakes coincides very closely with that of volcanoes. Regions of greatest seismicity are Circum-Pacific areas, with the epicentres and the most frequent occurrences along the *'Pacific Ring of Fire'*. It is said that as many as 70 per cent of earthquakes occur in the Circum-Pacific belt. Another 20 per cent of earthquakes take place in the *Mediterranean-Himalayan belt* including Asia Minor, the Himalayas and parts of north-west China. Elsewhere, the earth's crust is relatively stable and is less prone to earthquakes, though nowhere can be said to be immune to earth tremors.

QUESTIONS AND EXERCISES

1. With the aid of annotated diagrams, write a comparative account of landforms resulting from intrusive and extrusive igneous activities.
2. Distinguish the difference in appearance and origin of any *three* of the following pairs of terms associated with volcanicity.
   (a) sills and dykes
   (b) cinder cones and lava domes
   (c) geysers and hot springs
   (d) crater and caldera
   (e) laccolith and lopolith
3. Describe, with appropriate sketches, the major types of landforms originating from acid and basic lavas.
4. On a map of the world, locate the chief volcanic and earthquake areas. Write a descriptive account of any *one* major volcanic eruption or earthquake that has occurred in historical times. You should include the causes, effects and consequences of such a named occurrence.
5. The following terms are in one way or another connected with volcanoes and earthquakes. Choose *one* term from each of the sections A, B and C and write what you know about them:

Section A	*Section B*	*Section C*
magma	basalt plateau	Vulcano
lava	lava plain	tsunami
pyroclasts	parasitic cones	'Old Faithful'

4 Weathering, Mass Movement and Groundwater

The earth's crust is constantly undergoing geological changes caused by internal forces, which create new relief features. Orogenesis build new mountain ranges, uplift or depression of particular areas is caused by folding or faulting, and volcanic disturbances also modify the landscape. Meanwhile external forces are working vigorously to wear away the surface, and the interaction of these constructive and destructive forces gives rise to the great diversity of present-day landforms. The process of wearing away the earth causes a general lowering and levelling out of the surface. It is known as denudation and is carried out in four phases.

i. *Weathering:* the gradual disintegration of rocks by atmospheric or weather forces;
ii. *Erosion:* the active wearing away of the earth's surface by moving agents like running water, wind, ice and waves;
iii. *Transportation:* the removal of the eroded debris to new positions;
iv. *Deposition:* the dumping of the debris in certain parts of the earth, where it may accumulate to form new rocks.

All four phases of the denudation process are taking place simultaneously in different parts of the world at different rates, much depending on the nature of the relief, the structure of the rocks, the local climate and interference by man.

This chapter describes the work of weathering and the features it produces, while Chapters 5 to 10 deal with erosion, transportation and deposition by water, wind, ice and waves.

Weathering

The work of weathering in breaking up the rocks is of two kinds, namely chemical, and physical or mechanical weathering, but the processes involved in each are closely interrelated.

1. Chemical weathering

Chemical weathering is the basic process by which denudation proceeds. It is the extremely slow and gradual decomposition of rocks due to exposure to air and water. Air and water contain chemical elements, which though they may be in small quantities, are sufficient to set up chemical reactions in the surface layers of exposed rocks. Such reactions may weaken or entirely dissolve certain constituents of the rock, thus loosening the other crystals and weakening the whole surface. For example, in Malaysia, the surface of granite which has been exposed to the weather is found to be pitted and rough. This is because the granite is made of three main minerals: quartz, felspar and mica. The felspar is more quickly weathered than the quartz and thus the felspar crystals are worn away. The quartz crystals are eventually loosened in this way and form a coarse sandy residue.

When the surface of a rock is weathered some of the material which is loosened is removed by erosive agents such as wind or running water thus exposing a fresh surface to weathering, but much of the weathered material or *regolith* (remains of the rock) may stay in position forming the basis of soil. Regolith is simply the mineral remains of decomposed rocks, but soil contains organic materials, such as the roots of plants, fallen leaves, small animals such as worms, bacteria and so on. It is the organic content of soil which makes it fertile and allows crops to be grown.

When a soil cover exists, chemical weathering of the underlying rocks does not cease; on the contrary it is usually enhanced. This is because the soil absorbs rainwater and keeps the underlying rocks in contact with this moisture. The rainwater absorbs organic acids from the soil and thus becomes a stronger weathering agent than pure rainwater acting on bare rock.

There are three major chemical weathering processes.

(a) **Solution.** Many minerals are dissolved by water, especially when, as with rainwater, it contains enough carbon dioxide to make it a weak acid. Solution is the most potent weathering process in limestone regions because the rainwater attacks and dissolves the calcium carbonate of which the rock is chiefly formed. The dissolved calcium carbonate is carried away by the water, joints and cracks in the rock are quickly widened and whole systems of caves and passages are worn out (see Chapter 8). Limestone, however, is by no means the only rock to suffer from solution. All rocks are subject to solution to some extent, though the process is much slower than with limestone. The rate at which solution takes place is affected not only by the mineral composition of the rock but also by its structure, Sedimentary rocks often have pore-spaces between the grains in which air and water can lodge and thus attack the rock. The density of joints or cracks in the rock is also crucial to the speed of weathering. This factor is very clearly seen in Malaysia and Kazakhstan in the weathering of granite. Mostly, in tropical countries, where the heavy rainfall and warm climate both promote rapid chemical reactions, weathering often proceeds very rapidly. This produces the very deep regoliths or soils overlying the solid rocks. Often these regoliths contain corestones. These are pieces of solid rock which have resisted weathering while all the surrounding rock has been weathered. They are more resistant because they have fewer joints or cracks to harbour moisture and are thus more slowly weathered by solution processes (Fig. 34 and Plate 4.A).

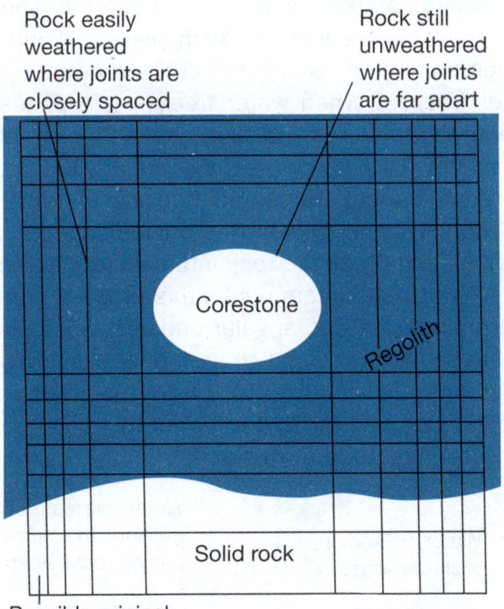

Fig. 34 Differential weathering in a rock such as granite where unevenly spaced joints may give rise to corestones and certain blocks remain unweathered. In jointed rocks, temperature change cracks up rectangular blocks.

4.A A solid corestone embedded in weathered material which has been created by chemical weathering or spheroidal solution processes, Torysh, Mangystau, Kazakhstan

Rates of weathering are also affected by climate. Warm wet climates promote rapid chemical weathering, while dry climates inhibit chemical weathering. Dry climates, however, provide good conditions for physical or mechanical weathering.

(b) **Oxidation.** Oxidation is the reaction of oxygen in air or water with minerals in the rock. For example, most rocks contain a certain amount of iron, which when it comes in contact with air is changed to iron oxide, familiar brownish crust or rust. Iron oxide crumbles easily and is fat more easily eroded than the original iron. It is thus removed, loosening the overall structure of the rocks and weakening them.

(c) **Decomposition by organic acids.** Within the soil which covers most rocks are bacteria whch thrive on decaying plant or animal material. These bacteria produce acids which, when dissolved in water, help to speed up the weathering of the underlying rocks. In some cases microorganisms and plants like mosses or lichens can live on bare rock, so long as the surface is damp. These absorb chemical elements from the rocks as food and also produce organic acids. They are thus agents of both chemical and mechanical weathering.

2. Physical or Mechanical weathering

Mechanical weathering is the physical disintegration of a rock by the actual prising apart of separate particles. This can happen even with completely fresh rock but the processes of physical weathering are able to work much more easily when the surface of the rock has already been weakened by the action of chemical weathering. Mechanical weathering takes place in several ways.

(a) **Repeated temperature changes.** In deserts, rocks are exposed to the blazing sun during the day and are intensely heated. The outer layers expand much faster than the cooler interior of the rocks and tend to pull away from the rest. At nightfall the temperature drops rapidly and the outer layers contract more rapidly than the interior, setting up internal stresses. Such stresses, repeated every day for months and years, cause the rocks to crack and split. Well-bedded and jointed rocks tend to split along the joints or cracks, breaking up into rectangular blocks. Shales and slates may split up into platy fragments because of their platy structure. In crystalline rocks such as granite the crystals of the various minerals (quartz, mica, felspar) will expand and contract at different rates, enhancing the stresses and accelerating the disintegration of the rocks. Fragments broken from large rock outcrops fall by gravity to the foot of the slope. They may form screes or may form a litter of angular chips and small boulders on the flatter ground.

Stresses and pressures will naturally be greatest near the surface and where there are sharp angles in the rocks. Rectangular blocks are thus gradually rounded by the splitting away of sharp corners. When the surface layers of rounded boulders gradually split off the process is called *onion peeling*, because the various layers look like the layers of an onion, peeled off one after another. The technical term for this process is *exfoliation* (Plate 4.B).

(b) **Repeated wetting and drying.** Exfoliation is not confined to desert areas. Similar stresses may be set up in rocks by repeated wetting and drying of the surface layers. This takes place especially in tropical regions, like Malaysia, where short downpours saturate the rocks and then the hot sun quickly dries them again. Repeated wetting and drying also occurs at the coast, where rocks may be rapidly dried by sun and wind between tides. When rocks are wetted the outer layers absorb a certain amount of moisture and expand. When they dry this moisture evaporates and they quickly shrink. When this happens repeatedly the outer layers split off. It should also be stressed that the wetting and drying of the rocks in deserts is probably just as important as temperature changes in mechanical weathering. The rocks dry very quickly indeed after being wetted by brief desert rainstorms.

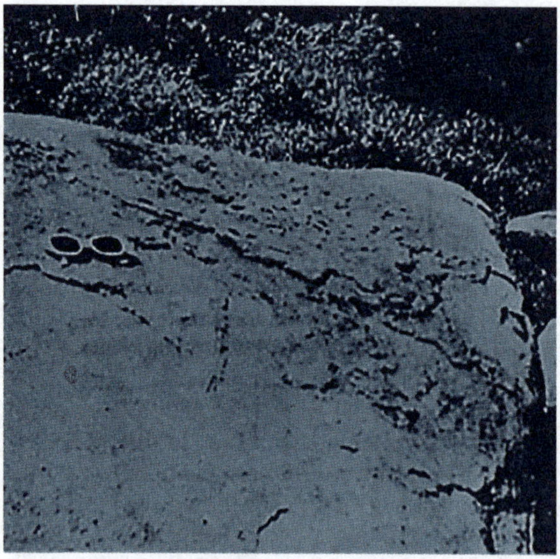

4.B When corestones are exposed to tropical weather conditions they are subject to repeated wetting and drying which cause the outer layers to peel off. This sandstone boulder shows several layers have split off in some areas. *G.C. Morgan*

(c) **Frost action.** In temperate latitudes frost is a potent rock breaker. All rocks contain cracks and joints, or pore spaces, and after a shower water or snow collects in such places. When the temperature drops at night or during the winter, this water freezes. When water freezes it expands by one-tenth its volume and exerts a bursting pressure of almost 140 kg per square cm (2,000 lb. to the square inch). Repeated freezing of this kind will deepen and widen the original cracks and crevices and break the rock into angular fragments (Fig. 35). On mountain peaks this process creates sharp pinnacles and angular outlines. Such peaks are described as *frost-shattered* peaks. Angular fragments of rock are prised from mountain-sides or cliff faces and fall to the foot of the slope where they accumulate to form screes.

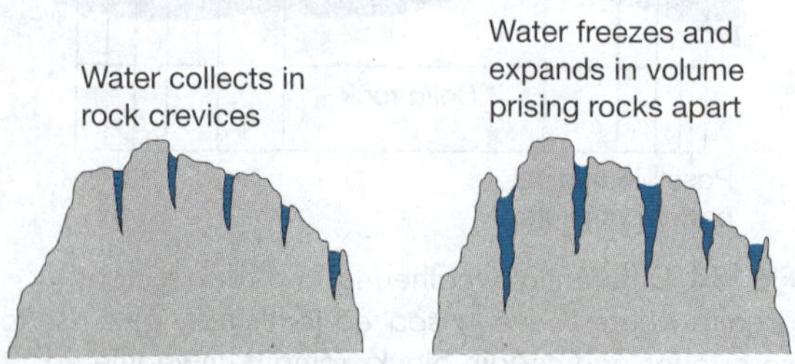

Fig. 35 Frost action as an agent of mechanical weathering

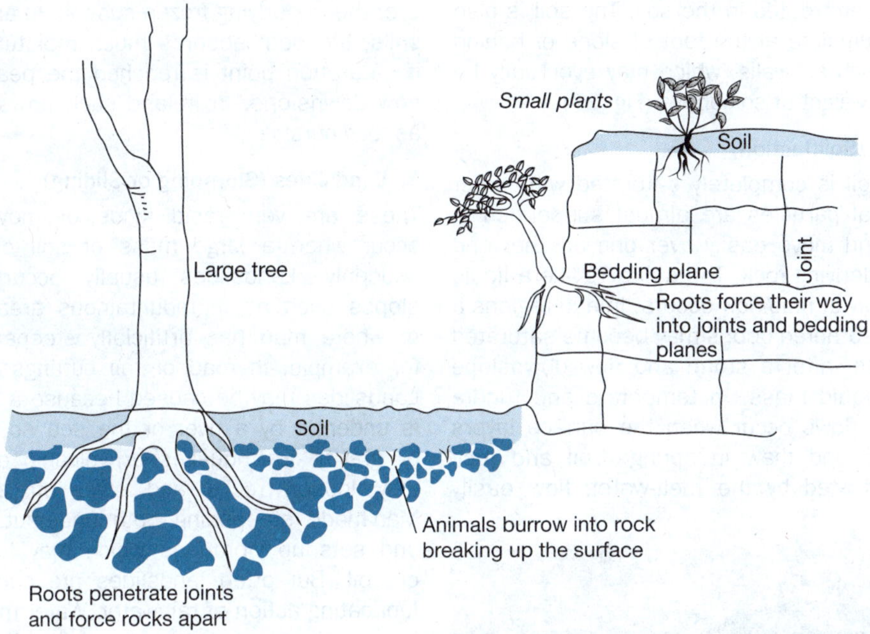

Fig. 36 Plant roots as agents of mechanical weathering

(d) **Biotic factors.** Small fragments of rock loosened by either chemical or mechanical weathering lodge in cracks and crevices in the rock and plants may sprout in such crevices. As they grow their roots penetrate the rocks below, usually along joints and other lines of weakness, prising them apart. You have often come across large trees growing near roads or the courtyards of houses that finally prise open the concrete or paving stones above their roots. The process is just the same on a smaller scale in a natural setting (Fig. 36).

Men, in the course of mining, road construction and farming, also contribute to mechanical weathering by excavating the rocks and rendering them more vulnerable to the agents of denudation.

Mass Movement

Mass movement is the movement of weathered materials down a slope due to *gravitational forces*. The movement may be gradual or sudden, depending on the gradient of the slope, the weight of the weathered debris and whether there is any lubricating moisture supplied by rainwater. Several kinds of mass movement are distinguished.

1. Soil Creep

This is a slow, *gradual* but more or less continuous movement of soil down hillslopes. The movement is not very noticeable, especially when the slope is fairly gentle or when the soil is well-covered with grass or other vegetation. Soil creep is most common in damp soils where the water acts as a lubricant so that individual soil particles move over each other and over the underlying rock. It is also found where continuous trampling by animals grazing on the slopes sets up vibrations which loosen the soil and cause it to move. Though the movement is slow and cannot readily be seen in action, the gradual movement tilts trees, fences, posts and

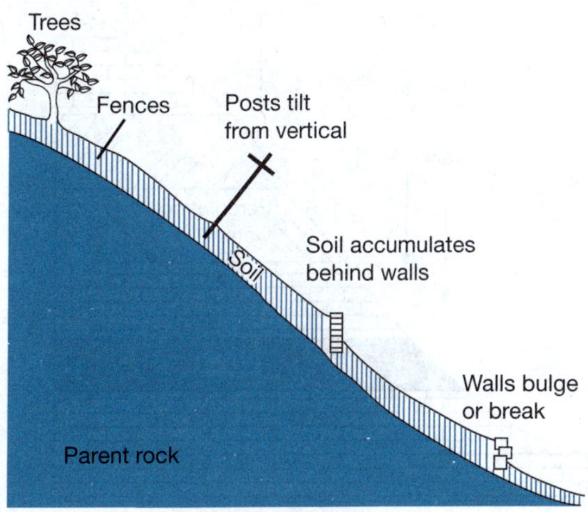

Fig. 37 Evidences of soil creep

so on which are rooted in the soil. The soil is also seen to accumulate at the foot of slope or behind obstacles such as walls, which may eventually be burst by the weight of soil above (Fig. 37).

2. Soil Flow (Solifluction)

When the soil is completely saturated with water the individual particles are almost suspended in the water and move easily over one another and over the underlying rock. The soil acts like a liquid and a *soil-flow* or *mud-flow* occurs. In arid regions a mantle of weathered debris may become saturated with rainwater after a storm and flow downslope as a semi-liquid mass. In temperate and tundra regions soil flows occur when the surface layers of frozen ground thaw in spring. Soil and rock debris, lubricated by the melt-water, flow easily over the underlying frozen subsoil. In areas of peat soils, the peat absorbs much moisture. However if saturation point is reached the peaty soil may flow downslope. In Ireland such flows are known as *'bog-bursts'*.

4.C A landslide after flood has damaged the road in a small town called Cemomoi in Bentong, Pahang, Malaysia

3. Landslides (Slumping or Sliding)

These are very rapid kinds of movement and occur when a large mass of soil or rock falls suddenly. Landslides usually occur on steep slopes such as in mountainous areas, on cliffs or where man has artificially steepened slopes, for example, in road or rail cuttings (Plate 4.C). Landslides may be caused because a steep slope is undercut by a river or the sea so that it falls by gravity. Earthquakes or volcanic disturbances may loosen rocks and start off a landslide. Man-made steepening both undercuts the slope and sets up vibrations which may loosen rocks or soil. But often landslides are caused by the lubricating action of rainwater. Water may collect in joints or bedding planes in rocks so that one layer slides over another, especially in areas of tilted strata. *Slumping* is particularly common where permeable debris or rock layers overlie impermeable strata such as clay. Water sinking through the permeable material is halted by the clay. The damp clay provides a smooth slippery surface over which the upper layers easily slide (Fig. 38).

Water may collect at the base of the regolith because it sinks readily into the weathered material but more slowly into the solid rock beneath. The water may allow the regolith to slide away from the underlying rock.

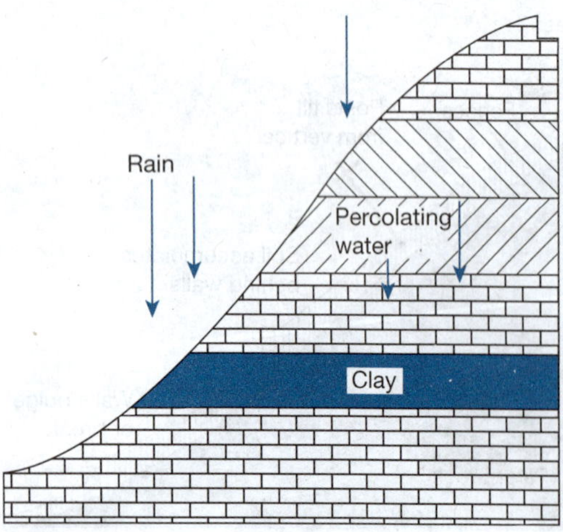

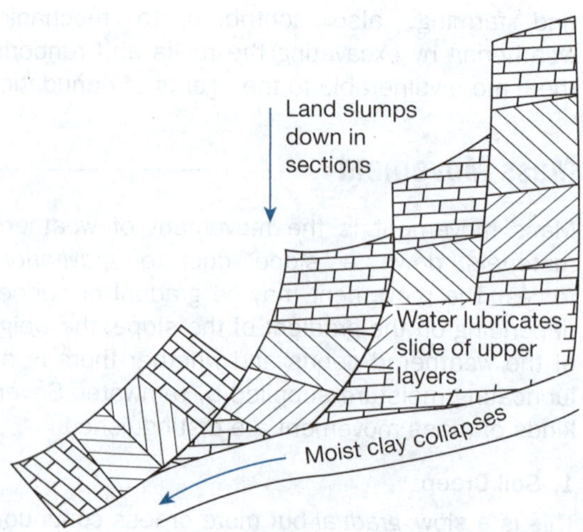

Fig. 38 Landslide

4.D (a) An effective way of preventing landslide by building a concrete wall

4.D (b) Currently, welded wire mesh continues to be the go-to solution for landslide mitigation and repairs

Man often enhances the possibility of landslides by clearing natural vegetation for agriculture or housing. Removal of the plant cover allows more water to penetrate the soil and rocks. In areas such as the Cameron Highlands, where steep slopes have been cleared, there is much evidence of minor slumps and slides, the old scars showing up clearly in the tea gardens. Extensive landslides, whether natural or man-induced, can have disastrous consequences, burying villages, railway lines or people. Spectacular landslides have taken place in many parts of the world, including South Wales, British Columbia, Hong Kong and the Cameron Highlands where the village of Ringlet was partially buried in 1961 and several houses were ruined.

Groundwater

The whole process of the circulation of water between the land, sea and atmosphere is known as the *hydrological cycle*. The movement of the water in the atmosphere and its effect on climate are dealt with in Chapters 13 and 14. The seas and oceans are discussed in Chapter 12. The effect of water on the land as an agent of weathering, erosion, transport and deposition is dealt with in this and the following chapters, especially Chapter 5.

When rain falls on the earth it is distributed in various ways. Some is immediately evaporated and thus returns to the atmosphere as water vapour. Some is absorbed by plants and only gradually returned to the atmosphere by *transpiration* from the leaves of plants. Much of it flows directly off slopes to join streams and rivers, eventually reaching the seas and oceans. This is known as run-off. A considerable proportion of the water received from rain or snow, however, percolates downwards into the soil and rocks, filling up joints and pore-spaces and forming what is known as groundwater. Groundwater plays an important part in weathering and mass movement and is also important as a means of natural water storage. It re-enters the hydrological cycle by way of springs.

The amount of water available to form groundwater depends to some extent on climate. In dry climates much precipitation may be quickly evaporated into the dry atmosphere and little moisture may percolate into the ground. In very humid conditions, where the surface of the ground may already be moist, much water may be moved as run-off. In moderately humid areas water both runs off and sinks into the ground. The proportion of the rainfall absorbed as groundwater may depend on the season of the year.

More important, however, is the nature of the rocks and how easily they absorb and retain water. Various rocks and soils differ greatly in their porosity and permeability; the amount of groundwater present and the depth at which it lies are governed by these characteristics. Porous rocks are those, like sandstone, which have many pore-spaces between the grains. Water is easily absorbed by such rocks and may be stored in the pore-spaces.

Permeable or pervious rocks are those which allow water to pass through them easily (Fig. 39). Thus most porous rocks are also permeable. However some rocks are porous but impermeable. Clay, for example, is highly porous since it is made up of innumerable very fine particles with pore-spaces between them. It thus absorbs a great deal of water. However, the pore-spaces are so small that the water does not move easily through the rock, which is thus impermeable. On the other hand, granite which is a crystalline rock and consequently non-porous is often pervious. Its individual crystals absorb little or no water but the rock may have numerous *joints* or *cracks* through which the water can pass, rendering it pervious or permeable. Some granites are, however, far more pervious than others.

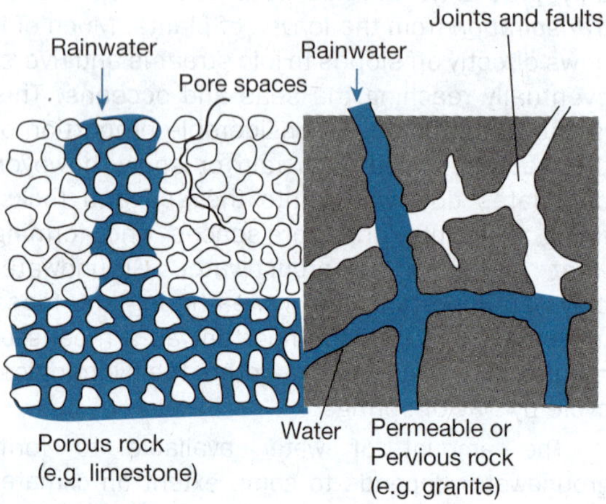

Fig. 39 Porosity and permeability of rocks

4.E Substantial downpour has triggered floods and caused extreme loss in Penampang area in Malaysia. The 2014 floods have affected 40,000 people from 70 villages.

The Water-Table

Water which seeps through the ground moves downward under the force of gravity until it reaches an impermeable layer of rock through which it cannot pass. If there is no ready outlet for the groundwater in the form of a spring, the water accumulates above the impermeable layer and saturates the rock. The permeable rock in which the water is stored is known as the aquifer (Fig. 40). The surface of the saturated area is called the *water-table*. The depth of the *water-table* varies greatly according to relief and to the type of rocks. The water-table is far below the surface of hill-tops but is close to the surface in valleys and flat low-lying areas where it may cause *waterlogging* and swampy conditions. The depth of

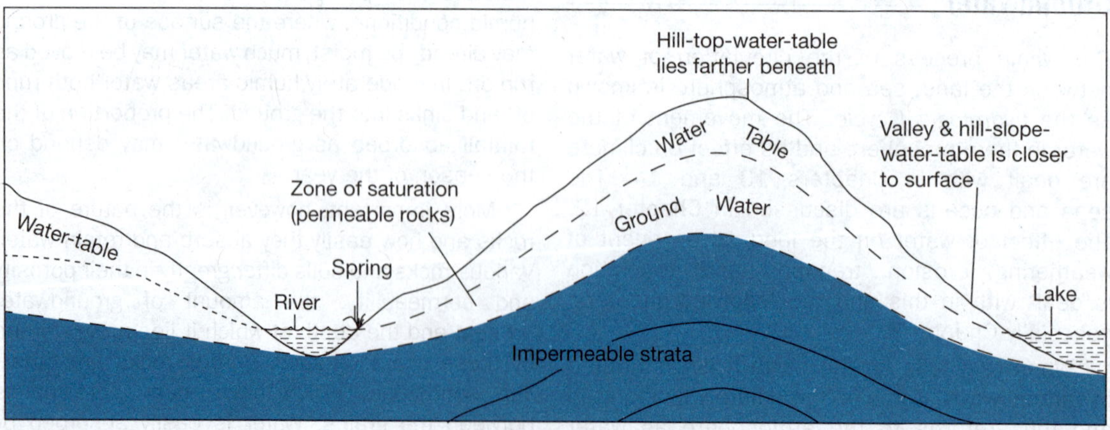

Fig. 40 Groundwater table and its relationship to the curvature of the land

the water-table also varies greatly with the seasons. When plenty of rain is available to augment groundwater supplies the water-table may rise, but in dry periods, no new supplies are available, and the water-table is lowered as groundwater is lost through seepages and springs (Fig. 40).

Springs and Wells

1. Springs

The groundwater stored in the rock is released onto the surface at points where the water-table reaches the surface. A spring is simply an outlet for such water. The water may seep gradually out of the rock or may gush out as a fountain. Springs are of several kinds due to the nature of the rocks and the position of the water-table. The main types are described below.

(a) In areas of *tilted strata,* where permeable and impermeable rocks alternate, water emerges at the base of the permeable layers (Fig. 41 a).

(b) In *well-jointed rocks* water may percolate downwards until it reaches a joint which emerges at the surface. The water may come to the surface through the joint (Fig. 41 b).

(c) Where a dyke or sill of impermeable rock is intruded through permeable rocks, it causes the water-table to reach the surface and the water issues as a spring (Fig. 41 c).

(d) In limestone or chalk escarpments, where the permeable rock lies between impermeable strata, water issues at the foot of the scarp as a *scarp-foot spring,* or near the foot of the dip-slope as a *dip-slope spring,* as illustrated in Fig. 41 d.

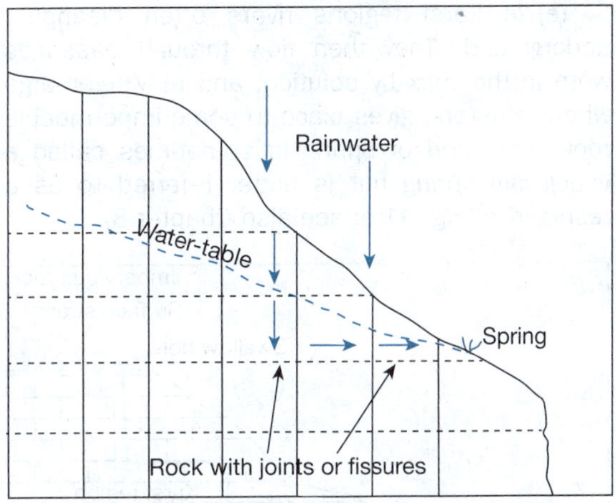

Fig. 41 (b) Spring emerges from rocks with joints

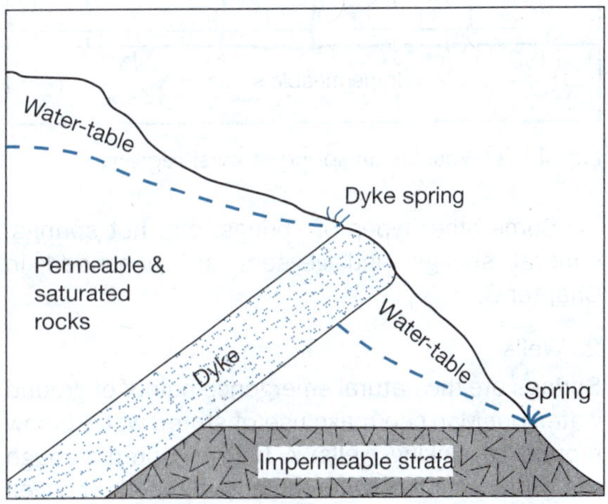

Fig. 41 (c) A dyke spring

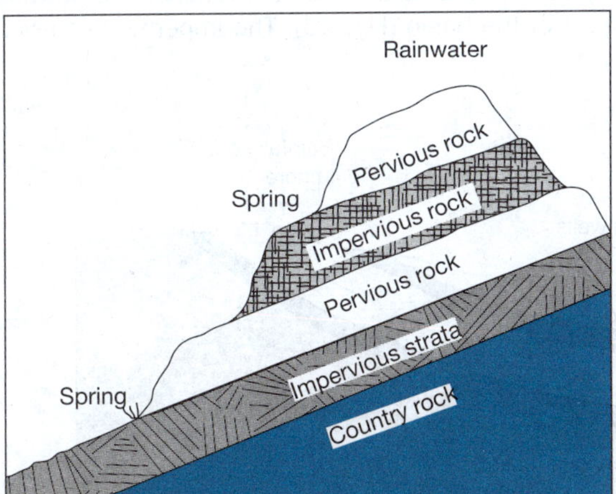

Fig. 41 (a) Spring seeps from edge of pervious rock lying above an inclined impervious strata

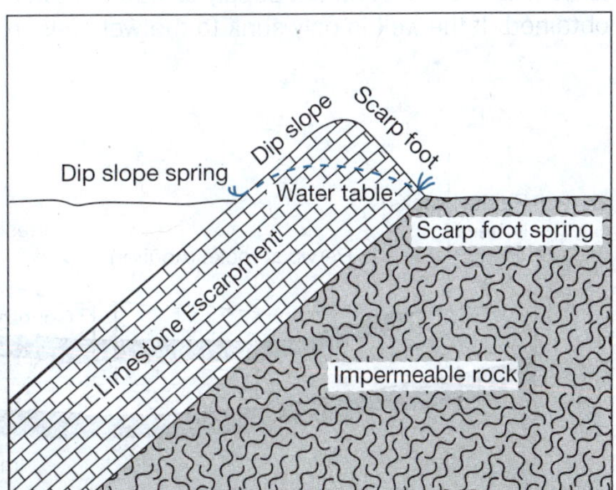

Fig. 41 (d) Scarp-foot spring and dip-slope spring

(e) In karst regions rivers often disappear underground. They then flow through passages worn in the rock by solution, and may re-emerge when limestone gives place to some impermeable rock. This kind of spring is sometimes called a *vauclusian spring* but is better referred to as a *resurgence* (Fig. 41 e; see also Chapter 8).

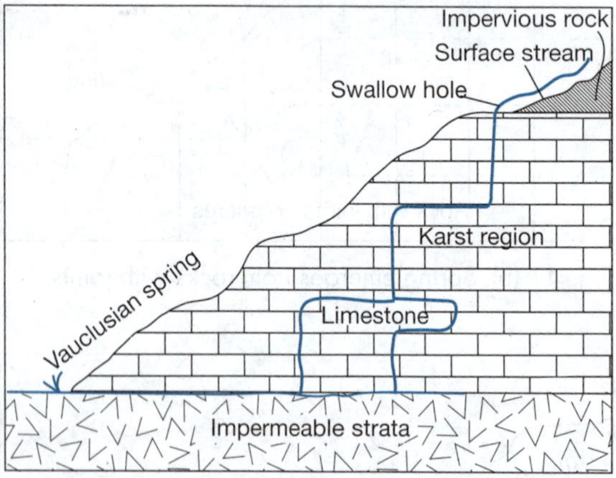

Fig. 41 (e) Vauclusian spring in karst regions

Some other types of springs, e.g. hot springs, mineral springs and geysers are described in Chapter 3.

2. Wells

Springs are the natural emergence points of ground water, but Man can make use of stored water below ground by sinking wells. A hole is bored through the earth until the water-table is reached. The well must be sunk to the depth of the permanent water-table (Fig. 42) if a constant supply of water is to be obtained. If the well is only sunk to the wet-season

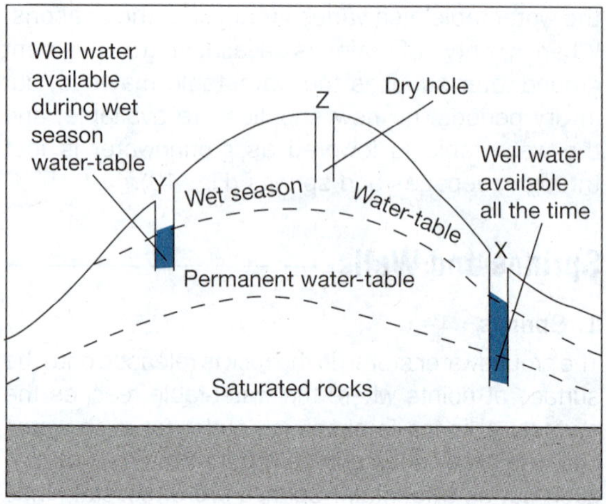

Fig. 42 Depth of wells and water-table mark

depth of the water-table, water will be unobtainable when the level drops in the dry season. When a well is bored, the water usually has to be raised by hand or by mechanical pumping. Wells are particularly important in arid areas where there is little surface water but where the underlying rocks contain groundwater.

A particularly important type of well is the *artesian well*, which owing to the nature of its formation is quite distinctive. Where rock layers have been down-folded into a basin shape, permeable strata such as chalk or limestone may be sandwiched between impermeable layers, such as clay. The permeable rocks may only come to the surface at the edges of the basin, but water falling on them will gradually seep downwards by the force of gravity until it reaches the lowest part of the basin (Fig. 43). The impermeable layer

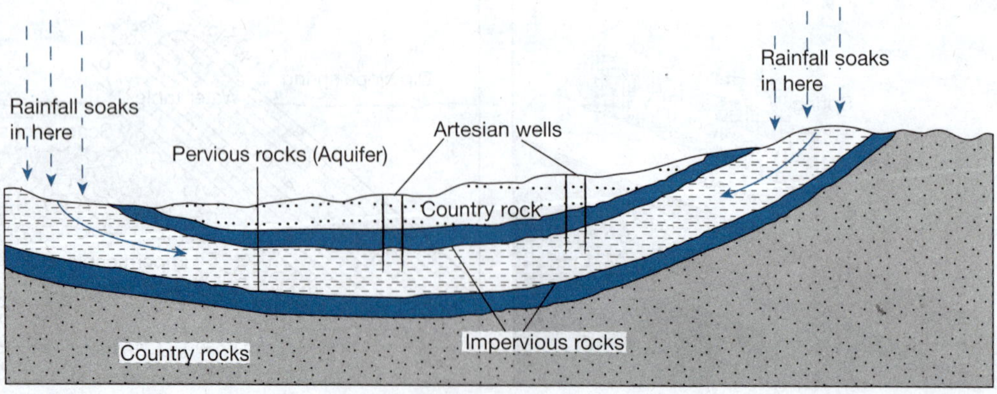

Fig. 43 Formation of an artesian basin where a pervious layer (aquifer) is between two impervious strata of rocks

below prevents the water from passing downwards while the impermeable layer on top prevents any possibility of the water escaping upwards. The aquifer is thus saturated to the brim of the basin.

The water is thus trapped in the aquifer under great pressure and when a well is bored, the pressure of water downwards from all around the basin is sufficient to force the water up the bore-hole so that it gushes onto the surface like a fountain. After a time the pressure decreases and it is necessary to pump up the water.

The depth of artesian wells varies from place to place, from a few feet to thousands of feet. The water may be used to supply the needs of an entire village as in the Great Plains of USA or for sheep farming as in Queensland and other parts of Australia. Fig. 44 shows the distribution of artesian wells in Australia. But the water is sometimes unsuitable for agricultural or irrigation purposes as it may be hot or contain an excessive amount of mineral salts.

Artesian wells are most valuable to Man when they can be used in desert areas, e.g. in parts of the Sahara and in Australia. The aquifers receive water in areas of higher rainfall, but the water accumulates in basins underlying arid regions.

Fig. 44 The distribution of artesian basins in Australia

All wells bored by Man tend to deplete groundwater resources because the water is extracted faster than under natural conditions and also much faster than it can be replenished by rainfall. In many areas groundwater supplies have been greatly reduced or even exhausted by Man as a result of carelessness and overexploitation.

QUESTIONS AND EXERCISES

1. (a) What do you understand by the term 'weathering'?
   (b) Name 4 natural forces that play a role in weathering.
   (c) Differentiate mechanical weathering from chemical weathering and give examples of each.
2. (a) Describe how gravitational forces and rainwater assist in the mass movement of weathered materials on hill slopes.
   (b) Distinguish soil creep from landslides, and locate places where such occurrences have taken place.
3. (a) What is meant by the following:
      i. hydrological cycle
      ii. water-table
      iii. acquifer.
   (b) For any *two* of the above, discuss their relationship with groundwater.
4. 'While the earth's crust is undergoing constructive changes to create new relief, external forces of nature are working vigorously to level this down.' Discuss.
5. Elaborate on any *three* of the following:
   (a) Exfoliation is the result of temperature changes in deserts.
   (b) Screes accumulate at the foot of steep mountains in temperate lands.
   (c) There are many ways in which springs can be formed.
   (d) Artesian wells have a distinct formation.

5 Landforms Made by Running Water

The Development of a River System

When rain falls, part of it sinks into the ground, some is evaporated back into the atmosphere and the rest runs off as rivulets, brooks, streams and tributaries of rivers that flow down to the sea. This running water forms a potent agent for denuding the earth's surface. Denudation is the *general lowering* of the earth's surface. This takes place because such agents of erosion as rivers, ice, wind and waves wear away the rocks and transport the eroded debris to lower land or right down to the sea. But erosion cannot take place unless the rocks are first weakened or shattered by exposure to the elements. Rain, frost and wind weather the rocks so that they can be eroded more easily. Unlike glaciers and snow, which are confined to the cold and temperate latitudes; waves which act only on coastlines; winds, which are only 'efficient' in deserts; the effect of running water is felt all over the globe *wherever water is present.* Running water is thus the most important single agent of denudation.

The source of a river may be a spring, a lake or a marsh, but it is generally in an *upland* region, where precipitation is heaviest and where there is a slope down which the run-off can flow. The uplands therefore form the catchment areas of rivers. The crest of the mountains is the divide or watershed from which streams flow down the slopes on both sides to begin their journey to the oceans. The initial stream that exists as a consequence of the slope is called the consequent stream. As the consequent stream wears down the surface by deepening its channel downwards, it is joined by several tributaries either *obliquely* or at *right angles* depending on the alignment and the degree of resistance of the rocks.

If the rocks are composed of homogeneous beds of uniform resistance to erosion, the tributaries will join the main valley obliquely as insequent streams. The drainage pattern so evolved will be *tree-like* in appearance, and is therefore described as dendritic drainage, after a Greek word *dendron* meaning 'tree' (Fig. 45). On the other hand, if the rocks are made up of alternate layers of hard and soft rocks, the tributaries tend to follow the pattern of the *rock structure*. If the outcrops of the rocks occur at right angles to the main valley, the tributaries will join it at right angles as subsequent streams. The drainage pattern so developed will be *rectangular* in shape and is called trellised drainage (Fig. 46).

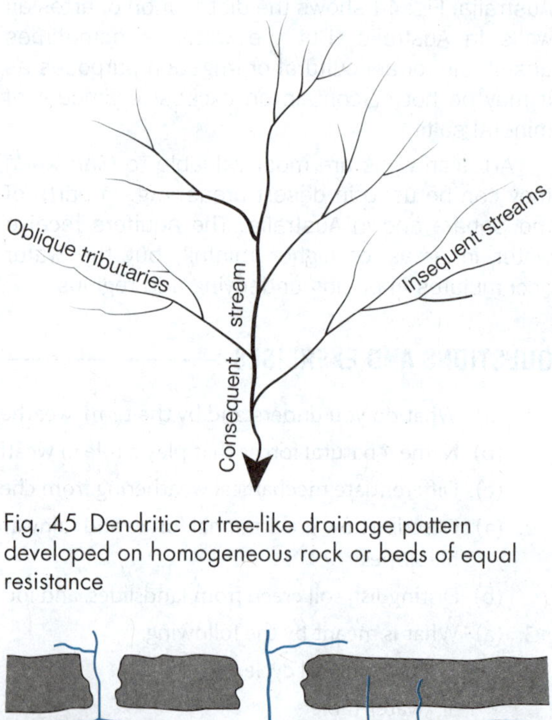

Fig. 45 Dendritic or tree-like drainage pattern developed on homogeneous rock or beds of equal resistance

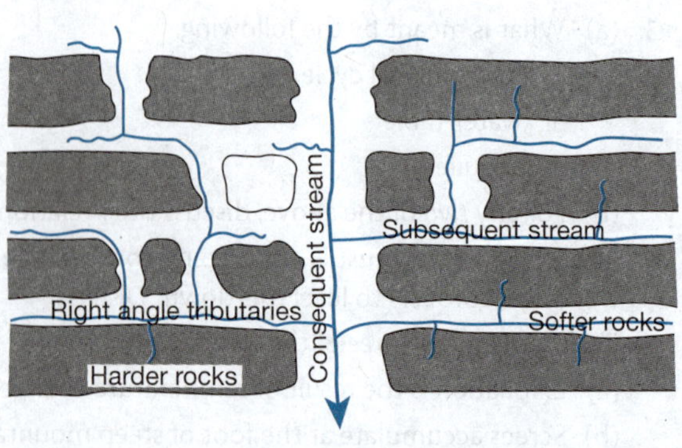

Fig. 46 Trellised or rectangular drainage pattern developed on alternating outcrops of harder and softer rocks

The Mechanism of Humid Erosion

Humid erosion covers the entire scope of sculpturing effects of running water from the action of rainwater to that of the rivers. Mass movements of earth and weathered materials on hill-slopes down to valleys are mainly due to the lubricating action of water which allows a mass of materials to move under gravity. This is particularly acute where the slopes are steep. The *slow* movement of soil down a hill-slope is call soil-creep. A more *sudden* movement due to the lubricating effect or rainwater may cause widespread landslides. In mountainous districts where the roads and railway tracks are cut through steep-sided valleys landslides may obstruct railway lines, cut off road communications and even bury villages and people.

The Processes of River Action

When a river flows it carries with it eroded materials. These comprise the river's load, and may be divided into *three* distinct types.

1. **Materials in solution.** These are minerals which are dissolved in the water.
2. **Materials in suspension.** Sand, silt and mud are carried along suspended in the water as the stream flows.
3. **The traction load.** This includes coarser materials such as pebbles, stones, rocks and boulders, which are rolled along the river bed.

It has been estimated that for every square mile of the earth's surface, more than 200 tons of solid materials in suspension and more than 50 tons of materials in solution are being carried off by running water every year. The Mississippi River which drains an area almost half the size of the United States itself, removes more than two million tons of eroded material into the Gulf of Mexico daily. Consequently the river basins are being lowered, and in the case of swift-flowing rivers like the Irrawaddy, its drainage basin is being lowered by about a foot in every 400 years! During floods the amount of rock debris swept off by rivers is very much greater. We can see this from the mud that colours the river-water during a heavy rain. The ability of a river to move the various grades of materials depends greatly upon the volume of the water, the velocity of the flow and lastly the size, shape and weight of the load. It is said that by doubling the velocity of a river, its transporting power is increased by more than 10 times! It is therefore not surprising to find huge boulders that are 'stranded' in normal times, but may be moved during seasonal floods. The movement of rivers is thus intermittent, acting vigorously in certain parts of the year and remaining less active at other times.

River Erosion and Transportation

In rivers, erosion and transportation go on simultaneously, comprising the following inter-acting processes.

1. **Corrasion or abrasion.** This is the mechanical grinding of the river's traction load against the *banks and bed* of the river. The rock fragments are hurled against the sides of the river and also roll along the bottom of the river. Corrasion takes place, in two distinct ways.

   (a) **Lateral corrasion.** This is the sideways erosion which widens the V-shaped valley.

   (b) **Vertical corrasion.** This is the downward action which deepens the river channel.

2. **Corrosion or solution.** This is the chemical or solvent action of water on soluble or partly-soluble rocks with which the river comes into contact. For example calcium carbonate in limestones is easily dissolved and removed in solution.

3. **Hydraulic action.** This is the mechanical loosening and sweeping away of materials by the river water itself. Some of the water splashes against the river banks and surges into cracks and crevices. This helps to disintegrate the rocks. The water also undermines the softer rocks with which it comes into contact. It picks up the loose fragments from its banks and bed and transports them away.

4. **Attrition.** This is the wear and tear of the transported materials themselves when they roll and collide into one another. The coarser boulders are broken down into smaller stones; the angular edges are smoothed and rounded to form pebbles. The finer materials are carried further downstream to be deposited.

The Course of a River

The course of a river may be divided into *three* distinct parts (Fig. 47): 1. The upper or mountain

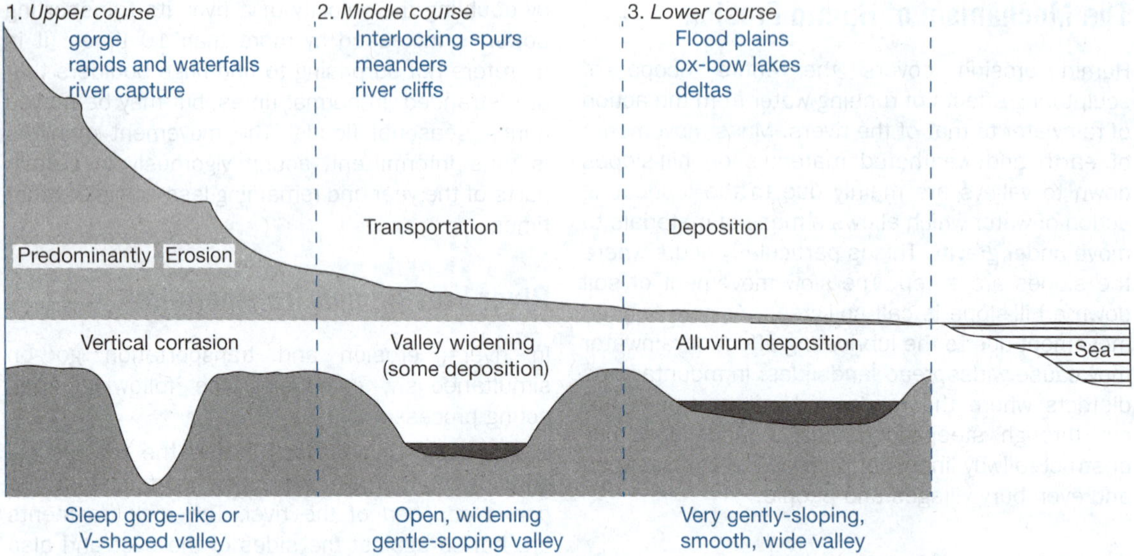

Fig. 47 The graded long profile and typical cross section of a river from source to mouth

course (in the stage of youth), 2. The middle or valley course (in the stage of maturity), 3. The lower or plain course (in the stage of old age).

1. The Upper or Mountain Course

This begins at the source of the river near the watershed, which is probably the crest of a mountain range. The river is very swift as it descends the steep slopes, and the predominant action of the river is vertical corrasion. The valley developed is thus deep, narrow and distinctively V-shaped. Down-cutting takes place so rapidly that *lateral corrasion* cannot keep pace. In some cases where the rocks are very resistant, the valley is so narrow and the sides are so steep that gorges are formed, e.g. the Indus Gorge in Kashmir. In arid regions, where there is little rainfall to widen the valley sides, and the river cuts deep into the valley-floor, precipitous valleys called canyons are formed, e.g. the Bryce Canyon, Utah, USA.

Some of the more outstanding features that are otten best developed in the upper course of a river include the following.

(a) **River capture.** This is also known as river piracy or river beheading. Its development is dependant on the different rate of back-cutting (headward erosion) into a divide. For instance, if one side of the divide is of greater gradient or receives more precipitation than the other, stream A in Fig. 48 will cut back more rapidly than stream B.

The famous Samaria Gorge on the island of Crete, Greece

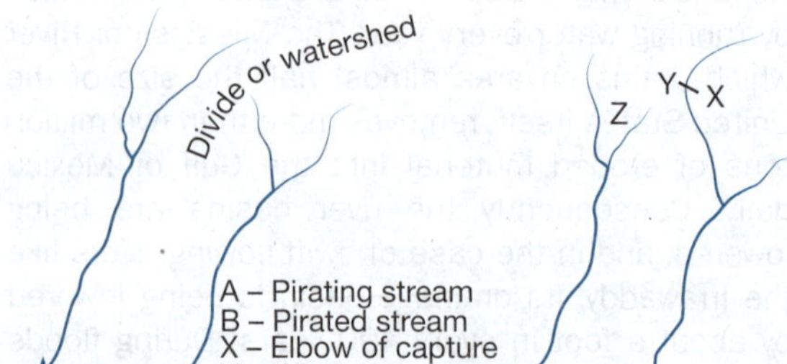

Fig. 48 River capture
(a) before capture (b) after capture

Its greater erosive power will succeed in enlarging its basin at the expense of the weaker stream. Stream A may eventually break through the divide and capture or pirate stream B. The bend at which the piracy occured is termed as the elbow of capture. The beheaded stream (Z) is called the misfit. The valley below the elbow is the wind gap, and may be valuable as a road and rail route. Examples of river capture abound. In Myanmar, the Upper Sittang has been captured by the Irrawaddy; in Northumberland, England, the Blyth and the Wansbeck are beheaded by the North Tyne.

(b) **Rapids, cataracts and waterfalls.** These are liable to occur at any part of the river course, but they are most numerous in the mountain course where changes of gradient are more abrupt and also more frequent. Due to the *unequal resistance* of hard and soft rocks traversed by a river, the outcrop of a band of hard rock may cause a river to 'jump' or 'fall' downstream. Rapids are formed (Fig. 49). Similar falls of greater dimensions are also referred to as ***cataracts***, of which there are five along the Nile that interrupt smooth navigation. When rivers plunge down in a sudden fall of some height, they are called waterfalls (Fig. 50). Their great force usually wears out a plunge-pool beneath. Waterfalls are formed in several ways.

i. When a bar of resistant rock lies transversely across a river valley, e.g. the Niagara Falls, USA, which is 167 feet (51 m) high and the Kaieteur Falls in Guyana, 741 (226 m) feet high.
ii. When a fault-line scarp caused by faulting lies across river, e.g. Victoria Falls on the River Zambezi, plunging 355 feet (108 m).
iii. When water plunges down the edge of a plateau like the River Congo which leaps for 900 feet (275 m) through a series of more than 30 rapids as Livingstone Falls.

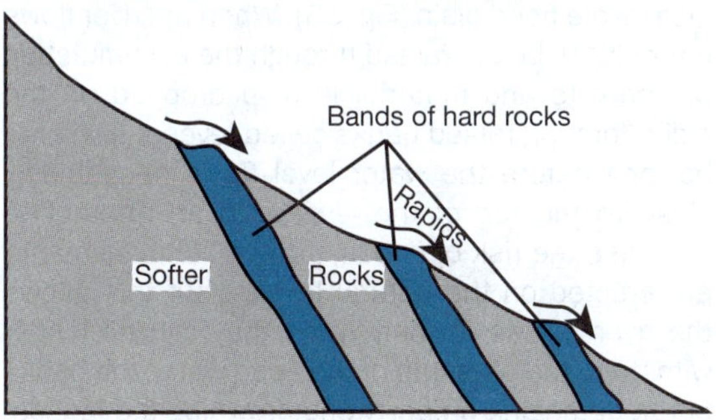

Fig. 49 Rapids, cataracts

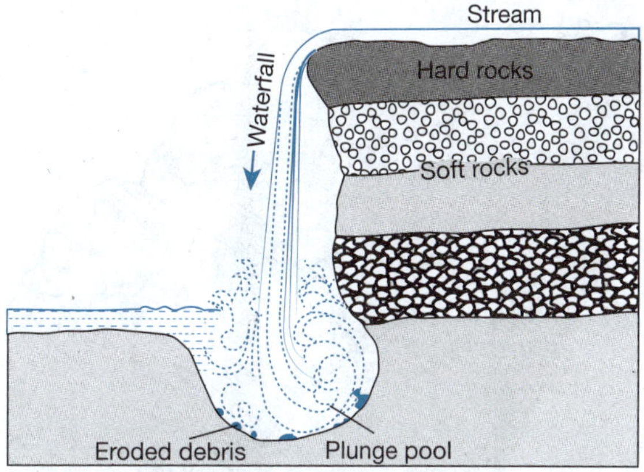

Fig. 50 A waterfall with plunge pool

iv. Glaciation produces hanging valleys where tributary streams reach the main U-shaped valley below as waterfalls, e.g. the Yosemite Falls of California with a total descent of 2,425 feet (740 m).

2. **The Middle or Valley Course**

In the middle course, lateral corrasion tends to replace vertical corrasion. Active erosion of the banks widens the V-shaped valley. The volume of water increases with the confluence of many tributaries and this increases the river's load. The work of the river is predominantly transportation with some deposition. Downstream, the interlocking spurs (Fig. 51) that project from both sides of the valley are cut back into a line of bluffs. Rain-wash, soil creep, landslides and gullying gradually widen the valley, cutting back the sides. The river's treble task of valley-cutting, bed-smoothing and debris-removal are being carried out in a more tranquil manner than in the mountain course though the velocity does not decrease. Some of the load is dropped or deposited. Again this depends on the *volume of flow,* for in the event of flood, the river's erosive power and its capability for load-carrying is greatly increased. The more outstanding features associated with the valley course are these.

(a) **Meanders.** As water flowing under gravity seldom flows straight for any long distance, a *winding* course soon develops. The irregularities of the ground force the river to swing in loops, forming meanders, a term derived from the winding River Meanderez in Asia Minor. The mechanism of meander formation is illustrated in Fig. 52.

(b) **River cliffs and slip-off slopes.** When the flow of water PQ (in Fig. 52) enters the bend of the river,

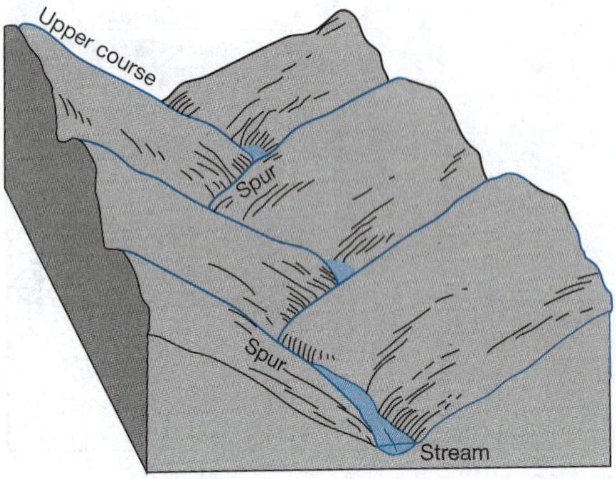

Fig. 51 Interlocking spurs

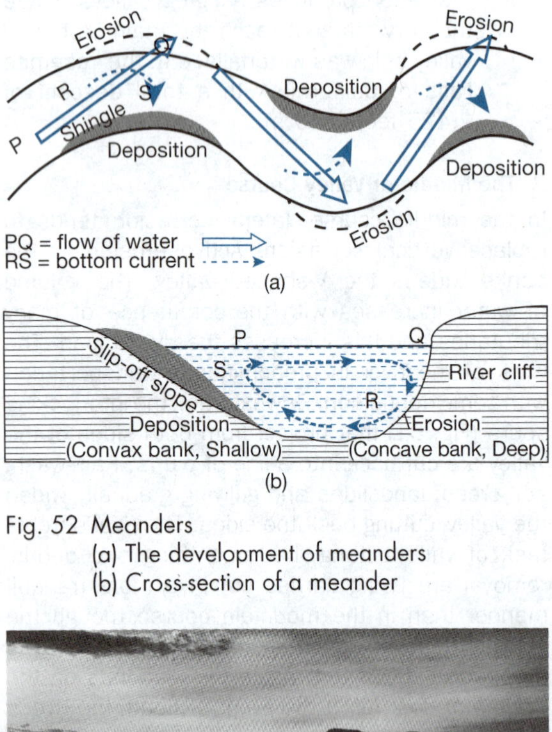

Fig. 52 Meanders
(a) The development of meanders
(b) Cross-section of a meander

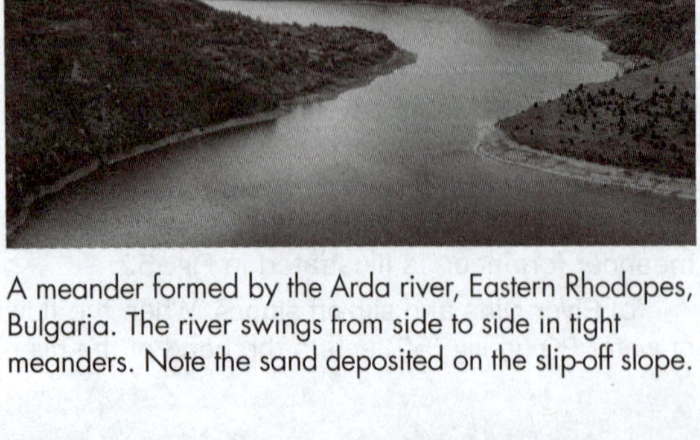

A meander formed by the Arda river, Eastern Rhodopes, Bulgaria. The river swings from side to side in tight meanders. Note the sand deposited on the slip-off slope.

it dashes straight into Q, eroding the outer bank into a steep river-cliff at Q. The water piles up on the outside of the bend because of the centrifugal force. A bottom current RS is set up in a corkscrew motion and is hurled back into midstream and the inner bank. Shingle is thus deposited here at S. where the slip-off slope is very gentle. The outer bank is therefore the bank of continuous erosion and the inner bank is the bank of continual deposition.

(c) **Interlocking spurs.** As the stream flows on, the meanders migrate progressively outwards with the interlocking spurs alternating with the undercut slopes as shown in Fig. 51. It must be pointed out at this stage that meanders in the middle course are only the beginning of the downstream swing, for bends are restricted by the interlocking spurs. In the lower course, the loops are enlarged across the level plain and meanders are fully developed.

3. The Lower or Plain Course

The river moving downstream across a broad, level plain is heavy with debris brought down from the upper course. Vertical corrasion has almost ceased though lateral corrasion still goes on to erode its banks further. The work of the river is mainly deposition, building up its bed and forming extensive *flood plains*. The volume of water is greatly swelled by the additional tributaries that join the main stream. Coarse materials are dropped and the finer silt is carried down towards the mouth of the river. Large sheets of materials are deposited on the level plain and may split the river into several complicated channels, so that it can be described as a braided stream. Some of the major plain course features are the following.

(a) **Flood plain.** Rivers in their lower course carry large quantities of sediments. During annual or sporadic *floods*, these materials are spread over the low-lying adjacent areas. A layer of sediment is thus deposited during each flood, gradually building up a fertile flood plain (Fig. 53). When the river flows normally its bed is raised through the accumulation of deposits and material is also dropped on the sides forming raised banks called levees. It will not be long before the water level flows dangerously close to the top of the levees. In an attempt to minimise the risk of floods, artificial embankments are erected on the natural levees, but this allows the river to rise further. When they can no longer withstand the pressure of the flood water, the banks burst, damaging property and drowning thousands. Disastrous floods of this nature frequently occur in the Yangtze, Mississippi, Po and Ganges plains. But the best known river for floods is the Hwang-Ho (Yellow River), 'China's Sorrow', where millions have perished. For example, in 1852 the Hwang-Ho breached its bank, killing a million people and did untold damage to farms and properties. The river's course was diverted over 300 miles away, draining into the Gulf of Pohai instead of the Yellow Sea. Nowadays, huge dredgers help to deepen the channels to avoid excessive sedimentation.

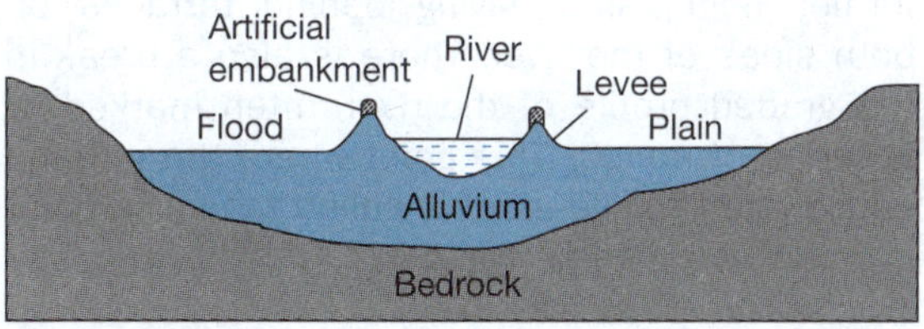

Fig. 53 Section of a flood plain (with levee and artificial embankment)

(b) **Oxbow lakes.** These are also known as cut-offs or bayous in the Mississippi basin. In the lower course of a river, a meander becomes very much more pronounced. The outside bend or concave bank is so rapidly eroded that the river becomes almost a complete circle. There will come a time when the river cuts through the narrow neck of the loop, abandoning an oxbow lake or '*mortlake*' (meaning dead lake). The river then flows straight. The oxbow lake will later degenerate into a swamp through subsequent floods that may silt up the lake. It becomes marshy, and eventually dries up (Fig. 54).

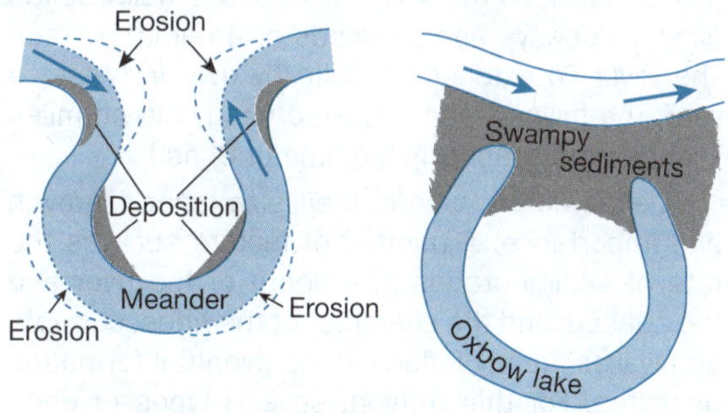

Fig. 54 The formation of an oxbow lake

(c) **Delta.** When a river reaches the sea, the fine materials it has not yet dropped are deposited at its mouth, forming a fan-shaped alluvial area called

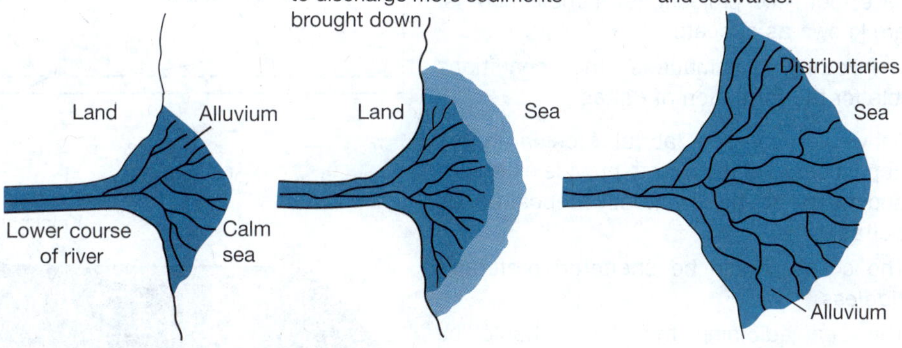

Fig. 55 The formation of deltas
(a) Stages in the formation of a delta

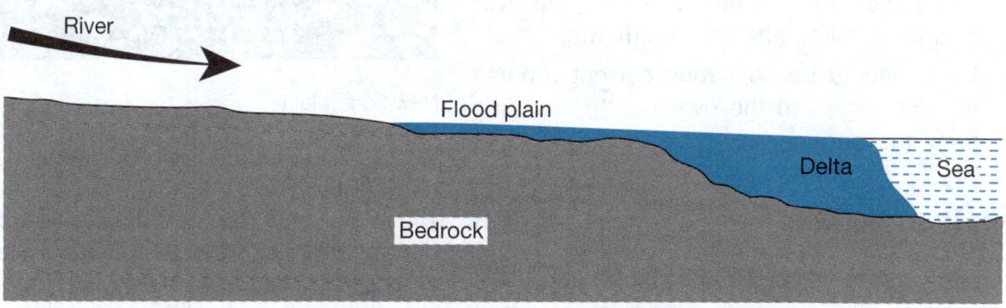

(b) Section through the lower course of a river, showing flood plain and delta a delta, a word which originated from the Greek letter Δ which closely resembled the triangular delta of the Nile (Fig. 55). This alluvial tract is, in fact, a seaward extension of the floodplain. Due to the obstruction caused by the deposited alluvium, the river may discharge its water through several channels called distributaries. Some deltas are extremely large. For instance, the Ganges delta is almost as big as the whole of West Malaysia. Deltas extend sideways and seawards at an amazing rate. The River Po extends its delta by over forty feet a year. The town of Adria, located nearly fifteen miles inland was a seaport in the time of Christ!

Deltas differ much in their size, shape, growth and importance. A number of factors such as the rate of sedimentation, the depth of the river and the seabed, and the character of the tides, currents and waves greatly influence the eventual formation of deltas. For this reason, several types of delta are recognisible. The Mississippi has a bird's-foot *delta*, with several main branches like the foot of a bird extending into the Gulf of Mexico. The Nile, Ganges and Mekong have the fan-shaped arcuate deltas with numerous distributaries. Some other rivers such as the Amazon, Ob and Vistula have their deltas partly submerged in coastal waters to form estuarine *deltas*. A few rivers like the Ebro of Spain have tooth-like projections at their mouths. These are known as cuspate deltas.

The following summarises the conditions favourable for the formation of deltas.

i. Active vertical and lateral erosion in the upper course of the river to provide extensive sediments to be eventually deposited as deltas.
ii. The coast should be sheltered preferably *tideless*.
iii. The sea adjoining the delta should be shallow or else the load will disappear in the deep waters.
iv. There should be no large lakes in the river course to 'filter off' the sediments.
v. There should be no strong current running at right angles to the river mouth, washing away the sediments.

River Rejuvenation

The earth's crust is far from stable and it is not surprising that, in the course of a river's development, parts may be uplifted or depressed, giving rise to certain characteristic features associated with rejuvenation, i.e. being young again.

A negative movement occurs when there is an *uplift of land* or a *fall in sea level.* This will steepen the slope so that active down-cutting is renewed. A fall in sea level leaves the floodplain at an increased altitude above the sea level. The river with its renewed vigour cuts into the former floodplain, leaving behind terraces on both sides of the river. There is also a break in the graded profile of the river, often marked by a series of rapids. This point where the old and rejuvenated profile meet is called the knick point or *rejuvenated head* (Fig. 56).

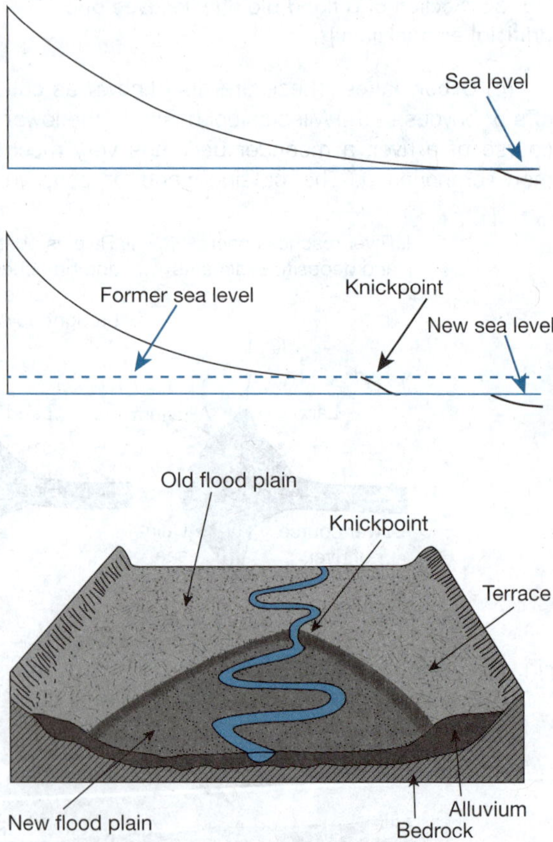

Fig. 56 River terraces and knickpoint due to rejuvenation
The rejuvenated river cuts down into previously deposited sediments to form a new valley leaving terraces at either side. At the head of rejuvenation the river falls to its new valley at a knickpoint

If rejuvenation occurs in the upper-course, the river valleys are deepened and steep-sided gorges are formed. In the middle and lower course vertical corrasion replaces lateral corrasion and the existing meanders are vertically eroded by the rejuvenated stream. A distinct new inner trench is cut in the old valley, and the river develops a deep valley with entrenched or incised meanders. The best developed incised meanders are those of the River Colorado, USA, where the uplift of 7,000 feet in the Tertiary period renewed down-cutting to a fantastic depth. In some parts of the Grand Canyon, the depth is almost a mile. It is 10 miles wide at the top and 300 miles long. Other examples are the River Moselle in Germany, the River Wear at Durham, England, and the Wye Valley, Monmouthshire.

A positive movement occurs when there is a *depression* of land or a *rise in sea level.* This will submerge the lands along the coast, 'drown' the valleys and weaken the erosive power of the river. The flow is checked and large quantities of sediment will be dropped. The lower course of the river may be partly in the sea and features of deposition are shifted upwards to the middle course. The upper course is little affected when there is a rise in sea level. In many areas where the sea has risen this was probably caused by the release of water locked up in the ice masses during the Quaternary Ice Ages.

The Human Aspects of Rivers

In many countries, rivers form the chief highway of commerce and transport. The Yangt-ze Kiang is navigable up to a thousand miles from its mouth. The Amazon, the world's greatest river is navigable 2,300 miles upstream to the foot of the Andes, though it is less extensively used. Even the Nile with its cataracts is navigable for its first 960 miles up to the First Cataract at Aswan. Other major rivers such as the Mississippi, St. Lawrence, Rhine, Danube, Congo, Murray, Darling, Mekong and Irrawaddy all serve as important waterways for their respective countries. Some of them are useful for transporting logs to the saw mills, others are used to export bulky goods and import foodstuffs and raw materials.

But all rivers undertake three closely interrelated activities *erosion, transportation and deposition.* Their work has therefore both advantages and disadvantages from a human point of view. Rapids and waterfalls, interrupt the navigability of a river. By depositing large quantities of sediments in the lower course, the river silts up ports preventing large steamers from anchoring close to the shores. Deltas are thus less satisfactory sites than estuaries for the siting of large ports. Though this can be overcome by the construction of *artificial harbours* or by dredging this is expensive and, in some instances, impracticable. Some rivers change their courses from time to time, others are made difficult for navigation by their seasonal variations in the amount of water discharged, and others may suffer from ill-drained marshes and stagnant waters, leading to ill health and water-borne disease. Many rivers flood, bursting levees and causing untold damage to crops. The floods may add a layer of fertile silt to the flood plain, but excessive flooding as in the Orinoco may discourage people from cultivating crops at all.

On the other hand, the advantages of rivers often outweigh the destruction that they cause. In the upper course, rivers with steep gorges and waterfalls, provide natural sites for the generation of hydroelectric power, leading to the establishment of metallurgical industries, engineering and aluminum smelting, which can be profitably run on cheap, abundant power. *Dams* constructed across rivers hold back floodwater which if allowed to flow downstream unchecked may cause widespread disastrous floods in the lower course, e.g. in the Indus and Ganges plains. In regions of insufficient rainfall such as Egypt and the Chao Phraya basin in Thailand irrigation canals fed by the main stream enable many crops to be successfully cultivated. The upper streams develop river captures and the resultant wind gaps may facilitate construction of upland roads and railways. The river valleys provide a convenient means of land *communication.*

The flood plains of large rivers with their thick mantles of fine silt are some of the richest agricultural areas of the world. They may support very dense populations and a chain of large cities may be strung along their banks. Many deltas are equally fertile, e.g. the Ganges delta accounts for almost all the jute grown for world consumption; the Nile delta produces superior quality cotton and several crops of rice a year. The productive hinterlands are able to support ports such as New Orleans for the Mississippi basin, Rotterdam for the Rhineland and Calcutta for the Indo-Gangetic Plain.

Freshwater fishing is important along many rivers and lakes. The organic matter brought down by the river waters provides valuable food for fish and for spawning purposes. Rivers supply water for domestic consumption, sewerage and other industrial purposes. In Lancashire, the soft-water from the Millstone Grit is used for washing, dyeing and bleaching textiles. Rivers form the political boundaries between many countries. The Mekong separates Laos from Thailand; and the Yalu forms a well defined border between North Korea and eastern Russia.

QUESTIONS AND EXERCISES

1. What are the characteristic features you would expect to find in a river valley at the stage of youth, maturity and old age? Illustrate some of the more outstanding features with diagrams and examples.
2. By reference to specific examples, describe the major constructive and destructive processes at work along the course of a river from its source to its mouth.
3. With the aid of annotated diagrams, explain the contrasting features of any *three* of the following pairs of features of a river:
   (a) dendritic and trellised drainage pattern
   (b) rapids and waterfalls
   (c) estuary and delta
   (d) tributaries and distributaries
   (e) river capture and river cliff
4. Explain any *three* of the following statements briefly:
   (a) Mass movement of earth is mainly due to the lubricating action of rainwater and gravitational forces.
   (b) Vertical corrasion is dominant in the upper course of a river.
   (c) The work of the river in the lower course is mainly depositional.
   (d) Ports are better sited on estuaries than on deltas.
   (e) Incised meanders are features of river rejuvenation.
5. *Either*: Describe and explain with relevant sketches the various types of river deltas.
   Or: Explain the ways in which river erosion occurs.

6 Landforms of Glaciation

The Ice Age and Types of Ice Masses

During the Pleistocene period or the Ice Ages, about 30,000 years ago, great continental ice sheets covered much of the temperate latitudes. It is estimated that more than 12 million square miles of the northern hemisphere were buried by ice, half of which was in North America and the rest in Europe, Greenland and the high mountains of Eurasia (Fig. 57). The warmer climate that followed caused the ice sheets to retreat. Today only two major ice caps are still present, in Greenland and Antarctica. The former covers an area of 720,000 square miles while the latter is more than 5 million square miles. They are made up of compact sheets of ice, hardened and crystallized to a depth of over a mile. In Marie Byrd Land, Antarctica, the ice cap was measured and found to be more than 14,000 feet thick! Under such a colossal weight, the land sinks gradually.

From the central dome of the ice cap the ice creeps out in all directions to escape as glaciers. The peaks of the loftier mountains project above the surface as nunataks. When the ice sheets reach right down to the sea they often extend outwards into the polar waters and float as ice shelves. They terminate in precipitous cliffs. When they break into individual blocks, these are called icebergs. While afloat in the sea, icebergs assume a tabular or irregular shape and only one-ninth of the mass is visible above the surface. They diminish in size when approaching warmer waters and are eventually melted, dropping the rock debris that was frozen inside them on the sea bed.

Apart from Greenland and Antarctica, glaciation is still evident on the highlands of many parts of the world, which lie above the snowline. This varies from sea level in the polar regions to 9,000 feet in the Alps and 17,000 feet at the equator, as on Mt. Kilimanjaro. Permanent snowfields are sustained by heavy winter snowfall and ineffective summer melting and evaporation. Where the slopes are gentle and the hollows are sheltered from both direct sunlight and strong winds, any snow that falls is rapidly accumulated. Part of the surface snow may melt during the day, but by nightfall it is refrozen. This process is repeated until it forms a hard, granular substance known as névé (in French) or firn (in German). Owing to gravitational forces, the neve of the upland snowfield is drawn towards the valley below. This is the beginning of the flow of the glacier – 'river of ice'. It normally assumes a tongue-shape, broadest at the source but becoming narrower downhill. Though the glacier is not a liquid, under the continual pressure from the accumulated snow above, it moves. The rate of movement is greatest in the middle where there

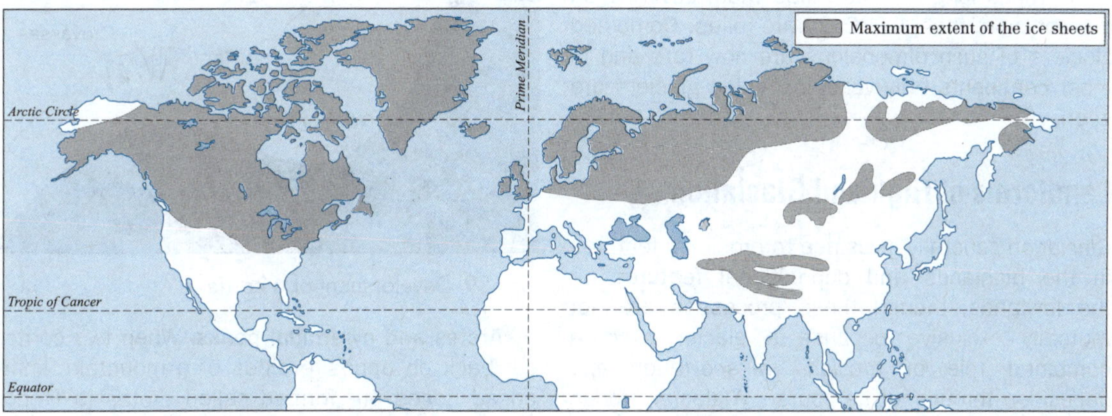

Fig. 57 The extent of continental ice sheets in the Ice Ages

is little obstruction. The sides and the bottom are held back by friction with the valley side spurs and the valley floor. If a row of stakes is planted across a glacier in a straight line, they will eventually take a curved shape down the valley, showing that the glacier moves faster at the centre than the sides (Fig. 58). In the Alps the average rate of flow is about three feet a day; in Greenland it may be more than 50 feet, but in Antarctica, where there is little heat to melt the ice, glaciers move only a few inches a day! The Aletsch Glacier in the Bernese Oberland of Switzerland is 10 miles long, affording some spectacular sights to Alpine tourists. Though it is the longest glacier in Europe, it is short compared with those of Alaska and the Himalayas which measure more than five times that length!

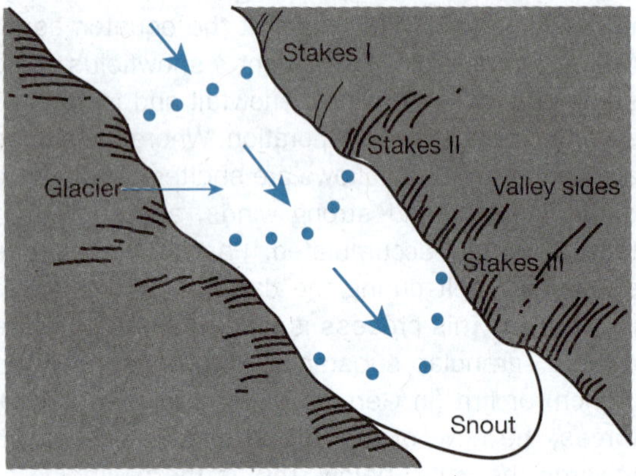

Fig. 58 The different rate of glacial movement. A glacier moves faster in the centre than the sides

At the foot of mountain ranges, several glaciers may converge to form an extensive ice-mass called a piedmont glacier. The best known piedmont glacier is the Malaspina Glacier of Alaska which is 65 miles long and 25 miles wide, covering an area of more than 1,600 square miles. Combined glaciers of such dimensions are now rare and in most continents only valley or Alpine glaciers are seen.

Landforms of Highland Glaciation

Glaciation generally gives rise to erosional features in the highlands and depositional features on the lowlands, though these processes are not mutually exclusive because a glacier plays a combined role of *erosion, transportation and deposition* throughout its course. A glacier erodes its valley by two processes *plucking* and *abrasion*. By plucking the glacier freezes the joints and beds of the underlying rocks, tears out individual blocks and drags them away. By abrasion, the glacier scratches, scrapes, polishes and scours the valley floor with the debris frozen into it. These fragments are powerful 'tools' of denudation. Large angular fragments cut deep into the underlying rocks so all glaciated floors bear evidence of striation or scratching. The finer materials smooth and polish the rock surfaces and produce finely ground rock flour. The rate of erosion is determined by several factors such as the velocity of flow, gradient of the slope, the weight of the glacier, the temperature of the ice and the geological structure of the valley.

The characteristic features of a glaciated highland are as follows.

1. **Corrie, cirque or cwm.** The downslope movement of a glacier from its snow-covered valley-head, and the intensive shattering of the upland slopes, tend to produce a depression where the *firn* or *névé* accumulates. The process of plucking operates on the back-wall, steepening it and the movement of the ice abrades the *floor*, deepening the depression into a steep, horse-shoe-shaped basin called a cirque (in French). It is also known as a corrie in Scotland and a cwm in Wales (Fig. 59). There is a rocky ridge at the exit of the corrie and, when the ice eventually melts, water collects behind this barrier, to form a corrie lake or tarn.

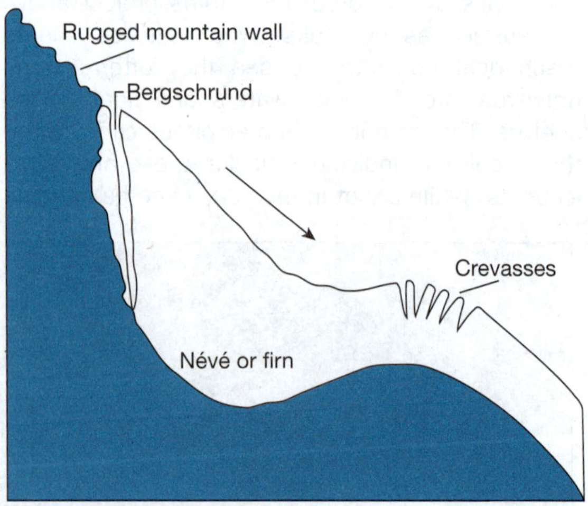

Fig. 59 Development of a corrie

2. **Arêtes and pyramidal peaks.** When two corries cut back on opposite sides of a mountain, knife-edged ridges are formed called aretes (a French word). A well-known British example of an arête

A glacial landscape in Switzerland *Swiss National Tourist Office*

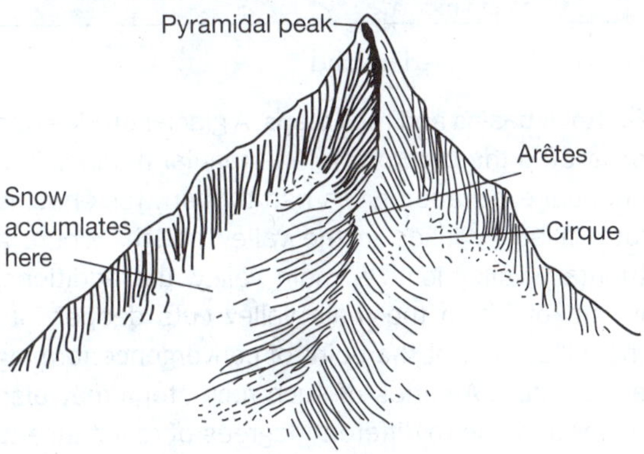

Fig. 60 Cirque, arête and pyramidal peak

is the Striding Edge on Helvellyn in Westmorland. Where three or more cirques cut back together, their ultimate recession will form an *angular horn* or pyramidal peak. The Matterhorn of Switzerland is a classic example (Fig. 60).

3. **Bergschrund.** At the head of a glacier, where it begins to leave the snowfield of a corrie, a deep vertical crack opens up called a bergschrund (in German) or rimaye (in French). This happens in summer when, although the ice continues to move out of the corrie, there is no new snow to replace it. In some cases not one but several such cracks occur. The bergschrund presents a major obstacle to climbers. Further down where the glacier

A U-shaped valley in Switzerland. The valley sides are steep but the floor is flat.

negotiates a bend or a precipitous slope, more crevasses or cracks are formed (Fig. 59).

4. **U-shaped glacial trough.** The glacier on its downward journey, fed by ice from several corries like tributaries that join a river, begins to wear away the sides and floor of the valley down which it moves. It scratches and grinds the bedrock, removing any rock debris and surface soil. It tends to straighten any protruding spurs on its course. The *interlocking spurs* are thus blunted to form truncated spurs and the floor of the valley is deepened (Fig. 61). A valley which has been glaciated takes a characteristic U-shape, with a wide, flat floor and very steep sides. After the disappearance of the ice, the deep sections of these long, narrow glacial troughs may be filled with water forming ribbon lakes, such as Loch Ness and Lake Ullswater in Great Britain. They are sometimes referred to as *trough lakes* or *finger lakes.*

5. **Hanging valleys.** The main valley is eroded much more rapidly than the tributary valleys as it contains a much larger glacier. After the ice has melted a tributary valley therefore 'hangs' above the main valley so that its stream plunges down as a waterfall (Fig. 61). Such tributary valleys are termed hanging valleys and may form a natural head of water for generating hydro-electric power.

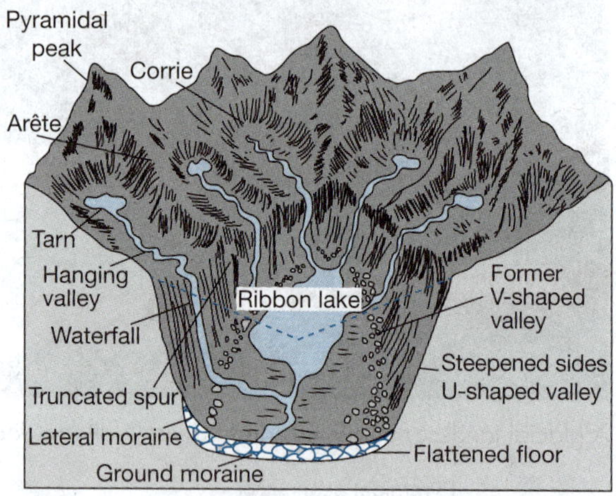

Fig. 61 A glaciated upland

6. **Rock basins and rock steps.** A glacier erodes and excavates the bed rock in an irregular manner. The unequal excavation gives rise to many rock basins later filled by lakes in the valley trough. Where a tributary valley joins a main valley, the additional weight of ice in the main valley cuts deeper into the valley floor at the point of convergence forming a rock step. A series of such rock steps may also be formed due to different degrees of resistance to glacial erosion of the bedrocks.

7. **Moraines.** Moraines are made up of the pieces of rock that are shattered by frost action, imbedded in the glaciers and brought down the valley. Those that fall on the sides of the glacier, mainly screes, form lateral moraines. When two glaciers converge, their inside lateral moraines unite to form a medial moraine. The rock fragments which are dragged along beneath the frozen ice are dropped when the glacier melts and spread across the floor of the valley as ground moraine. The glacier eventually melts on reaching the foot of the valley, and the pile of transported materials left behind at the snout is the terminal moraine or *end moraine* (Fig. 62). The deposition of the end moraines may be in several succeeding waves, as the ice may melt back by stages so that a series of recessional moraines are formed.

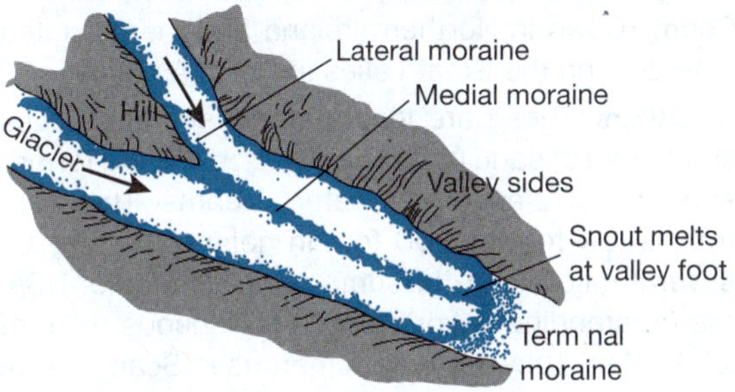

Fig. 62 The glacial moraines

If the glacier flows right down to the sea it drops its load of moraine in the sea. If sections break off as icebergs, morainic material will only be dropped when they melt (Fig. 63). Where the lower end of the trough is drowned by the sea it forms a deep, steep- sided inlet called a fiord, typical of the Norwegian and south Chilean coasts.

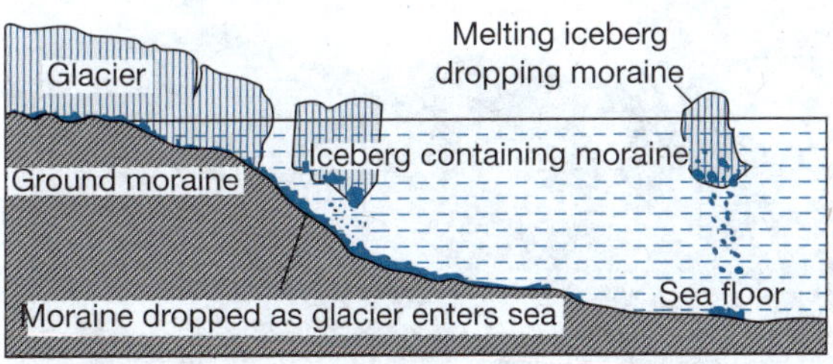

Fig. 63 A glacier ending at the sea

Landforms of Glaciated Lowlands

Landforms of glaciated lowlands are mainly *depositional* in nature, brought about by both *valley glaciers* and *continental ice sheets.* The former leaves behind the eroded materials in only restricted areas. The imprint of ice sheets on the landscape is far more widespread because they advanced through large areas during the Ice Ages, scouring and removing any surface soil and rock debris on their way. As a result, it has been estimated that almost a third of the total land surface of Europe and North America is littered with glacial and fluvio-glacial materials of all descriptions – moraines, boulder clay, tills, drifts, rock-flour, gravels and sands. Many of them are being re-eroded, resorted and redeposited elsewhere by present-day rivers.

Most of the glaciated lowlands have depositional features, but where rock masses project above the level surface, they result in striking features of erosion, such as the roche moutonnee and crag and tail:

1. **Roche Moutonnee.** This is a resistant residual rock hummock. The surface is striated by ice movement. Its upstream side is smoothed by abrasion and its downstream side is roughened by plucking, and is much steeper. The term roche moutonnee is used to describe such a feature because it resembles a sheepskin-wig once worn in France (Fig. 64). Roches moutonnees are found in both highland and lowland glaciated regions.

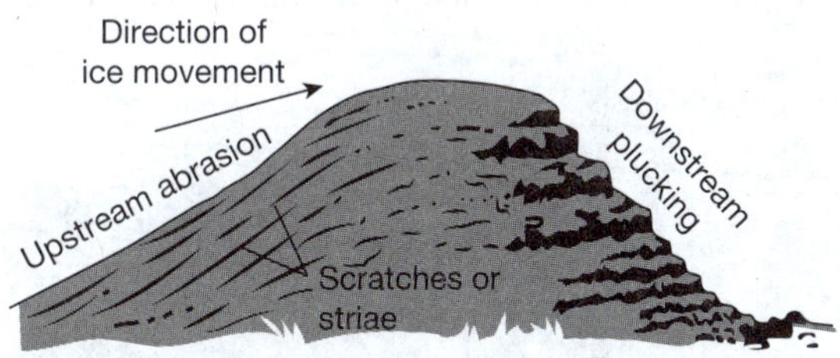

Fig. 64 Roche moutonnee

2. **Crag and Tail.** The crag is a mass of hard rock with a precipitous slope on the upstream side, which protects the softer leeward slope from being completely worn down by the oncoming ice. It therefore has a gentle tail, strewn with the eroded rock debris. The classic example is the *Castle Rock of Edinburgh,* Scotland. Edinburgh Castle is located on the crag and the High Street on the tail. (Fig. 65).

The remaining glaciated lowland features are of a depositional nature (Fig. 66). The following are the typical ones.

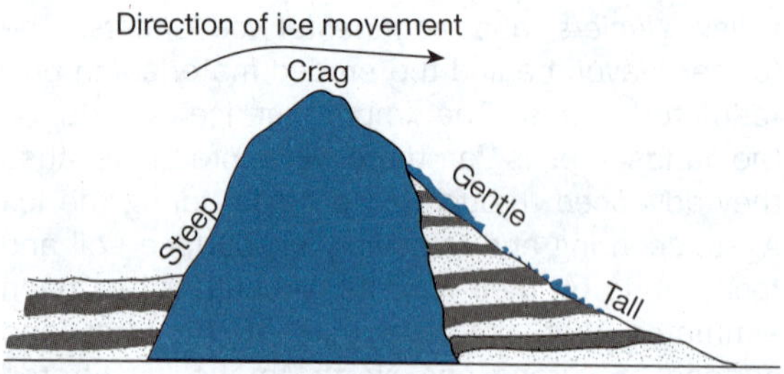

Fig. 65 Crag and tail

3. **Boulder clay or glacial till.** This is an unsorted glacial deposit comprising a range of eroded materials – boulders, angular stones, sticky clay and fine rock flour. It is spread out in sheets, not mounds, and forms gently undulating till or drift plains. The landform is rather monotonous and featureless. The degree of fertility of such glacial plains depends very much on the composition of the depositional materials. Some of the boulder clay plains such as East Anglia and the northern Mid-West of USA form rich arable lands.

4. **Erratics.** These are boulders of varying sizes that were transported by ice. They came with the advancing glaciers or ice sheets but when the ice melted, they were left 'stranded' in the regions of deposition. They are called erratics because they are composed of materials entirely different from those of the region in which they are found. Such erratics are thus most useful in tracing the source and direction of the ice movement. Sometimes the erratics may be found perched in precarious positions just as the ice dropped them and they are then termed perched blocks. Examples of such blocks are commonly encountered in both lowland and highland areas in Europe, e.g. Silurian grits are found perched on the Carboniferous Limestone of the Pennines. Their presence in large numbers is a hindrance to farming.

5. **Drumlins.** These are swarms of oval, elongated 'whale-back' hummocks composed wholly of boulder clay, with their elongation in the direction of the ice flow, that is on the downstream side. They are low hills varying from a few yards to 400 feet in height and may be a mile or two long. They appear a little steeper at the onset side and taper off at the leeward end. They are arranged diagonally and so are commonly described as having a *basket of eggs topography.* Large numbers of them are found in County Down in Northern Ireland and the glaciated plain around the Great Lakes in North America.

6. **Eskers.** These are long, narrow, sinuous ridges composed of sand and gravel which mark the former sites of sub-glacial melt-water streams. They vary from a few feet to 200 feet in height and may be several miles long. In some parts of Maine, USA, the outstanding eskers form a continuous ridge of 100 miles! They are very numerous in Scandinavia, e.g. the Punkaharju Esker of Finland. As eskers are made up of highly porous sand and gravel, water is rapidly drained off from their crests and they may

A drumlin field

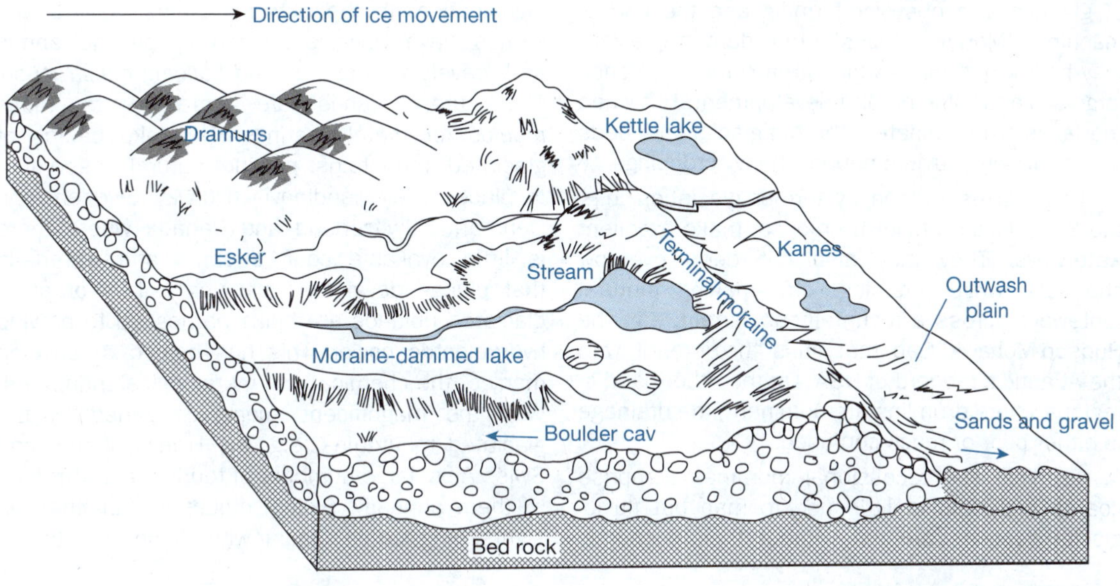

Fig. 66 Glacial depositional features in the outwash plain

not support many trees, though in Finland they often form tree-covered ridges between lakes.

7. **Terminal moraines.** These are made up of the coarse debris deposited at the edge of the ice-sheet, to form hummocky and hilly country such as the Baltic Heights of the North European Plain (Fig. 66).

8. **Outwash plains.** These are made up of fluvio-glacial deposits washed out from the terminal moraines by the streams and channels of the stagnant ice mass. The melt-waters sort and re-deposit the material in a variety of forms from the low hilly heathlands, such as the Luneburg Heath of the North European Plain, to undulating plains, where terraces, alluvial fans and deltaic deposits of the melt-water streams make up the landscape. Kames, small rounded hillocks of sand and gravel may cover part of the plain. Where the deposition takes the form of alternating ridges and depressions, the latter may contain kettle lakes and give rise to characteristic *knob and kettle* topography.

The Human Aspects of Glaciated Landforms

Though the Ice Ages were at their height over 30,000 years ago, the effects of glaciation on both landforms and human activities have profound influence in many parts of the world today. Their most striking impact is felt in the temperate regions of Europe and North America which were once under continental ice sheets. Further south and on the high mountains all over the world, slow-moving glaciers are still shaping the landscape in the Alps, Andes, Rockies and Himalayas. Glacial influences on Man's economic activities are both favourable and unfavourable, depending on the intensity of glaciation, the relief of the region and whether the effects are of an erosional or depositional nature.

In *hilly regions* such as the mountain slopes of Scandinavia, ice sheets and glaciers have removed most of the top soil, leaving them quite bare of vegetation. Soils that do exist are so *thin* that they are incapable of supporting effective agriculture. Glacial drifts in the valleys and benches or alps which were not affected by glaciers have good pastures during summer. Cattle are driven up to graze on the grass and return to the valley bottom in winter. This form of animal-migration type of farming is called transhumance. Extensive boulder clay plains such as those of East Anglia and the Mid-West of USA are some of the most fertile agricultural plains known. The loess plains of Europe and central USA, with a high proportion of humus are good farming land too. On the other hand, the *sandy or gravelly* outwash plains e.g. the heath-covered *geest* of northern Germany, the *marshy boulder clay* deposits of central Ireland, the *barren* ice-scoured surfaces of the Canadian and Baltic Shields are infertile. The presence of numerous erratic and perched blocks in parts of Britain and in Alberta, Canada, many of them of gigantic size obstruct farming and the use of machines. Morainic deposits may dam, or glaciers may hollow out, lakes which greatly inconvenience large-scale farming or land development. But when the lakes are eliminated, the old glacial lake beds with their rich alluvium support heavy cropping.

Large lakes formed by former glaciation, e.g. the Great Lakes of North America, make excellent waterways. They may also cut deep overflow channels while draining off, making natural routeways across a mountainous terrain, e.g. the Hudson-Mohawk Gap that links the interior with the Atlantic seaboard of USA. On the other hand in regions where drumlins are dominant, the drainage is either poor or much confused.

Terminal and recessional moraines comprise coarse materials of little use to man but fluvio-glacial deposits are not without their economic significance. In the outwash plains, eskers and kames have been excavated to provide sands and gravels for *highway and building construction.* The purest sands are extracted to make *moulds* for metal castings. The lake basins of glaciated mountains provide natural reservoirs. In places like Scandinavia (Norway, Sweden, and Denmark), Switzerland and Canada where there is little available coal, streams and waterfalls that plunge down from hanging valleys or other glaciated uplands are being harnessed to provide hydroelectric power. This has helped to develop many of the chemical and metallurgical industries. With the magnificent scenery provided by the glaciated mountains, e.g. the French, Italian and Swiss Alps, large numbers of tourists are attracted to them annually. Skiing, mountain climbing and sightseeing are all popular with Alpine tourists.

QUESTIONS AND EXERCISES

1. Choose any *three* of the following glacial features: corrie, arete, erratic, hanging valley, kettle lake, nunatak. For each of them:
   (a) Describe its physical appearance.
   (b) Account for its mode of formation.
   (c) Locate and name an area where an example could be seen.
2. (a) Distinguish between valley glaciers and continental ice sheets.
   (b) Explain why glaciation in the uplands produced erosional features while that of the lowlands produced mainly depositional features.
3. The following lowland glacial features are all, in fact, small ridges, but are quite different in their process of formation:
   (a) State which of them are of erosional or depositional nature.
   (b) Pick out their distinctive differences in both appearance and formation.

   roche moutonnee, drumlin, esker, crag and tail, kames.
4. Briefly explain any *three* of the following.
   (a) Glaciated valleys assume a characteristic U-shaped.
   (b) The middle of a glacier moves faster than the sides.
   (c) In glaciated lowlands, eskers, kames and other morainic deposits are extensively quarried.
   (d) Glacial soils vary greatly in their fertility.
   (e) Erratics and perched blocks are the best indicators of the source and direction of ice movement.
5. With the aid of diagrams, attempt to explain the difference between any *three* of the following pairs of terms connected with glaciation.
   (a) Valley glacier and piedmont glacier
   (b) Bergschrund and crevasses
   (c) Corrie lake and ribbon lake
   (d) Interlocking spurs and truncated spurs
   (e) Terminal moraine and recessional moraine.

7 Arid or Desert Landforms

Types of Deserts

About a *fifth* of the world's land is made up of deserts, some rocky, others stony and the rest sandy. Deserts that are absolutely barren and where nothing grows at all are rare and they are better known as *true deserts.*

If you look at the world map carefully, you will find that there is a certain definite pattern to the location of the world's deserts (Fig. 67). You will realize that almost all the deserts are confined within the 15° to 30° parallels of latitude north and south of the equator. They lie in the trade wind belt on the western parts of the continents where Trade Winds are offshore. They are bathed by cold currents which produce a 'desiccating effect' so that moisture is not easily condensed into precipitation. *Dryness or* aridity is the key note. Such deserts are tropical hot deserts or 'Trade Wind deserts'. They include the great Sahara Desert; Arabian, Iranian and Thar Deserts; Kalahari, Namib, and Atacama Deserts; the Great Australian Desert and the deserts of south-west USA, and northern Mexico. In the continental interiors of the mid-latitudes, the deserts such as the Gobi and Turkestan are characterized by extremes of temperatures.

The work of winds and water in eroding elevated uplands, transporting the worn-off materials and depositing them elsewhere, has given rise to *five* distinct kinds of desert landscape.

1. **Hamada or rocky desert.** This consists of large stretches of bare rocks, swept clear of sand and dust by the wind. The exposed rocks are thoroughly smoothed and polished. The region is bare and sterile.

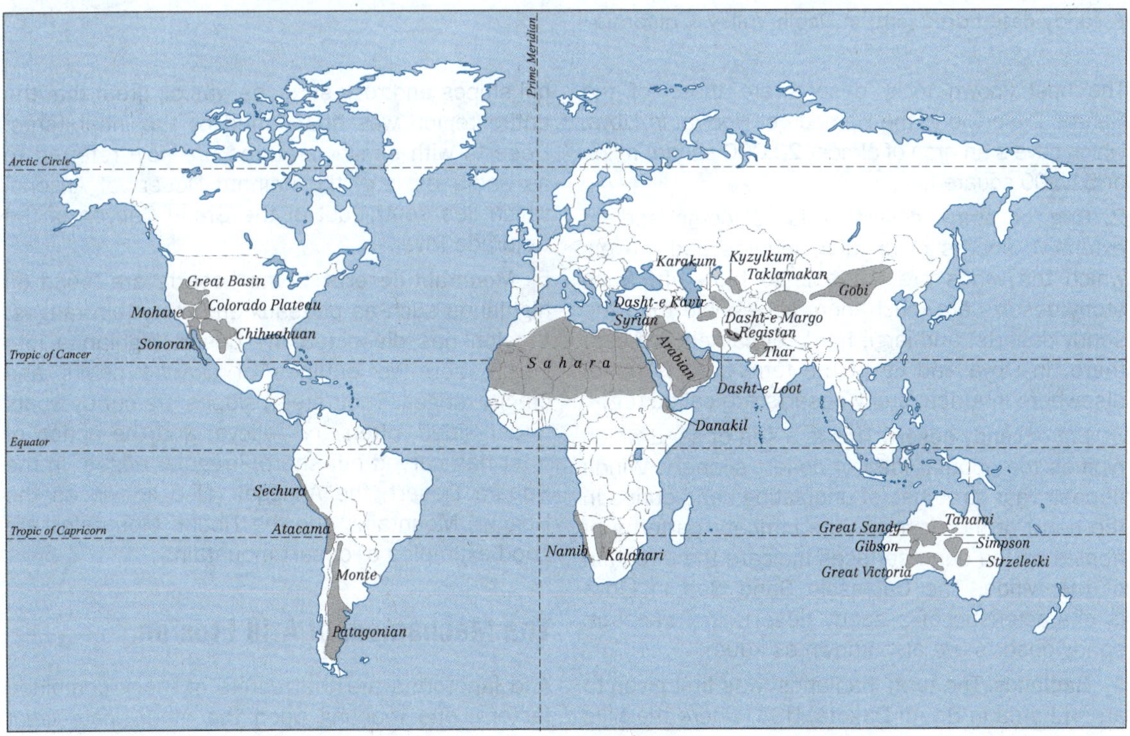

Fig. 67 World distribution of major deserts

A sandy desert area (erg) in Death Valley, California

The best known rocky deserts are those of the Sahara Desert, e.g. the Hamada el Homra, in Libya, which covers an area of almost 20,000 square miles or 51,800 square km.

2. **Reg or stony desert.** This is composed of extensive sheets of angular pebbles and gravels which the winds are not able to blow off. Such stony deserts are much more accessible than the sandy deserts, and large herds of camels are kept there. In Libya and Egypt the term serir is used; elsewhere in Africa, stony deserts are called reg.

3. **Erg or sandy desert.** This is a sea of sand which typifies the popular idea of desert scenery. Winds deposit vast stretches of undulating sand dunes in the heart of the deserts. The intricate patterns of ripples on the dune surfaces indicate the direction of the winds. The Calanscio Sand Sea in Libya is characteristic of a sandy desert. In Turkestan, sandy deserts are also known as koum.

4. **Badlands.** The term 'badlands' was first given to an arid area in South Dakota, USA, where the hills were badly eroded by occasional rainstorms into gullies and *ravines*. The extent of water action on hill slopes and rock surfaces was so great that the entire region was abandoned by the inhabitants. Deserts with similar features are now referred to as badlands, e.g. the Painted Desert of Arizona, which lies south-east of the Grand Canyon of the Colorado River.

5. **Mountain deserts.** Some deserts are found on highlands such as plateaux and mountain ranges. Erosion has dissected the desert highlands into harsh, serrated outlines of chaotic peaks and craggy ranges. Their steep slopes are cut by wadis (steep-sided, often dry, valleys) and the action of frost has carved out sharp, irregular edges. In the Sahara Desert, the Ahaggar (also known as the Hoggar) Mountains and the Tibesti Mountains are good examples of desert mountains.

The Mechanism of Arid Erosion

Arid landforms are the results of many combined factors, one reacting upon the other. *Insufficient rainfall* (often less than 5 inches) coming at most irregular periods, coupled with very high temperatures (87°F or 30°C is the average) and a *rapid rate of evaporation,* are the chief causes of aridity. Sub-aerial denudation through the processes of *weathering* (mechanical and chemical), *wind action* and the work of *water* have combined to produce a desert landscape that is varied and distinctive.

Weathering. This is the most potent factor in reducing rocks to sand in arid regions. Even though the amount of rain that falls in the desert is small, some manage to penetrate into the rocks and sets up chemical reactions in the various minerals. Intense heating during the day and rapid cooling at night by radiation, set up stresses in the already weakened rocks so that they eventually crack. As heat penetrates rocks slowly when the outer surface of rocks is being heated by the hot sun, the inner rocks remain quite cool. The heating of the rocks causes the outer surface to expand and so prise itself off from the interior rocks, so that it peels off in successive very thin layers. Such an onion-peeling process of mechanical weathering is called exfoliation. Angular rock debris is found in abundance as screes at the foot of upstanding rocks. Similarly, when water gets into the cracks and joints of rocks and the temperature at night suddenly drops to below freezing point, the water freezes and therefore expands by 10 per cent of its volume. Successive freezing will prise off fragments of rock which accumulate as screes. These rock fragments become the 'teeth' or *tools* of wind erosion.

Action of winds in deserts. The wind though not the most effective agent of erosion, transportation and deposition, is more efficient in arid than in humid regions. Since there is little vegetation or moisture to bind the loose surface materials, the effects of wind erosion are almost unrestrained.

Wind erosion is carried out in the following ways.

1. **Deflation.** This involves the *lifting and blowing away* of loose materials from the ground. Such unconsolidated sands and pebbles may be carried in the air or rolled along the ground depending on the grain size. The finer dust and sands may be removed miles away from their place of origin, and be deposited even outside the desert margins. Deflation results in the *lowering* of the land surface to form large depressions called deflation hollows. The Qattara Depression of the Sahara Desert lies almost 450 feet (137 m) below sea level.

2. **Abrasion.** The sand-blasting of rock surfaces by winds when they hurl sand particles against them is called abrasion. The impact of such blasting results in rock surfaces being scratched, polished and worn away. Abrasion is most effective at or near the base of rocks, where the amount of material the wind is able to carry is greatest. This explains why telegraph poles in the deserts are protected by a covering of metal for a foot or two above the ground. A great variety of desert features are produced by abrasion.

3. **Attrition.** When wind-borne particles roll against one another in collision they wear each other away so that their sizes are greatly reduced and grains are rounded into millet seed sand. This process is called attrition.

Landforms of Wind Erosion in Deserts —

In the combined processes of abrasion, deflation and attrition, a wealth of characteristic desert landforms emerge.

1. **Rock pedestals or mushroom rocks.** The sand-blasting effect of winds against any projecting rock masses wears back the softer layers so that an irregular edge is formed on the alternate bands of hard and soft rocks. Grooves and hollows are cut in the rock surfaces, carving them into fantastic and grotesque-looking pillars called rock pedestals (Fig. 68). Such rock pillars will be further eroded near their bases where the friction is greatest. This process of *undercutting* produces rocks of mushroom shape called mushroom rocks or gour in the Sahara.

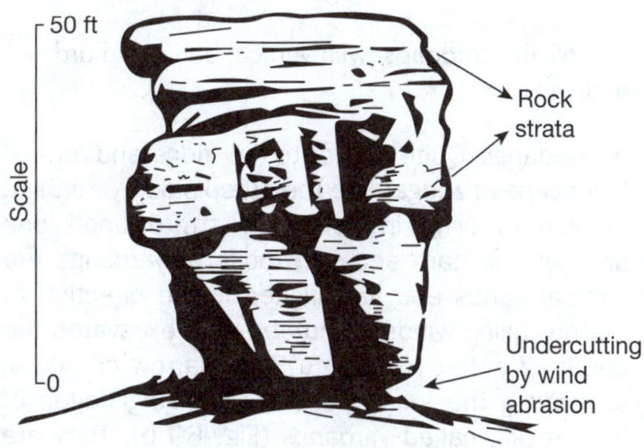

Fig. 68 Rock pedestals or gour

2. **Zeugen.** These are tabular masses which have a layer of soft rocks lying beneath a surface layer of more resistant rocks. The sculpting effects of wind abrasion wear them into a weird-looking *ridge and furrow* landscape. *Mechanical weathering* initiates their formation by opening up joints of the surface rocks. Wind *abrasion* further 'eats' into the underlying softer layer so that deep furrows are developed. The hard rocks then stand above the furrows as ridges or zeugen (Fig. 69 a), and many even overhang. Such tabular blocks of zeugen may stand 10 to 100 feet above the sunken furrows. Continuous abrasion by wind gradually lowers the zeugen and widens the furrows.

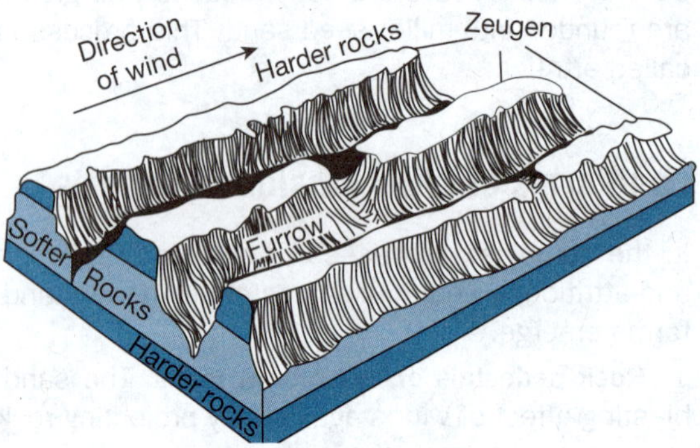

Fig. 69 (a) Zeugen (with horizontal strata of hard and soft rocks)

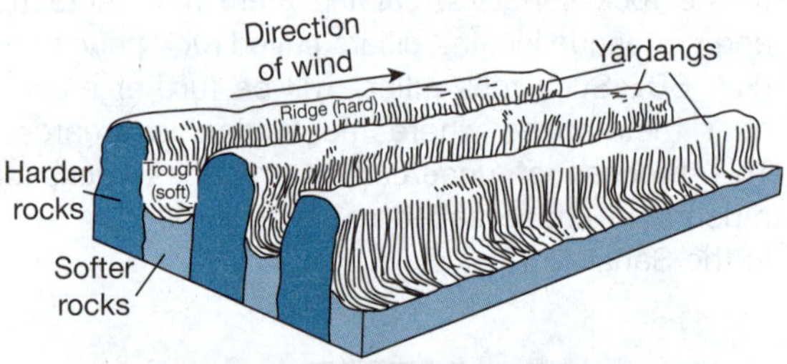

Fig. 69 (b) Yardangs (with vertical bands of hard and soft rocks)

3. **Yardangs.** Quite similar to the 'ridge and furrow' landscape of zeugen are the steep-sided yardangs. Instead of lying in horizontal strata upon one another, the hard and soft rocks of yardangs are vertical bands and are aligned in the direction of the prevailing winds. Wind abrasion excavates the bands of softer rocks into long, narrow corridors, separating the steep-sided overhanging ridges of hard rocks, called *yardangs* (Fig. 69 b). They are commonly found in the Atacama Desert, Chile, but the more spectacular ones with yardangs rising to 25–50 feet are best developed in the interior deserts of Central Asia where the name originated.

4. **Mesas and buttes.** Mesa is a Spanish word meaning 'table'. It is a flat, table-like land mass with a very resistant horizontal top layer, and very steep sides. The hard stratum on the surface resists denudation by both wind and water, and thus protects the underlying layers of rocks from being eroded away. Mesas may be formed in canyon regions, e.g. Arizona, or on fault blocks, e.g. the Table Mountain of Cape Town, South Africa. Continued denudation through the ages may reduce mesas in area so that they become isolated flat-topped hills called buttes. Many of them in arid countries are separated by deep gorges or canyons (Fig. 70).

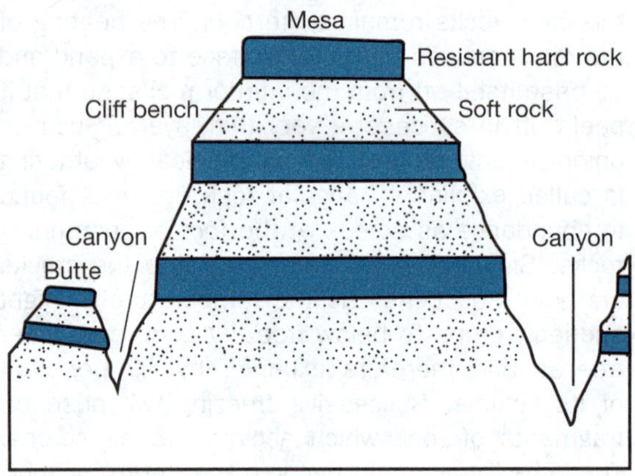

Fig. 70 Mesa and butte

5. **Inselberg.** This is a German word meaning 'island-mountain'. They are isolated residual hills rising abruptly from the level ground. They are characterized by their very steep slopes and rather rounded tops. They are often composed of granite or gneiss, and are probably the relics of an

Fig. 71 Round-topped, steep-sided inselbergs

Ayers Rock, an inselberg in the Australian Desert

original plateau which has been almost entirely eroded away. *Inselbergs* are typical of many desert and semi-arid landscapes in old age, e.g. those of northern Nigeria, Western Australia and the Kalahari Desert (Fig. 71).

6. **Ventifacts or dreikanter.** These are pebbles faceted by sand-blasting. They are shaped and thoroughly polished by wind abrasion to shapes resembling Brazil nuts. Rock fragments, mechanically weathered from mountains and upstanding rocks, are moved by wind and smoothed on the windward side. If wind direction changes another facet is developed. Such rocks have characteristic *flat facets* with *sharp edges*. Amongst the ventifacts those with *three* wind-faceted surfaces are called dreikanter. These wind-faceted pebbles form the desert pavement, a smooth, mosaic-like region, closely covered by the numerous rock fragments and pebbles.

7. **Deflation hollows.** Winds lower the ground by blowing away the unconsolidated materials, and small depressions may form. Similarly, minor *faulting* can also initiate depressions and the eddying action of oncoming winds will wear off the weaker rocks until the water table is reached. Water then seeps out forming oases or swamps, in the deflation hollows or depressions. The Faiyum (or Fayum) Depression in Egypt lies 130 feet (40 m) below the sea level. Large areas in the western USA, stripped of their natural vegetation for farming, were completely *deflated* when strong winds, moved materials as duststorms, laying waste crops and creating what is now known as the Great Dust Bowl. In a duststorm, winds may lift dust hundreds of feet high and carry it thousands of miles away.

Landforms of Wind Deposition in Deserts

Materials eroded and transported by winds must come to rest somewhere. The finest dust travels enormous distances in the air, and may be moved completely out of the desert. It has been estimated that some dust grains travel as far as 2,300 miles

(3,700 km) before they are finally deposited on land or sea. The dust from the Sahara Desert is sometimes blown across the Mediterranean to fall as *'blood rains'* in Italy or on the glaciers of Switzerland. Dust that settles in the Hwang-Ho (or Huang He) basin from the Gobi Desert has accumulated over past centuries to a depth of several hundred feet! As wind-borne materials are sifted according to their coarseness, it can be expected that the coarser sands will be too heavy to be blown out of the desert limits. They remain as dunes or other depositional landforms within the deserts themselves. Since they are *rarely static,* their migration pattern depends on a number of factors: the size of the particles they carry, the direction and velocity of the winds, the location and nature of the surfaces over which the particles are transported and the presence or absence of water and natural vegetation.

The following are some of the major features of wind deposition.

1. **Dunes.** Dunes are, in fact, *hills of sand* formed by the accumulation of sand and shaped by the movement of winds. They may be active or live dunes, constantly on the move, or inactive fixed dunes, rooted with vegetation. Dunes are most well represented in the erg desert where a sea of sand is being continuously moved, reshaped and redeposited into a variety of features. Because of their great contrast in shape, size and alignment, they have been given a long list of fanciful names, such as attached dune or head dune, tail dune, advanced dune, lateral dune, wake dune, star dune, pyramidal dune, sword dune, parabolic blow-out dune, hairpin dune, smoking dune and transverse dune. However, the following two types of common dunes, barchans and seifs, will be described in more detail.

(a) **Barchan.** These are crescentic or moon-shaped dunes which occur individually or in groups. They are live dunes which advance steadily before winds that come from a particular prevailing direction. They are most prevalent in the deserts of Turkestan and in the Sahara. Barchans are initiated probably by a chance accumulation of sand at an obstacle, such as a patch of grass or a heap of rocks. They occur transversely to the wind, so that their horns thin out and become lower in the direction of the wind due to the reduced frictional retardation of the winds around the edges. The *windward* side is *convex* and *gently-sloping* while the *leeward side,* being sheltered, is *concave* and *steep* (the slip-face) (Fig. 72). The crest of the sand dune moves forward as more sand is accumulated by the prevailing wind. The sand is *driven up* the windward side and, on reaching the crest, *slips down* the leeward side so that the dune advances. The rate of advancement varies from 25 feet a year for the high dunes measuring up to 100 feet high, to 50 feet a year, for the lower dunes which may be only a dozen feet high.

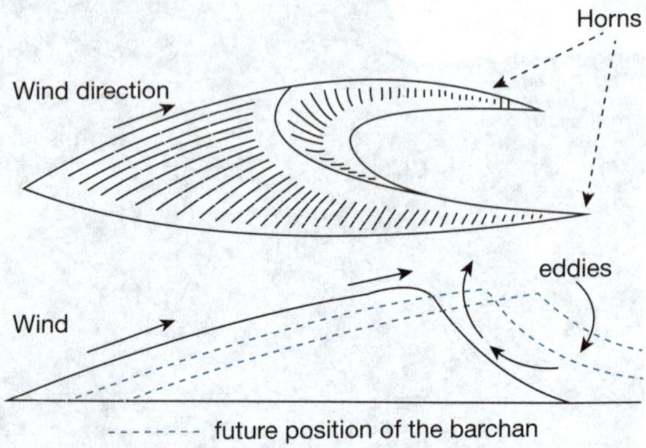

Fig. 72 Crescentic sand dune – barchan

The *migration* of the barchans may be a threat to desert life for they may encroach on an oasis burying palm trees or houses. Long-rooted sand-holding trees and grasses are therefore planted to halt the advance of the dunes thus preventing areas of fertile land from being devastated. Under the action of winds, barchans take a chaotic changing pattern. Several barchans may coalesce into a line of irregular ridges, ever-changing with the direction of the winds. Ergs or sandy deserts are thus most difficult to cross.

(b) **Seifs or longitudinal dunes.** Seif is an Arabic word meaning 'sword'. They are long, narrow ridges of sand, often over a hundred miles long lying parallel to the direction of the *prevailing winds.* The high, serrated ridges may attain a height of over 200 feet. The crestline of the seif rises and falls in alternate peaks and saddles in regular successions like the teeth of a monstrous saw. The dominant winds blow straight along the corridor between the lines of dunes so that they are swept clear of sand and remain smooth. The eddies that are set up blow towards the sides of the corridor, and, having less power, drop the sand to form the dunes.

In this manner, the prevailing winds increase the length of the dunes into tapering linear ridges while the occasional cross winds tend to increase their height and width. Extensive seif dunes are found in the Sahara Desert, south of the Qattara Depression; the Thar Desert and the West Australian Desert (Fig. 73).

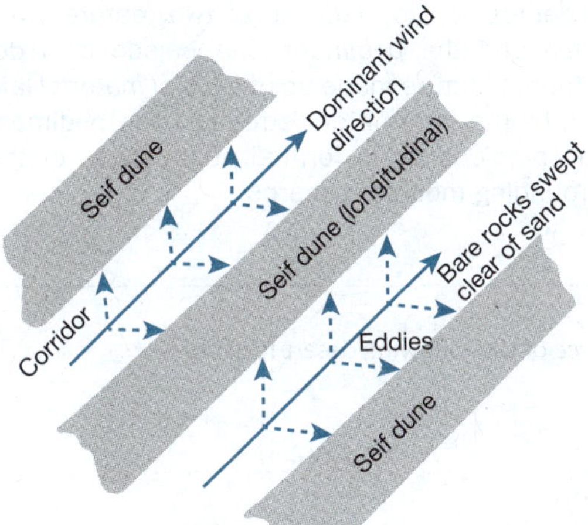

Fig. 73 Longitudinal dunes – seifs

2. **Loess.** The fine dust blown beyond the desert limits is deposited on neighbouring lands as loess. It is a yellow, friable material and is usually very fertile. Loess is in fact, fine loam, rich in lime, very coherent and extremely porous. Water sinks in readily so that the surface is always dry. Streams have cut deep valleys through the thick mantle of soft loess and badland topography may develop. It is so soft that roads constructed through a loess region soon sink and their walls rise steeply.

The most extensive deposit of loess is found in north-west China in the loess plateau of the Hwang-Ho (Huang He) basin. It is estimated to cover an area of 290,000 square miles (750,000 square km), and the deposits have accumulated to a depth of 200 to 500 feet (about 60 to 150 m)! In China, such yellowish wind-borne dust from the Gobi Desert is called *'Hwangtu' – the yellow earth!* But the original term *loess* actually comes from a village in Alsace, France, bearing that name, where such deposits occurred. Similar deposits also occur in some parts of Germany, France and Belgium, and are locally called limon. They are also wind-borne but were blown from material deposited at the edge of ice-sheets during the Ice Ages. In parts of the Mid-West, USA. loess was derived from the ice sheets which covered northern North America and is termed adobe.

Landforms due to Water Action in Deserts

Few deserts in the world are entirely without rain or water. The annual precipitation may be small, 5 to 10 inches, and comes in irregular showers. But thunderstorms do occur and the rain falls in torrential downpours, producing devastating effects. A single rainstorm may bring several inches of rain within a few hours, drowning people who camp in dry desert streams and flooding mud-baked houses in the oases. As deserts have little vegetation to protect the surface soil, large quantities of rock wastes are transported in the sudden raging torrents, or flashfloods. Loose gravels, sand and fine dust are swept down the hill sides. They cut deep gullies and ravines forming *badland topography.* Subsequent downpours widen and deepen the gullies when they wash down more soft rocks from the surface. There is so much material in the flash floods that the flow becomes *liquid* mud. When the masses of debris are deposited at the foot of the hill or the mouth of the valley, an alluvial cone or fan or 'dry delta' is formed, over which the temporary stream discharges through several channels, depositing more material. The pasty alluvial deposits are subjected to rapid evaporation by the hot sun and downward percolation of water into the porous ground, and soon dry up leaving *mounds of debris.*

Apart from gullies there are many larger dry channels or valleys. These are deepened by vertical corrasion by raging torrents during the occasional cloudbursts. These are the wadis and are dry for most of the time. Some desert streams are fed by the melting snow of the distant mountains outside the deserts and rivers flow as exotic streams. The water carves out steep walls, which rise abruptly from the stream bed. In Algeria such gorges are termed chebka.

In arid and semi-arid areas the outflowing streams from the upland regions are both short and intermittent. They drain into the lower depressions so that drainage is almost entirely internal. Sometimes water collected in a depression or a desert basin does not

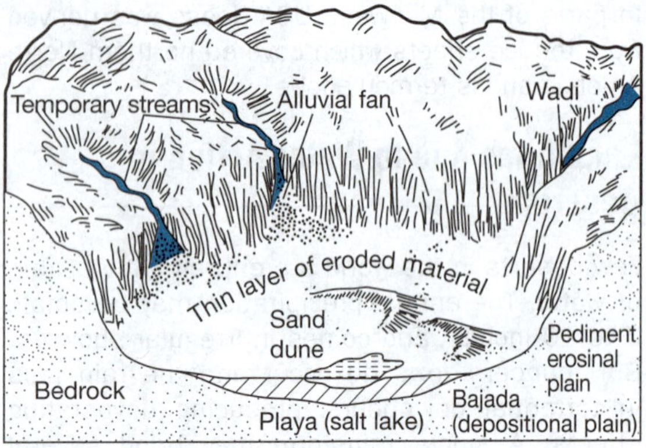

Fig. 74 Intermont desert basin

completely disappear by evaporation or seepage, and a temporary lake is formed. Such lakes contain a high percentage of salts, because of high evaporation, and are glistening white when they dry up. The lakes and the alluvial plains formed by them are called playas, salinas or salars in the United States and Mexico, and shotts in northern Africa (Fig. 74). The floor of the depression is made up of two features, the *bajada* and the *pediment.* The bajada is a depositional feature made up of *alluvial material* laid down by the intermittent streams. The pediment is an *erosional plain* formed at the base of the surrounding mountain scarps.

QUESTIONS AND EXERCISES

1. Draw annotated diagrams and explain very briefly any *three* of the following desert features.
   (a) yardangs
   (b) barchans
   (c) pediments
   (d) inselbergs
   (e) wadis
2. Attempt a simple classification of deserts. Justify your basis of classification by bringing out their distinct differences in appearance, formation and outstanding features.
3. With the aid of diagrams, explain the major differences between any *three* of the following pairs of desert landforms.
   (a) zeugen and yardangs
   (b) mesas and inselbergs
   (c) crescentic barchans and longitudinal seifs
   (d) bajadas and pediments
   (e) ventifacts and dreikanter
4. Explain concisely the processes of deflation, abrasion and deposition by winds. With the aid of diagrams explain *two* topographical features formed by any two of the above processes.
5. The following terms are closely related to desert landforms. For any *four* of them, define with reference to examples what the terms mean.
   (a) erg landscape
   (b) loess deposits
   (c) badland topography
   (d) rock pedestals
   (e) Great Dust Bowl
   (f) flash floods

8 Limestone and Chalk Landform

Limestone and Chalk

Limestone and chalk are *sedimentary rocks* of organic origin derived from the accumulation of corals and shells in the sea. In its pure state, limestone is made up of *calcite* or calcium carbonate, but where magnesium is also present it is termed dolomite. Chalk is a very pure form of limestone, white, and rather soft. Limestone is soluble in rainwater, which, with carbon dioxide from the air, forms a weak acid. A region with a large stretch of limestone therefore possesses a very distinct type of topography. It is then termed a karst *region,* a name derived from the Karst district of former Yugoslavia where such topography is particularly well developed. In the present geographical scenario, Karst remains a remarkable Karst plateau region that stretches across the border of southwestern Slovenia and northeastern Italy.

Characteristic Features of a Karst Region

Generally speaking, karst regions have a bleak landscape, occasionally broken by precipitous slopes. There is a general absence of surface drainage as most of the surface water has gone underground. Streams rising on other rocks only flow over limestone for a short distance and then disappear underground. For the greater part of their course, they cut their way along the joints and fissures of the rock wearing out a system of underground channels. The surface valleys are therefore dry. When the water penetrates to the base of the limestone and meets non-porous rocks it re-emerges onto the surface as a spring or resurgence.

Limestones are well jointed and it is through these joints and cracks that rainwater finds its way into the underlying rock. Progressive widening by solution enlarges these cracks into trenches and a most intriguing feature called limestone pavement is developed. The enlarged joints are called grikes and the isolated, rectangular blocks are termed clints. The limestone pavements may have been formed beneath the soil and are now exposed by the removal of the soil cover (Fig. 75).

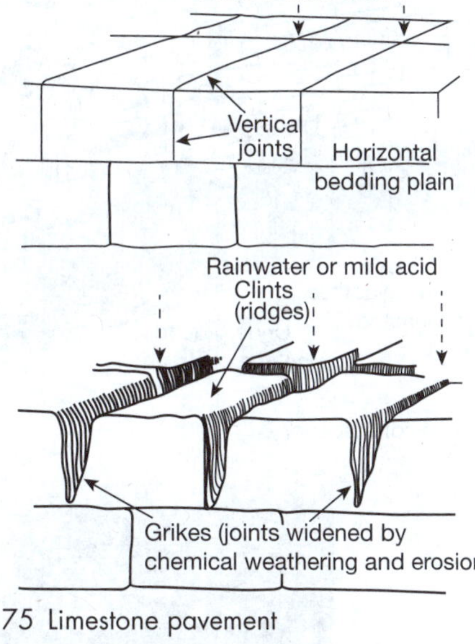

Fig. 75 Limestone pavement

A limestone escarpment overlooking the beautiful Lyth Valley in Cumbria, UK. Notice that the valley is cultivated but the limestone is bleak and treeless.

On the surface of the limestone are numerous swallow holes, which are small depressions carved out by solution where rainwater sinks into the limestone at a point of weakness. They are also known as sink holes. Gaping Ghyll in Yorkshire is a fine example. These holes grow in size through continuous solvent action.

Once water has sunk into the limestone it etches out caverns and passages along joints or bedding planes. When the roof of an underground tunnel collapses, a precipitous limestone gorge, such as the Cheddar Gorge, is formed. Where a number of swallow holes coalesce a larger hollow is formed and is called a doline (Fig. 76). Several dolina may merge

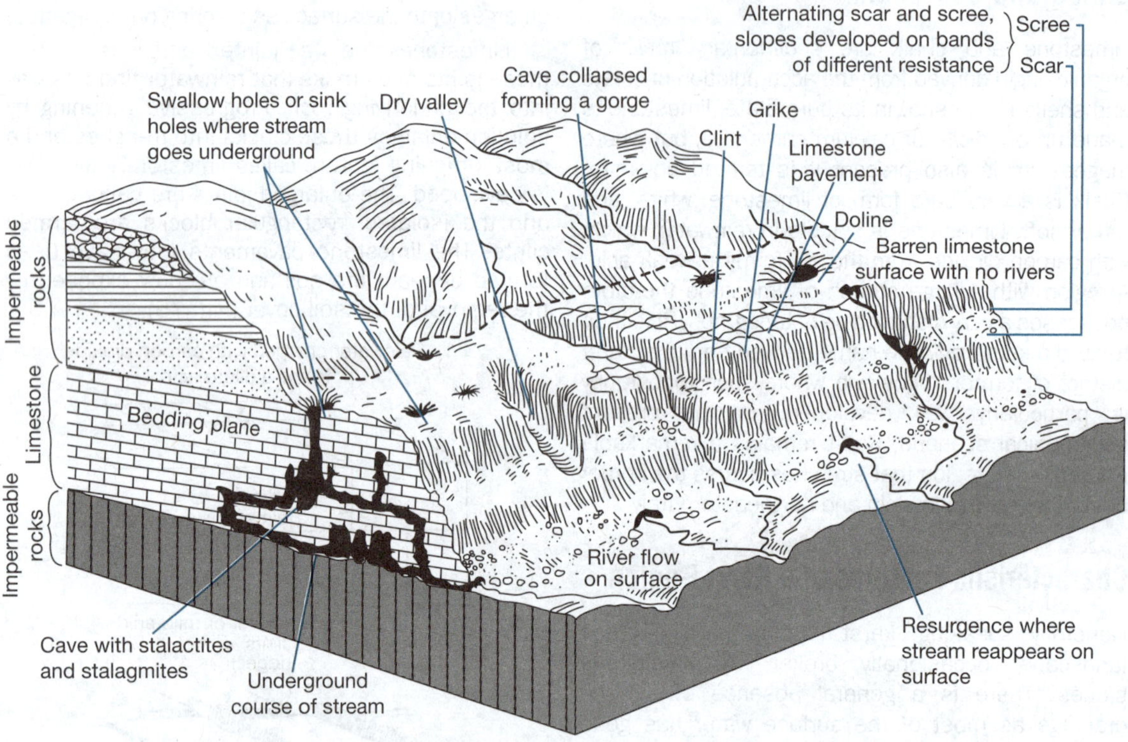

Fig. 76 Limestone scenery

A limestone pavement

as a result of subsidence to form a larger depression called an uvala. Some of them are a mile across, containing much clayey soil from the limestones, weathered after their subsidence.

In Slovenia, some very large depressions called polje may be as large as a hundred square miles but these are partly due to faulting. During the rainy season, parts of the floor which are at or near the water table may become temporary lakes, but the drier areas are fertile and may support large villages.

Where subterranean streams descend through swallow holes to underground passages, the region may be honeycombed with caves and *caverns*, some containing ponds and lakes. The most spectacular underground features that adorn the limestone caves are stalactites, stalagmites and pillars. Stalactites are the sharp, slender, downward-growing pinnacles that hang from the cave-roofs. The water carries calcium in solution and when this lime-charged water evaporates, it leaves behind the solidified crystalline calcium carbonate. As moisture drips from the roof it trickles down the stalactite and drops to the floor where calcium is deposited to form stalagmites. They are shorter, fatter and more rounded. Over a long period, the stalactite hanging from the roof is eventually joined to the stalagmite growing from the floor to form a pillar (Fig. 77). Such features are commonly seen in any well-developed limestone caves, e.g. Batu Caves, Selangor in Malaysia; Mammoth Cave, Kentucky and Carlsbad Caverns, New Mexico both in USA; and Postojna Cave, Slovenia.

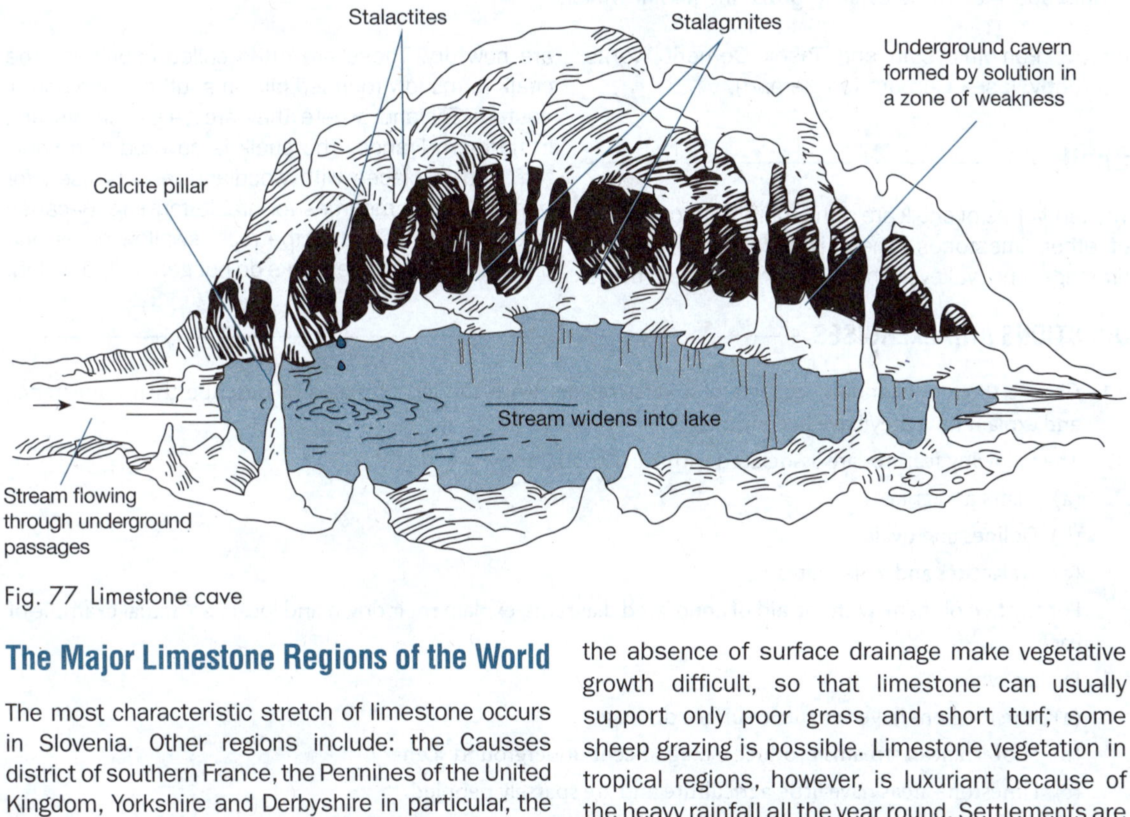

Fig. 77 Limestone cave

The Major Limestone Regions of the World

The most characteristic stretch of limestone occurs in Slovenia. Other regions include: the Causses district of southern France, the Pennines of the United Kingdom, Yorkshire and Derbyshire in particular, the Kentucky region of the USA, the Yucatan Peninsula of Mexico, the Cockpit Country of Jamacia, and the limestone hills of Perlis, Malaysia.

Human Activities of Karst Regions

Karst regions are often barren and at best carry a thin layer of soil. The porosity of the rocks and the absence of surface drainage make vegetative growth difficult, so that limestone can usually support only poor grass and short turf; some sheep grazing is possible. Limestone vegetation in tropical regions, however, is luxuriant because of the heavy rainfall all the year round. Settlements are scattered and the population is often sparse. The only mineral of importance is lead which occurs in veins in association with limestone. Besides this, good quality limestones are often used as building materials or quarried for the cement industry. In West Malaysia, the limestone outcrops of the Kledang Range and the Main Range are quarried

The Burren region, Clare, Ireland. The limestone landscape of the Burren is well known for the old tradition of 'Winterage' – allowing cattle to graze the hills in winter.

for the Pan-Malaysian and Tasek Cement Works (currently, Tasek Corporation Berhad).

Chalk

The landforms of chalk are rather different from those of other limestones. There is little or no surface drainage and valleys which once contained rivers are now dry. These are often called coombes. The chalk forms low rounded hills in southern and south-eastern England, where they are called downs and in northern France. The chalk is covered with short turf, and in places with woodland, and is used for pasture and sometimes for arable farming. Because of the friable nature of the rock, swallow holes and underground cave networks do not generally develop.

QUESTIONS AND EXERCISES

1. Choose *three* outstanding features of a karst region. With the aid of diagrams describe their appearance and explain how they have been formed.
2. The following features are associated with karst topography.
   (a) Clints and grikes
   (b) Dolines and uvalas
   (c) Stalactites and stalagmites
   For any *two* of them, with the aid of annotated diagrams, explain their origin and locate an actual example of each.
3. Explain why:
   (a) Karst regions have very little surface drainage.
   (b) Subterranean streams produce a magnificent underground scenery.
   (c) Limestone areas have little agriculture and are sparsely peopled.
4. With the aid of labelled diagrams, describe and account for the development of physical features which result from the action of *water* in:
   (a) limestone regions
   (b) arid deserts
   (c) granite uplands
5. Draw a large diagram of a karst region and indicate the following: swallow holes, limestone gorge, dry valleys, limestone pavement with clints and grikes. Describe briefly how any *two* of them have been formed.

9 Lakes

General

Lakes are amongst the most varied features of the earth's surface. They occupy the hollows of the land surface in which water accumulates. They vary tremendously in size, shape, depth and mode of formation. The tiny ones are no bigger than ponds or pools, but the large ones are so extensive that they merit the name of seas, e.g. the Caspian Sea which is 760 miles long (1,220 km), as much as 3,360 feet (1,025 m) deep, with a total area of 149,200 square miles (386,400 sq. km), and is bigger than the whole of Malaysia!

Lakes may exist *temporarily* filling up the small depressions of undulating ground after a heavy shower. But those which are deep and carry more water than could ever be evaporated remain *permanent*. Most of the lakes in the world are *freshwater lakes* fed by rivers and with outflowing streams, e.g. Lake Geneva (Switzerland), Lake Poyang (China) and the Great Lakes of North America. In regions of low precipitation and intense evaporation where there are few rivers strong enough to reach the sea, streams drain into a lake forming a basin of *inland drainage*. Because of the intense evaporation these lakes are saline. For example, the Dead Sea has a salinity (salt content) of 250 parts per thousand, and the Great Salt Lake of Utah, USA. has a salinity of 220 parts per thousand. But, the Black Sea, into which drain many large rivers, has a salinity of less than 17 parts per thousand! *Playas* or salt lakes, are a common feature of deserts.

It must be pointed out that lakes are only temporary features of the earth's crust; they will eventually be eliminated by the double process of draining and silting up. In regions of unreliable rainfall, lakes dry up completely during the dry season. In the hot deserts lakes disappear altogether by the combined processes of evaporation, percolation and outflow. Though the process of lake elimination may not be completed within our span of life, it takes place relatively quickly in terms of geological time.

The Formation and Origin of Lakes

The following are the various ways in which lakes can be formed. Each of them is placed in a specific category, though in a few cases the lakes could have been formed by more than one single factor.

1. **Lakes Formed by Earth Movement**

(a) **Tectonic lakes.** Due to the warping, sagging, bending and fracturing of the earth's crust, tectonic depressions occur. Such depressions give rise to lakes of immense sizes and depths. They include Lake Titicaca, occupying a huge depression in the intermont plateau of the Andes, 12,500 feet (3,810 m) above sea level the highest lake in the world; and the Caspian Sea, 149,200 square miles (386,400 sq. km), the largest lake, almost five times larger than its nearest rival, Lake Superior.

(b) **Rift valley lakes.** Due to faulting, a rift valley is formed by the sinking of land between two parallel faults, deep, narrow and elongated in character. Water collects in these troughs and their floors are often below sea level. The best known example is the East African Rift Valley which runs through Zambia, Malawi, Tanzania, Kenya and Ethiopia, and extends along the Red Sea to Israel and Jordan over a total distance of 3,000 miles (4,828 km). It includes such lakes as Lakes Tanganyika (4,710 feet or 1,436 m deep, the world's second deepest lake), Malawi, Rudolf, Edward, Albert, as well as the Dead Sea 1,286 feet (392 m) below mean sea level, the world's lowest lake (Fig. 78).

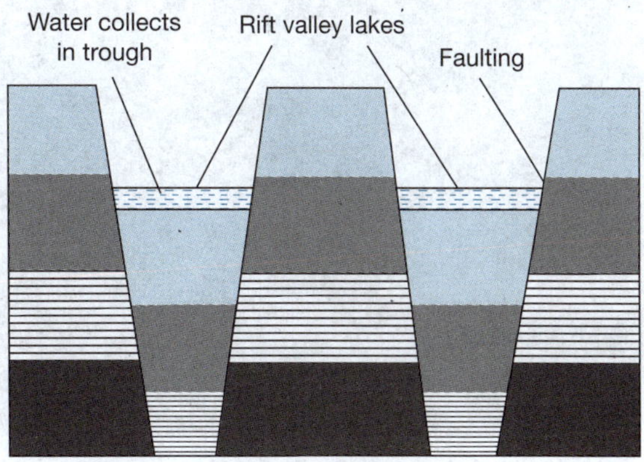

Fig. 78 Earth movement

2. **Lakes Formed by Glaciation**

(a) **Cirque lakes or tarns.** A glacier on its way down the valley leaves behind circular hollows in the heads of the valleys up in the mountains. Such hollows are the armchair-shaped cirques or corries. Their over-deepened floors may be filled with water to become cirque lakes, e.g. Red Tarn in the English Lake District (Fig. 79). Those that occupy glacial troughs are long and deep and are termed ribbon lakes, e.g. Lake Ullswater.

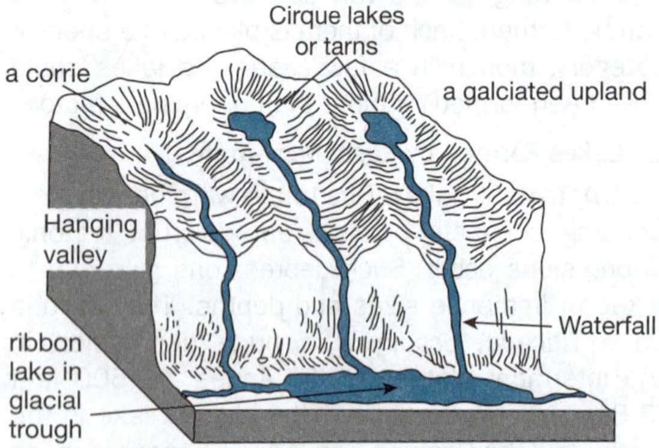

Fig. 79 Glaciation

(b) **Kettle lakes.** These are depressions in the outwash plain left by the melting of masses of stagnant ice. They are irregular because of the uneven morainic surface and are never of any great size or depth, e.g. the meres of Shropshire in England, and the kettle lakes of Orkney in Scotland.

(c) **Rock-hollow lakes.** These are formed by ice-scouring when valley glaciers or ice sheets scoop out hollows on the surface. Such lakes of glacial origin are abundant in Finland, indeed the Finns call their country *Suomi* – the Land of Lakes. It is said that there are over 35,000 glacial lakes in Finland!

(d) **Lakes due to morainic damming of valleys.** Valley glaciers often deposit morainic debris across a valley so that lakes are formed when water accumulates behind the barrier. Both lateral and terminal moraines are capable of damming valleys, e.g. Lake Windermere of the Lake District, England.

(e) **Lakes due to the deposition of glacial drifts.** In glaciated lowlands with a predominant drumlin

Blea Water in Westmorland, England, a typical corrie lake

landscape, where drainage is poor, there are intervening depressions. These depressions are often waterlogged, forming small lakes like those of County Down in Northern Ireland.

3. Lakes Formed by Volcanic Activity

(a) **Crater and caldera lakes.** During a volcanic explosion the top of the cone may be blown off leaving behind a natural hollow called a *crater.* This may be enlarged by subsidence into a *caldera.* These depressions are normally dry, bounded by steep cliffs and roughly circular in shape. In dormant or extinct volcanoes, rain falls straight into the crater or caldera which has no superficial outlet and forms a crater or caldera lake. The outstanding ones are the Crater Lake in Oregon, USA which in fact occupies a caldera; Lake Toba in northern Sumatra and Lake Avernus near Naples (Fig. 80).

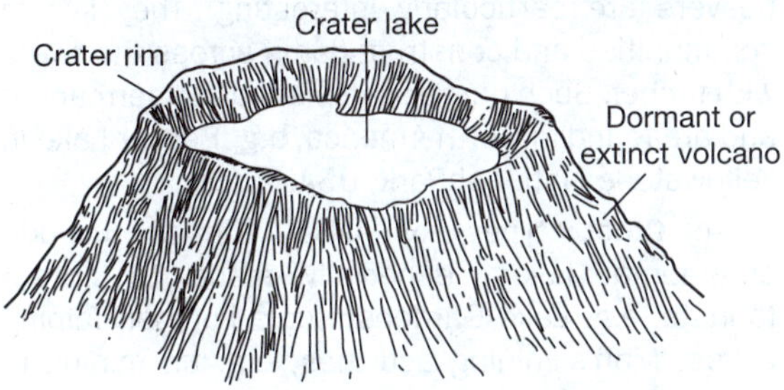

Fig. 80 Volcanic activity

(b) **Lava-blocked lakes.** In volcanic regions a stream of lava may flow across a valley, become solidified and thus dam the river forming a lake, e.g. a lava flow blocks the Jordan valley forming the Sea of Galilee (also called Lake Tiberias or Kinneret) which is an inland lake, rather elongated in shape.

(c) **Lakes due to subsidence of a volcanic land surface.** The crust of a hollow lava flow may collapse the subsidence leaves behind a wide and shallow depression in which a lake may form, e.g. Mývatn of Iceland.

4. Lakes Formed by Erosion

(a) **Karst lakes.** The solvent action of rainwater on limestone carves out solution hollows. When these become clogged with debris lakes may form in them. The collapse of limestone roofs of underground caverns may result in the exposure of long, narrow lakes that were once underground, e.g. the Lac de Chaillexon (French name) or the Lac des Brenets (Swiss name) in the Jura Mountains.

The large depressions called poljes, which normally do not have surface outlets, may contain lakes. During wet periods these may cover most of the polje floor but they shrink during dry periods due to seepage (Fig. 81). An example is Lake Scutari that lies on the border of Albania and Montenegro in Southern Europe.

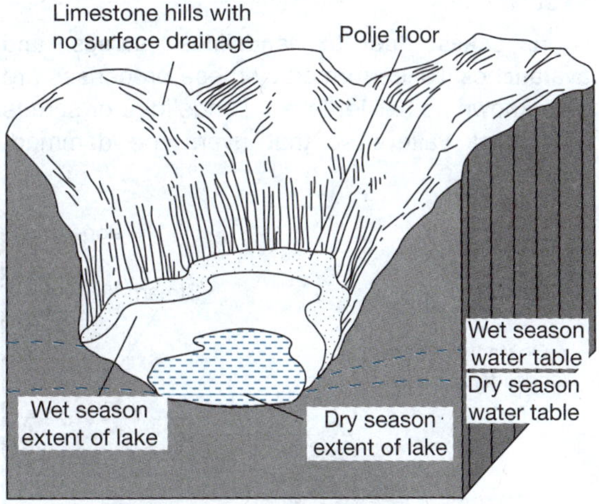

Fig. 81 A karst lake formed above the groundwater table in a limestone region

Solution is important in other rocks such as rock salt. Local subsidence may occur when the underlying beds of rock salt are gradually removed in solution. Many of the meres of Cheshire, England, were probably caused by this, and are also the result of salt-mining operations.

(b) **Wind-deflated lakes.** The deflating action of winds in deserts creates hollows. These may reach ground water which seeps out forming small, shallow lakes. Excessive evaporation causes these to become salt lakes and playas. These are found in the Qattara Depression in Egypt, and the Great Basin of Utah, USA.

5. Lakes Formed by Deposition

(a) **Lakes due to river deposits.** A river may shorten its course during a flood by cutting across its meandering loops, leaving behind a horseshoe-shaped channel as an oxbow lake, e.g. those that occur on the floodplains of Lower Mississippi, USA and Rio Grande, Mexico.

(b) **Lakes due to Marine Deposits.** The action of winds and waves may isolate lagoons along coasts by building spits or bars. As these lagoons of shallow water are enclosed only by a narrow spit of land, comprising mud, sand and shingle, they may drain away at low tide. They are commonly found off the deltas of large rivers such as the Nile and the Ganges. In East Germany and Poland, lagoons are called haffs. Strong onshore winds are capable of pushing *coastal sand dunes* landwards, and these may enclose marshy lagoons. This type of lagoon is well developed in the Landes of south-west France.

(c) **Lakes due to landslides, screes and avalanches.** Lakes formed by these processes are also known as barrier lakes. Landslides or screes may block valleys so that rivers are dammed.

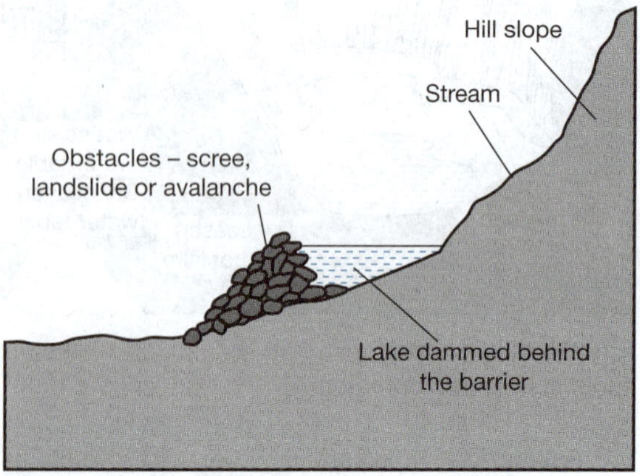

Fig. 82 Deposition (a barrier lake formed by the deposition of an obstacle)

Such lakes are short-lived, because the loose fragments that pile across the valleys soon give way under the pressure of water. When they suddenly give way, the dammed water rushes down, causing floods. Examples of lakes of this type are, Lake Gormire in Yorkshire (England), blocked by landslides; Ffynnon Llugwy on Snowdon blocked by screes (Fig. 82).

6. **Lakes Formed by Human and Biological Activities**

(a) **Man-made lakes.** Besides the natural lakes, man has now created artificial lakes by erecting a *concrete dam* across a river valley so that the river water can be kept back to form reservoirs (Fig. 83).

Amongst such man-made lakes, the most imposing is Lake Mead above the Hoover Dam on the Colorado River, USA.

(b) **Lakes made by animals.** Animals like beavers are particularly interesting. They live in communities and construct dams across the rivers with timber. Such beaver dams are quite permanent and are found in North America, e.g. Beaver Lake in Yellowstone National Park, USA.

(c) **Other types of lakes.** These include ornamental lakes, especially made to attract tourists, e.g. Lake Gardens, Kuala Lumpur, Taiping Lakes. Man's mining activities, e.g. tin mining in West Malaysia, have created numerous lakes. Inland fish culture has necessitated the creation of many *fishing lakes*.

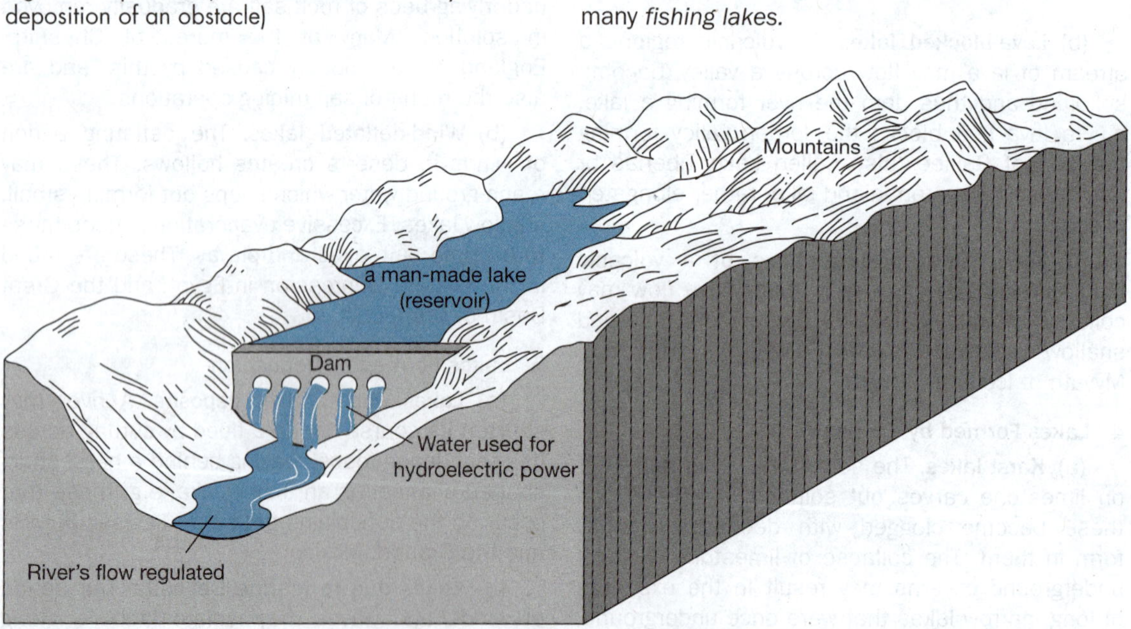

Fig. 83 Human activities (a lake made by constructing a concrete dam across a river valley)

Lakes and Man

A careful examination of the lakes of the world will reveal their immense human significance. In countries where they are found in abundance, such as Finland, Canada, USA, Sweden and the East African states, lakes, together with other inland waterways, have played a dominant role in the human, economic, social and cultural life of the people. The pattern of settlement, commerce and communication is very closely related to the distribution of the water features.

The following are the major uses of lakes and their associated human activities.

1. **Means of communication.** Large lakes like the Great Lakes of North America provide a cheap and convenient form of transport for heavy and bulky goods such as coal, iron, machinery, grains and timber. The Great Lakes-St. Lawrence waterways penetrate more than 1,700 miles into the interior. They are thus used as the chief arteries of commerce. It is estimated that the annual tonnage passing through the Sault-Ste. Marie Canal, or the Soo Canal, between Lake Huron and Lake Superior is greater than the combined annual tonnage of the Suez and Panama Canals.

2. **Economic and industrial development.** Early settlements and town sites were very much influenced by the presence of lakes. Lakes are an even more decisive factor when they are drained by large rivers with outlets to the sea. The Great Lakes-St. Lawrence waterways were responsible for the development of the interior wheat farms and lakeside industries. Raw materials, minerals and fuels were economically handled and assembled in the *HOMES* district (Lakes *H*uron, *O*ntario, *M*ichigan, *E*rie and *S*uperior), which has since become one of the greatest industrial districts of the world. Similarly, Lakes Poyang, Tung Ting and other lakes of the central Yangtze basin have greatly assisted in the commercial and industrial development of *Wuhan* (*Wu*chang, *Han*yang and *Han*kow).

Some of the lakes of Finland scoured out by ice action

3. **Water storage.** Lakes of either natural or artificial origin are vital sources of *domestic* water supply to surrounding towns and industrial cities. For example, Lake Thirlmere (in England) supplies water to Manchester, Loch Katrine (in Scotland) to Glasgow, Lake Vyrnwy (in Wales) to Liverpool. The Okhla Reservoir supplies Delhi, and the Vetarna, Vihar and Tulsi lakes supply Mumbai.

4. **Hydroelectric power generation.** In mountainous districts, lakes or man-made reservoirs are used to furnish *a good* head of water to generate hydroelectric power. Natural lakes are preferred to artificial reservoirs because the volume of water that flows from them varies very little throughout the year. For instance, the Niagara River flowing from Lake Erie to Lake Ontario has a very regular supply of water for its power stations, whereas the Catawba River in the Carolinas which does not flow from a lake, has very little water during the dry season. Cotton mills have been forced to close down during the period of drought due to insufficient power supplies to run the mills. The Aswan Dam on the Nile in Egypt and the Sukkur Barrage (previously known as Lloyd Barrage) on the Indus at Sukkur suffer from similar defects. The Abu Bakar Dam of the Cameron Highlands supplies much hydroelectricity for central West Malaysia.

5. **Agricultural purposes.** As mentioned earlier most lakes will eventually be eliminated, and when they dry up, their former beds are covered with thick layers of fertile alluvium. They make excellent agricultural land like the fertile Vale of Pickering in Yorkshire, or the rich Red River Valley of Canada which was in fact the former site of Lake Agassiz.

Modern multipurpose dams, besides generating hydroelectric power also supply water for irrigation, e.g. the Sennar Dam on the Blue Nile in Sudan, the Burrinjuck Dam on the Murrumbidgee in Australia, and the Hirakud Dam (Odisha) on the Mahanadi in India.

6. **Regulating river flows.** A river with large lakes in its basin seldom experiences serious floods or lack of water. By absorbing the excess water during heavy rain, a lake reduces the effects of serious flooding downstream. In the dry season, it releases its water so that a steady flow of the river is maintained. Because lakes retain part of the sediment load, rivers leaving lakes have clearer water. Lakes that have such functions include the Poyang and Tung Ting on the Yangtze Kiang, Tonle Sap on a tributary of the Mekong, and Lake Constance on the upper Rhine. Where such lakes are not available, and flooding is a serious problem, artificial reservoirs are constructed, e.g. the Hoover Dam on the River Colorado and the Bhakra and Nangal Dams on the Satluj in India.

7. **Moderation of climate.** Large and deep lakes which are heated more slowly than the land by day and cooled more slowly than the land by night, exercise an appreciable effect in moderating the climate of a region in the same way as oceans affect adjoining land masses. Water in the lakes *cools the air in summer* by absorbing part of the heat and *warms it in winter* by releasing the heat. For example, the eastern shores of Lakes Erie, Ontario and Huron have a much milder winter than those of the west, because the oncoming breezes are warmed and early frosts are minimized. This part of the Lake Peninsula is therefore important for grapes and fruit farming. Large lakes like Lake Michigan and the Caspian Sea, also exert a slight influence on the cloudiness and precipitation of the region. Their large expanse of water acts almost like part of the ocean, and helps to precipitate atmospheric moisture into rain. The leeward side of Lake Michigan records a little more precipitation than the windward side, though the actual amount is often not easily noticeable. Small lakes have practically no effect at all on either temperature or rainfall.

8. **Source of food.** Many large lakes have important supplies of protein food in the form of freshwater fish. Sturgeon is commercially caught in the Caspian Sea, salmon and sea trout in the Great Lakes, and in Tonle Sap in Cambodia, fishing is a leading occupation. Amateur fishermen have found fishing in lakes and rivers a most rewarding pastime. In many countries, artificial lakes have been created for inland fish breeding. This is particularly important in China and Japan.

9. **Source of minerals.** Salt lakes provide valuable rock salts. In the Dead Sea, the highly saline water is being evaporated and produces common salt, almost indispensable for human well-being. Borax is mined in the salt lakes of the Mojave Desert.

Gypsum is mined in Cheshire, and Stassfurt, a small distance from Berlin, is so rich in potash and other chemical deposits, that they have given rise to a wide range of chemical industries. In both these areas the salts are obtained from deposits formed in earlier geological period.

10. **Tourist attraction and health resorts.** Some of the world's best frequented holiday and health resorts are located on lakesides for example, Lake Geneva, Lake Lucerne, Lake Lugano, Lake Como, Lake Placid (New York), Lake Vaner and Lake Vatter, (Sweden), the English Lake District (UK) and Taiping Lakes (Malaysia). The glacier-formed lakes of the Alps have made the tourist industry a national occupation of the Swiss.

QUESTIONS AND EXERCISES

1. Locate the following lakes on an outline map of the world: Lake Tanganyika, Great Salt Lake, Lake Toba, Lake Como, Lake Victoria, Lake Scutari, and Lake Mead. Also,
   (a) with the aid of sketch maps, explain their mode of formation.
   (b) state their specific value to the countries they serve.
   (c) name another lake outside that country which has fairly similar origins.
2. Explain how each of the following types of lakes are formed. Quote an example of each and locate them in clear sketch maps.
   (a) oxbow lake
   (b) kettle lake
   (c) crater lake
   (d) karst lake
3. (a) With the help of large, labelled diagrams, explain how lakes may be formed by any *three* of the following.
   i. glaciation
   ii. earth movement
   iii. volcanic activity
   iv. erosion
   v. deposition
   (b) Quote three actual examples of each
   (c) State three uses of man-made lakes
4. Rivers may be dammed for
   (a) generating hydroelectricity
   (b) controlling floods
   (c) irrigating crops
   (d) supplying drinking water
   (e) assisting inland water transport

   For any *four* of them, locate a dam and a river in which the damming has taken place. Explain briefly how each of the above purposes has been successfully achieved.
5. Each of the following terms are in one way or another connected with lake formation and uses. For any *five* of them give a concise explanation of their implications and give a good example of each.
   (a) basin of inland drainage
   (b) tectonic lakes
   (c) haffs
   (d) beaver dams
   (e) playas
   (f) barrier lakes
   (g) tarns

10 Coastal Landforms

The Action of Waves, Tides and Currents

The coastline, under the constant action of the waves, tides and currents, is undergoing changes from day to day. On calm days, when winds are slight, waves do little damage to the shoreline and may instead help to build up beaches and other depositional features. It is in storms that the ravages of the waves reach their greatest magnitude. The average pressure of Atlantic waves on adjacent coasts is about 600 lb. per square foot in the summer and treble that in winter. During storms, the pressure exerted is more than 6,000 lb. or 3 tons per square foot! Movements of such intensity will wear down not only the cliffs but also sea walls and buildings. *Tides and currents,* on contact with the shores, make very little direct attack on the coastline. Tides affect marine erosion mainly by extending a *line* of erosion into a zone of erosion. This zone corresponds to the area between the low water level and the high water level. Currents help to move eroded debris and deposit it as silt, sand and gravel along the coasts.

The Mechanism of Marine Erosion

The most powerful agents of marine erosion are waves. Their origin is due to the sweeping of winds over the water surface, which sets a series of undulating swells surging forward. These become higher and swifter. A normal wave in an open ocean may measure 20 feet or 6 metres high (the vertical height between the crest and the trough) and 400 feet or 122 metres long (the wave length or the horizontal distance between one crest and another). During storms this is greatly increased, depending on the speed and duration of the winds. On approaching shallow water near the shores, their speed is reduced, and the waves are curved or refracted against the alignment of the coast. Shallow water, when it is less than the height of the waves, checks their forward movement, the crests curl over and break into the shores in a mass of foam as breakers. The water that finally rushes up the beach and hurls rock debris against the land is termed swash. The water is sucked back and retreats as backwash. Another element in offshore drift is the undertow, which flows near the bottom away from the shore. This current exerts a pulling effect which can be dangerous to sea-bathers (Fig. 84).

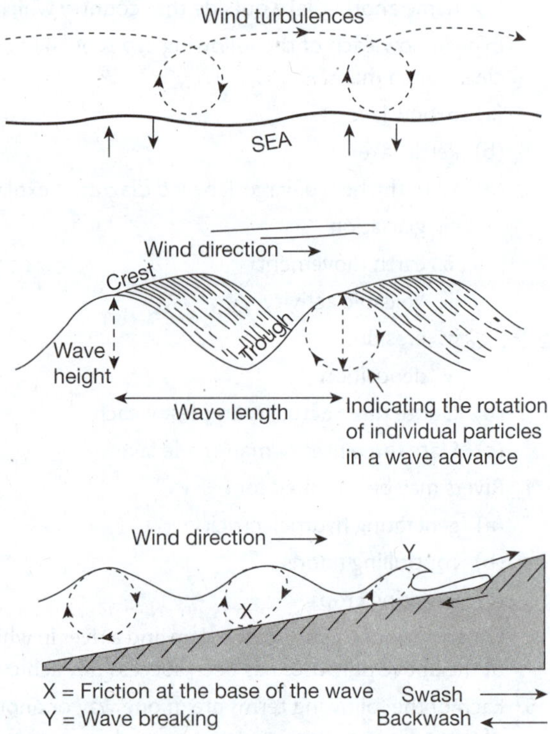

Fig. 84 The mechanism of wave motion

Marine agents of erosion operate in the following ways to transform the coastal landscape.

1. **Corrasion.** Waves armed with rock debris of all sizes and shapes charge against the base of the cliffs, and wear them back by corrasion. Oncoming currents and tides complete the work by sweeping the eroded material into the sea.

2. **Attrition.** The constantly moving waves that transport beach materials such as boulders, pebbles, shingle and fine sand also hurl these fragments against one another, until they are broken down by attrition into very small pieces. The

grinding and polishing of such fragmental materials against cliff faces and against each other is largely responsible for the fine sand which forms the beaches that are so typical of the seaside resorts.

3. **Hydraulic action.** In their forward surge, waves splashing against the coast may enter joints and crevices in the rocks. The air imprisoned inside is immediately compressed. When the waves retreat, the compressed air expands with explosive violence. Such action repeated again and again soon enlarges the cracks and rock fragments are prised apart.

4. **Solvent action.** On limestone coasts, the solvent action of sea water on calcium carbonate sets up chemical changes in the rocks and disintegration takes place. This process is limited to limestone coasts.

The rate of marine erosion depends on the nature of the rocks, the amount of rock exposed to the sea, the effects of tides and currents, and human interference in coast protection. Other effects such as vulcanicity, glaciation, earth movement and organic accumulations have also to be considered.

Coastal Features of Erosion

1. **Capes and bays.** On exposed coasts, the continual action of waves on rocks of varying resistance causes the coastline to be eroded irregularly. This is particularly pronounced where hard rocks, e.g. granites and limestones, occur in alternate bands with softer rocks, e.g. sand and clay. The softer rocks are worn back into inlets, coves or bays and the harder ones persist as headlands, promontories or capes (Fig. 85). Along the Dorset coast of southern England, Swanage Bay and Durlston Head are examples. Even where the coast is of one rock type irregularities will be caused by variation within the rock. Thus, Penang Island (Malaysia), made of granite, has many bays and headlands. Very large indentations such as the Persian Gulf or the Bay of Bengal are due to other causes such as submergence or earth movement.

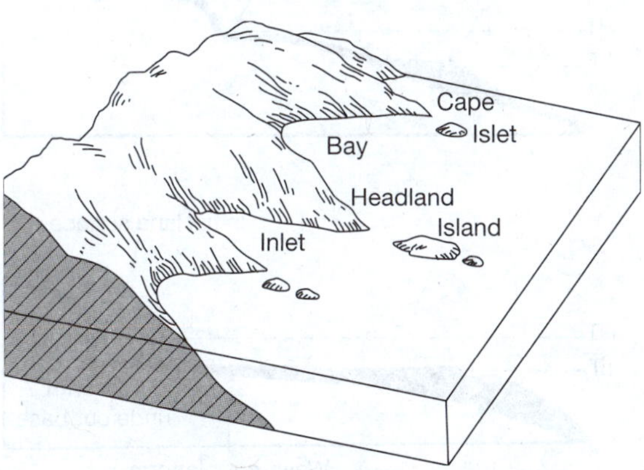

Fig. 85 Coastal features of differential erosion

2. **Cliffs and wave-cut platforms.** Generally, any very steep rock face adjoining the coast forms a cliff. The rate of recession will depend on its geological structure, that is the stratification and jointing of the rocks and their resistance to wave attack. If the beds dip seawards, large blocks of rock will be dislodged and fall into the sea. The cliff will rise in a series of 'steps' as shown in Fig. 86. On the contrary, if the beds dip landwards as illustrated in Fig. 87, the cliff will be more resistant to wave erosion. Some of the best-known cliffs are the chalk cliffs of the English Channel and include Beachy Head which is 500 feet or 152 metres high, the Seven Sisters near the mouth of the Cuckmere and the 'White Cliffs' of Dover.

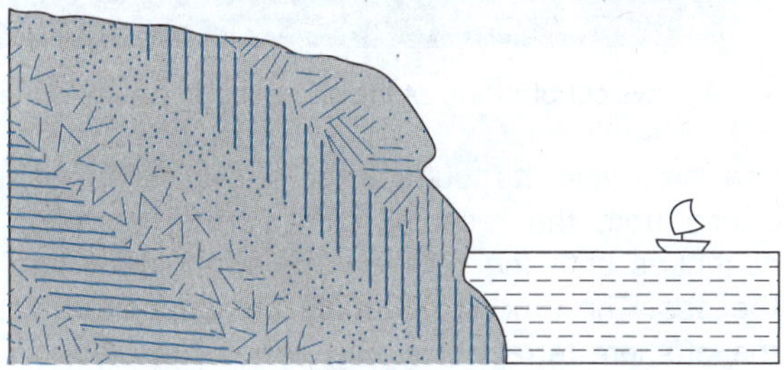
Fig. 86 Cliff beds dipping seawards

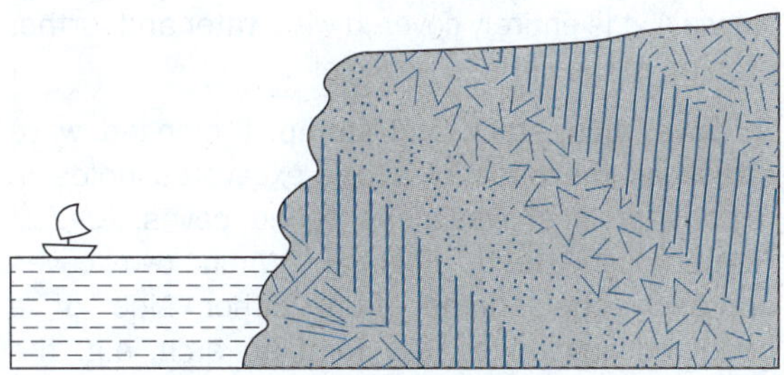
Fig. 87 Cliff beds dipping landwards

At the base of the cliff the sea cuts a notch, which gradually undermines the cliff so that it collapses.

As a cliff recedes landwards under the pounding of waves, an eroded base is left behind, called a wave-cut platform. The platform, the upper part of which is exposed at low tide, slopes gently

A wave-cut platform at the shoreline in South Wales, UK

seawards and its surface is strewn with rock debris from the receding cliff. Further abrasion continues until the pebbles are swept away into the sea. The eroded materials are deposited on the offshore terrace (Fig. 88). When the platform attains a greater width (e.g. 30 miles in the case of the wave-cut platform of Strand-flat off Western Norway), it is entirely covered with water and further erosion of the cliffs is negligible.

3. **Cave, arch, stack and stump.** Prolonged wave attack on the base of a cliff excavates holes in regions of local weakness called caves, e.g. at Flamborough Head, England. When two caves approach one another from either side of a headland and unite, they form an arch, e.g. the Neddie Eye near Wick, Scotland. Further erosion by waves will ultimately lead to the total collapse of the arch. The seaward portion of the headland will remain as a pillar of rock known as a stack. One of the finest examples of a stack is the Old Man of Hoy in the Orkneys which is of Old Red Sandstone and is 450 feet (137 m) high. Equally outstanding are the Needles, Isle of Wight, which are a group of stacks cut in chalk and diminishing in size seawards. In the course of time, these 'stubborn'

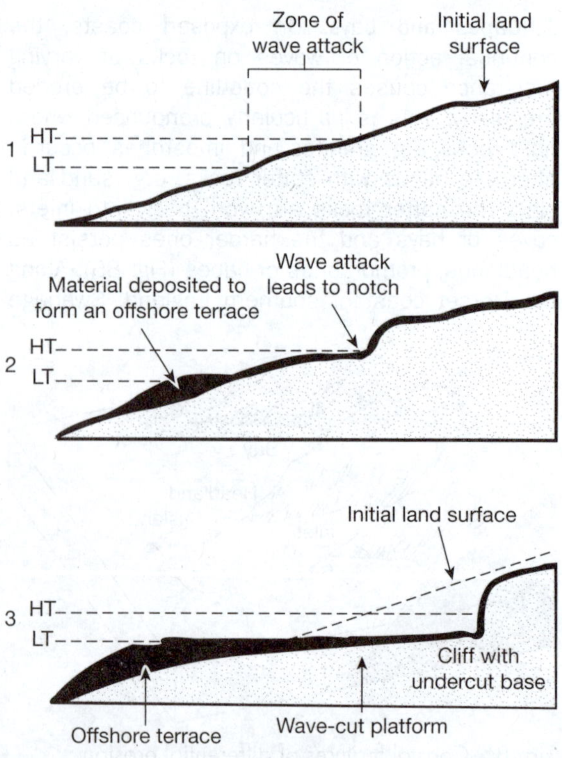

Fig. 88 The development of shore profile

stacks will gradually be removed. The vertical rock pillars are eroded, leaving behind only the stumps which are only just visible above the sea level, e.g. those of the St. Kilda group, off the Outer Hebrides, Scotland (Fig. 89).

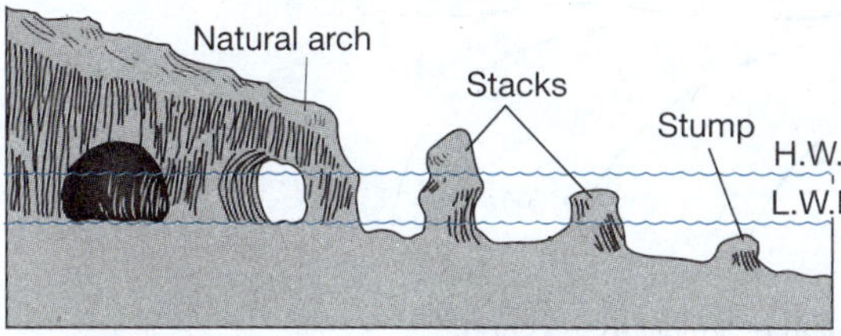

Fig. 89 Arch, stacks and stumps. Where two caves are eroded on either side of a headland they may eventually join to form a natural arch. If the top of the arch collapses stacks are formed. These are gradually worn down until they become stumps exposed only at low tide

4. **Geos and gloups.** The occasional splashing of the waves against the roof of a cave may enlarge the joints when compressed air is trapped inside. A natural shaft is thus formed which may eventually pierce through to the surface. Waves breaking into the cave may force water or spray or just air out of this hole. Such a shaft is termed a gloup (from the noise made by the water gurgling inside) or blow-hole (Fig. 90). An example is at Holborn Head in Caithness Scotland. The enlargement of blow-holes and the continued action of waves weakens the cave roof. When the roof collapses a long, narrow inlet or creek develops. Such deep clefts, which may be 100 feet (30.5 m) deep and equally long, are called geos, e.g. the Wife Geo, near Duncansby Head, Scotland (Fig. 91).

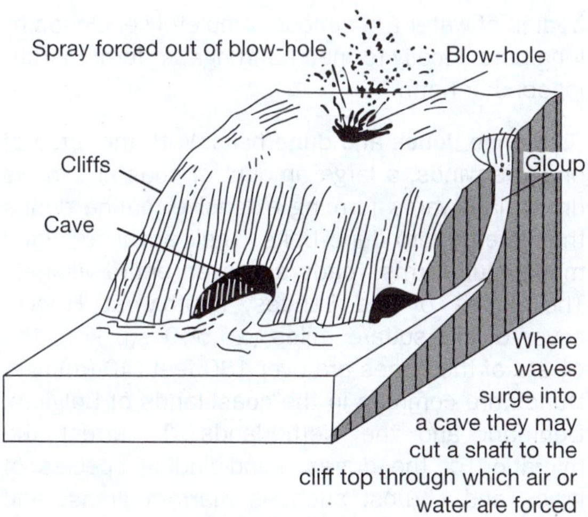

Fig. 90 Gloup

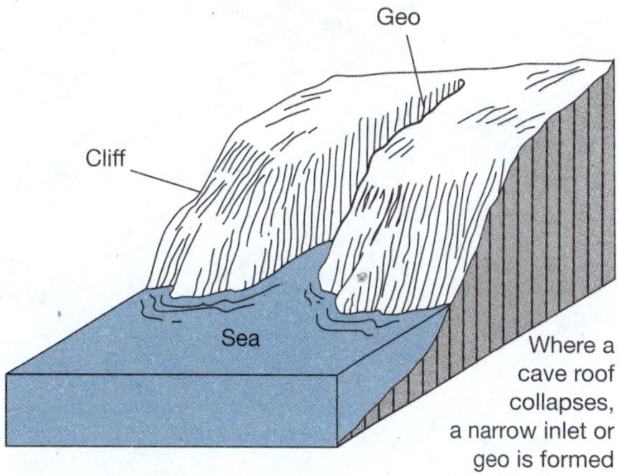

Fig. 91 Geo

Coastal Features of Deposition

1. **Beaches.** Sands and gravels loosened from the land are moved by waves to be deposited along the shore as beaches. This is the most dominant form of the constructive work of the sea. The eroded material is transported along the shore in several distinct ways. The longshore drift which comes obliquely to the coast carries the material along the shore in the direction of the dominant wind (Fig. 92). At the same time, the backwash removes part of the material seawards along the bed of the sea, and deposits it on the offshore terrace and even beyond. Finer materials such as silt and mud are deposited in the shallow, waters of a sheltered coast.

A natural arch

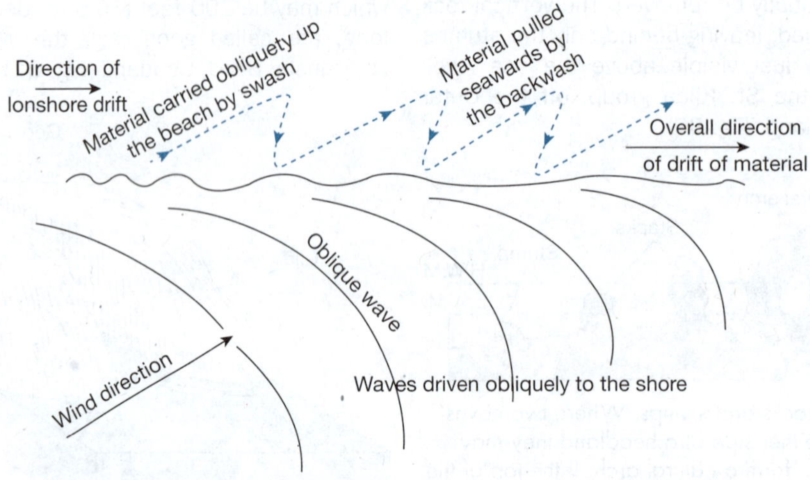

Fig. 92 Longshore drift

The constant action of the waves automatically sorts out the shoreline deposits in a graded manner. The coarser materials (cobbles and boulders) are dropped by the waves at the top of the beach. The finer materials (pebbles and sand grains) which are carried down the beach by the backwash are dropped closer to the sea. On smooth lowlands, beaches may continue for miles, like those of the east coast of West Malaysia, but in upland regions where the land descends abruptly into the sea, such as the Chilean coast, long beaches are absent.

2. **Spits and bars.** The debris eroded by waves is continually moved by longshore drift and where there is an indentation in the coast, such as the mouth of a river or a bay, material may continue to be deposited across the inlet. As more materials are added, they will pile up into a ridge or embankment of shingle forming a tongue or spit, with one end attached to the land and the other end projecting into the sea (Fig. 93), e.g. Calshot Spit, Southampton Water, England or those along the coast of Kelantan. Oblique waves may curve the spit into a hook or re-curved spit. When the ridge of shingle is formed across the mouth of a river or the entrance to a bay, it is called a bar. The most remarkable example of a bar is Chesil Beach in Dorset, England, which extends for over 16 miles (25.7 km) along the coast, linking the Isle of Portland with mainland, and enclosing a lagoon called the Fleet. Such a connecting bar that joins two land masses is better known as tombolo. On the Baltic coast of Poland and Germany, large

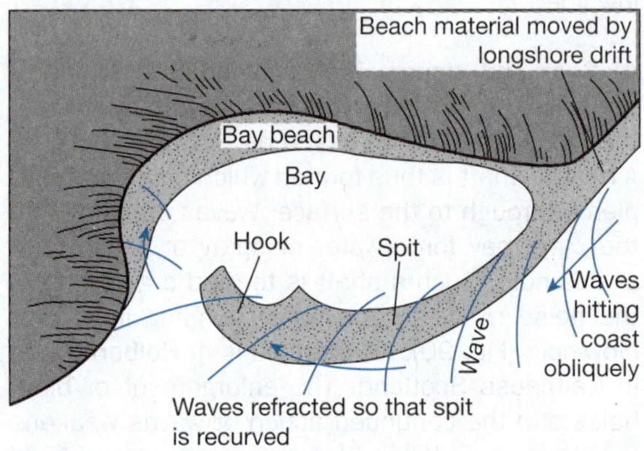

Fig. 93 Development of spit

bodies of water are almost completely enclosed by long bars, locally termed nehrungs, to form marshy lagoons or haffs.

3. **Marine dunes and dune belts.** With the force of onshore winds, a large amount of coastal sand is driven landwards forming extensive marine dunes that stretch into dune belts. Their advance inland may engulf farms, roads and even entire villages. The dunes of the Landes, south-west France, cover 6,000 square miles (15,540 sq. km); the crests of the dunes are over 130 feet (40 m) high. Dunes are common in the coast-lands of Belgium, Denmark and the Netherlands. To arrest the migration of the dunes, sand-binding species of grass and shrubs, such as marram grass, and pines are planted.

Types of Coasts

Despite a great variety of coastal features coastlines may be divided into two basic types.

1. **Coastlines of submergence.** These are due to the sinking of the land or the rise of the sea, including such coasts as ria coasts, fiord coasts, estuarine coasts and Dalmatian or longitudinal coasts.

2. **Coastlines of emergence.** These are due to the uplift of the land or a fall in the sea level. They are less common and are represented by the uplifted lowland coast and the emergent upland coast.

Coastlines of Submergence

1. **Ria coasts.** During the Ice Age a great deal of water was locked up in ice. The warmer climate that followed melted much of the ice. Subsequently there was an increase in the waters of the oceans and the sea level rose appreciably. In some cases, it is estimated that there was a rise of almost 300 feet (91 m)!

In upland coastal regions where the mountains run at right angles to the sea, that is transverse or discordant to the coast (Fig. 94), a rise in the sea level submerges or drowns the lower parts of the valleys to form long, narrow branching inlets separated by narrow headlands. They differ from fiords in two important respects, i.e. they are not glaciated, and their depth increases seawards. A ria coast is typical of the Atlantic type of coast like those of north-west France, north-west Spain, south-west Ireland, Devon and Cornwall. As rias are generally backed by highland, they support few large commercial ports though they have deep water and offer sheltered anchorage. They have been extensively used for siting fishing ports and naval bases such as Plymouth and Brest.

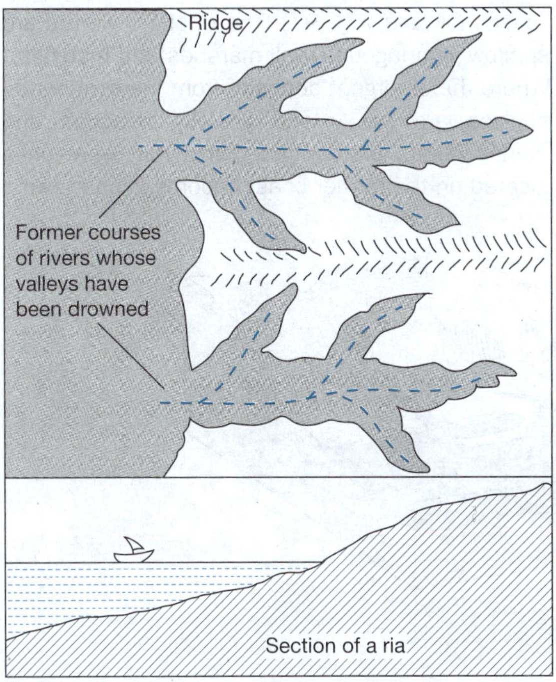

Fig. 94 A ria coast (discordant, Atlantic type)

2. **Fiord coasts.** Fiords are *submerged U-shaped* glacial troughs. They mark the paths of glaciers that plunged down from the highlands. They have steep walls, often rising straight from the sea, with tributary branches joining the main inlet at right angles. Due to the greater intensity of ice erosion fiords are deep for great distances inland but there is a shallow section at the seaward end formed by a ridge of rock and called the threshold (Fig. 95). Off the fiord coast are numerous islands or skerries which, with the shallow thresholds, sometimes only 200 feet (61 m) deep, complicate coastal navigation. Fiord coasts are almost entirely confined to the higher latitudes of the temperate regions which were once glaciated, e.g. Norway, Alaska, British Columbia, southern Chile and the South Island of New Zealand. Some of the large fiords are extremely long and deep. For example, the Sogne Fiord of Norway is 110 miles (177 m) long, 4 miles (6.4 m) wide and almost 4,000 feet (1,219 m) deep in its mid-channel. Despite their deep and sheltered water, few large ports are located in fiords. Their mountainous background with

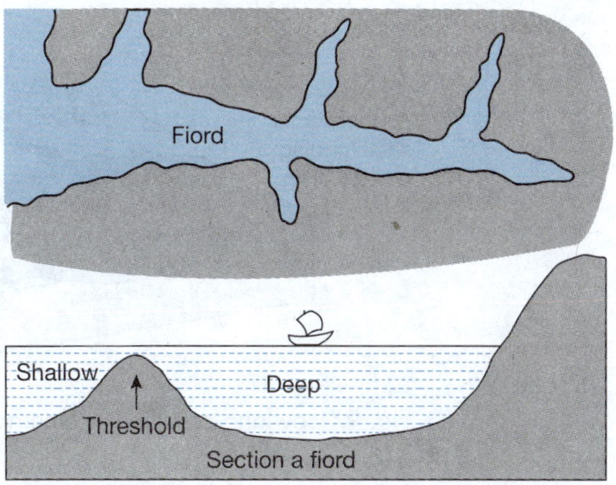

Fig. 95 A fiord coast (submergent and glaciated)

poor accessibility inland, attract few settlements. Agriculture is confined to the deltaic fans, built up where streams flow down to the fiords. The few towns that exist either as fishing or market centres, e.g. Trondheim, are only of local importance.

3. **Dalmatian coast.** This is the longitudinal coast where mountains run parallel or concordant to the coast. The name is taken from the coast of Dalmatia, Yugoslavia, along the Adriatic Sea, where the submergence of the coastline produces long, narrow inlets with a chain of islands parallel to the coast. The elongated islands are the crests of former ranges and the narrow sounds were the former longitudinal valleys (Fig. 96). The Dalmatian type of coast is also typical of the Pacific coast where the ranges are parallel to the coast, e.g. western coasts of North and South America but there the coastline is more regular. Like the ria and fiord coasts, the mountainous nature of the Dalmatian coastline hinders communication inland. It has deep, sheltered harbours but no distinguished ports. On the Pacific coast, however, there are some important ports such as San Francisco.

4. **Estuarine coasts.** In submerged lowlands, the mouths of rivers are drowned so that funnel-shaped estuaries are formed. If their entrances are not silted by moving sandbanks, they make excellent sites for ports, e.g. the estuaries of the Thames, Elbe and Plate are the sites of such great seaports as London, Hamburg and Buenos Aires. Tidal effects further enhance the value of the ports and even when there is a little silting, modern dredges help to keep the ports open all the time.

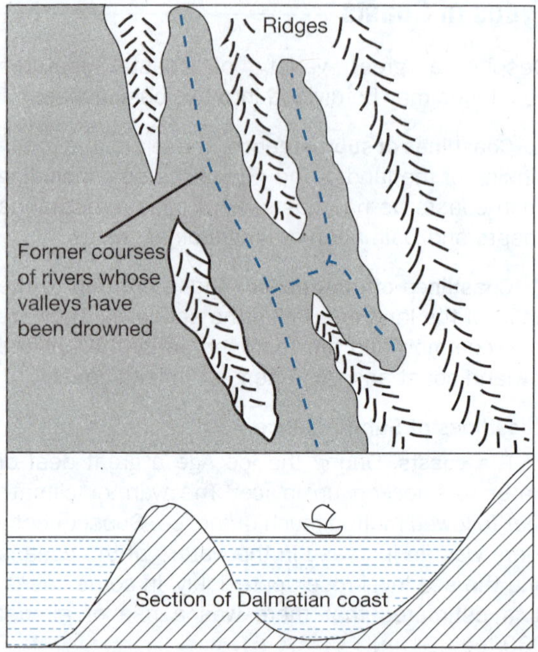

Fig. 96 A Dalmatian coast (concordant, Pacific type)

Coastlines of Emergence

1. **Uplifted lowland coast.** The uplift of part of the continental shelf produces a smooth, *gently sloping coastal lowland* (Fig. 97). The offshore waters are shallow with lagoons, salt-marshes and mud-flats. Where the emergent deposits from the continental shelves are sandy and gravelly, beaches and marine dunes are formed. Ports that were once located on the former coast become inland towns.

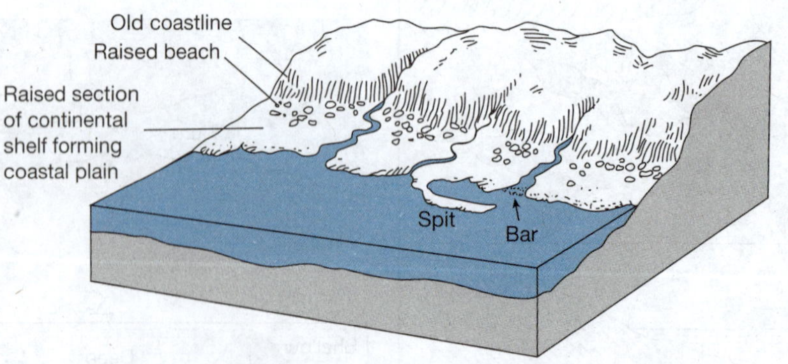

Fig. 97 Lowland coastline of emergence

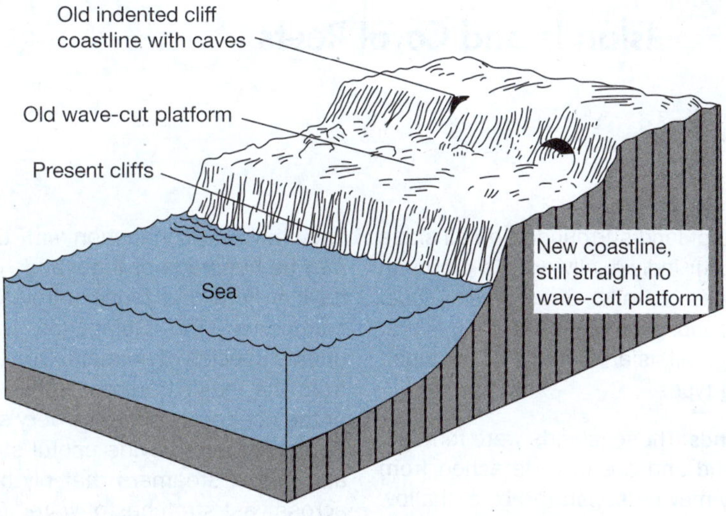

Fig. 98 Upland emergent coastline

Examples of uplifted lowland coasts include the south-eastern USA, western Finland, eastern Sweden and parts of coastal Argentina south of the Rio de la Plata.

2. **Emergent upland coast.** Faulting and earth movement may thrust up coastal plateaux so that the whole region is raised, with consequent emergent features. A raised beach is the most prominent. The raised beach is beyond the reach of the waves, though it may still possess arches, stacks and other coastal features. The emergent upland coast is quite straight with steep cliffs and deeper offshore water, for the waves have not yet eroded lines of weakness or carved a wave-cut platform (Fig. 98). It has little potential for good port sites. Examples of emergent upland coasts are found in Scotland, the western coast of the Deccan, India and the western Arabian coast facing the Red Sea.

QUESTIONS AND EXERCISES

1. By reference to specific examples describe some of the major coastal features resulting from the constructive and destructive work of the sea.
2. With the aid of annotated diagrams, describe the appearance and formation of any *three* of the following pairs of features of coastal landforms.
   (a) cliff and wave-cut platform
   (b) geo and blow-hole
   (c) arch and stack
   (d) spits and bars
3. How can shorelines be classified? Describe any *one* method of classification and briefly explain some of the major shoreline features that you have classified.
4. With the help of diagrams, explain the distinct differences between the following coastlines of submergence.
   (a) ria coast
   (b) fiord coast
   (c) Dalmatian coast
   (d) estuarine coast
5. Choose any *three* of the following terms connected with marine landscape. Explain the meaning of each and state its role in transforming the coastline.
   (a) longshore drift
   (b) undertow
   (c) concordant coast
   (d) raised beach
   (e) tombolo

11 Islands and Coral Reefs

An island is a piece of land surrounded on all sides by water. It may occur individually or in a group, in open oceans or seas. Smaller ones of only local significance are found even in lakes and rivers. Generally speaking, all islands may be grouped under the following types.

1. **Continental islands.** These islands were formerly part of the mainland and are now detached from the continent. They may be separated by a shallow lagoon or a deep channel. Their separation could be due to subsidence of some part of the land or to a rise in sea level, so that the lowland links are submerged by the sea. Their former connection with the neighbouring mainland can be traced from the similar physical structure, flora and fauna that exist on both sides of the channel. In the course of time, modification by men and other natural forces may give rise to different surface features. But even then, the basic structural features will remain the same. Continental islands may appear as:

(a) **Individual islands.** These lie just outside the continent, very much associated with the characteristic features of the mainland of which they were once part. Some of the outstanding examples are Newfoundland, separated from the mainland by the Strait of Belle Isle; Madagascar, by the Mozambique Channel; Sri Lanka by the Palk Strait; Tasmania by the Bass Strait and Taiwan by the Taiwan Strait.

(b) **Archipelagoes or island groups.** These comprise groups of islands of varying sizes and shapes, e.g. the British Isles, the Balearic Islands of the Mediterranean and also those of the Aegean Sea.

(c) **Festoons or island arcs.** The islands form an archipelago in the shape of a loop around the edge or the mainland, marking the continuation of mountain ranges which can be traced on the continent, e.g. the East Indies, the Aleutian Islands, Ryukyu Islands, Kuril Islands and other island arcs of the Pacific coasts.

2. **Oceanic islands.** These islands are normally small and are located in the midst of oceans. They have no connection with the mainland which may be hundreds or thousands of miles away. They have a flora and fauna unrelated to those of the continents. The Galapagos Islands have many unique species of animals. Due to their remoteness from the major trading centres of the world, most of the oceanic islands are very sparsely populated. Some of them provide useful stops for aeroplanes and ocean steamers that ply between continents across vast stretches of water. Generally speaking, oceanic islands fall into one of the following groups.

(a) **Volcanic islands.** Many of the islands in the oceans are in fact the topmost parts of the cones of volcanoes that rise from the ocean bed. Most of them are extinct, but there are also some active ones. The best known volcanic peak of the Pacific Ocean is Mauna Loa in Hawaii, which is 13,680 feet (4,170 m) above sea level. Tracing downwards, Mauna Loa is found to have been built up from the ocean floor at a depth 18,000 feet (5,486 m) below the water surface! Other volcanic islands have emerged from the submarine ridges of the oceans.

The volcanic islands are scattered in most of the earth's oceans. In the Pacific Ocean, they occur in several groups such as Hawaii, the Galapagos Islands and the South Sea islands. In the Atlantic are the Azores, Ascension, St. Helena, Madeira and the Canary Islands. Those of the Indian Ocean are

Rarotonga in the Cook Islands, a volcanic island in the Pacific

Mauritius and Reunion. In the Antarctic Ocean are the South Sandwich Islands, Bouvet Island and many others.

(b) **Coral islands.** Unlike the volcanic islands, the coral islands are very much lower and emerge just above the water surface. These islands, built up by coral animals of various species, are found both near the shores of the mainland and in the midst of oceans. Coral islands include the Marshall Islands, Gilbert and Ellice Islands of the Pacific; Bermuda in the Atlantic and the Lakshadweep and Maldives of the Indian Ocean.

Coral Reefs

In tropical seas many kinds of coral animals and marine organisms such as coral polyps, calcareous algae, shell-forming creatures and lime-secreting plants live in large colonies. Though they are very tiny creatures, their ability to secrete calcium carbonate within their tiny cells has given rise to a peculiar type of marine landform. They exist in numerous species of many forms, colours and shapes. Under favourable conditions, they grow in great profusion just below the water level. Taking coral animals as a whole, the polyps are the most abundant and also the most important. Each polyp resides in a tiny cup of coral and helps to form coral reefs. When they die, their limy skeletons are cemented into coralline limestone. There are also non-reef-building species such as the 'precious corals' of the Pacific Ocean and the 'red coral' of the Mediterranean which may survive in the colder and even the deeper waters. As a rule they thrive well only in the warmer tropical seas.

The reef-building corals survive best under the following conditions.

1. The water temperature must not fall below 68°F. (20°C.). This virtually limits the areal distribution of corals to the tropical, and sub-tropical zones. Again they will *not flourish* where there are *cold currents* because of the upwelling of the cold water from the depths that cools the warm surface water. This explains why coral reefs are generally absent on the western coasts of continents. On the other hand the warming effect of the warm currents, e.g. the Gulf Stream, means that corals are found far to the north of the West Indies in the Atlantic Ocean. The Pacific and the Indian Oceans, however, have the most numerous coral reefs.

2. The depth of the water should not exceed 30 fathoms or 180 feet (55 m), because beyond this depth sunlight is too faint for photosynthesis to take place. This is essential for the survival of the microscopic algae, on which the coral polyps depend. Shallow water of less than 100 feet (30.5 m) is ideal. But there should always be plenty of water as polyps cannot survive for too long out of water.

3. The water should be saltish and free from sediment. Corals therefore survive best in the moving ocean water well away from the silty coasts or muddy mouths of streams. The corals are best developed on the seaward side of the reef, where constantly moving waves, tides and currents maintain an abundant supply of clear, *oxygenated water.* They also bring an adequate supply of food in the form of microscopic organisms.

An aerial view of Tupai atoll, also called Motu Iti in Society Island group, French Polynesia

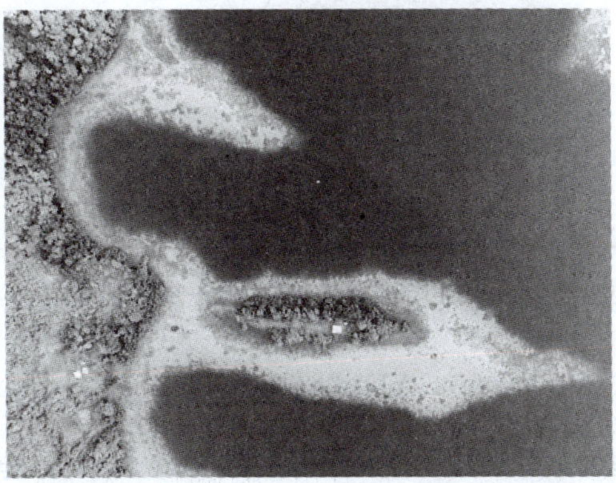

A fringing reef found in a remote part of the Solomon Islands

Types of Coral Reefs

There are three main types of coral reefs.

1. **Fringing reefs.** A fringing reef is a coralline platform lying close to the shore extending outwards from the mainland. It is sometimes separated from the shore by a shallow lagoon. It is widest when fringing a protruding headland but completely absent when facing the mouth of a stream. The outer edge grows rapidly because of the splashing waves that continuously renew the supply of fresh food. The reefs may be about a mile wide, lying just above the level of low water and sloping steeply downwards on the seaward side to a depth of about 100 feet or 30.5 metres (Fig. 99).

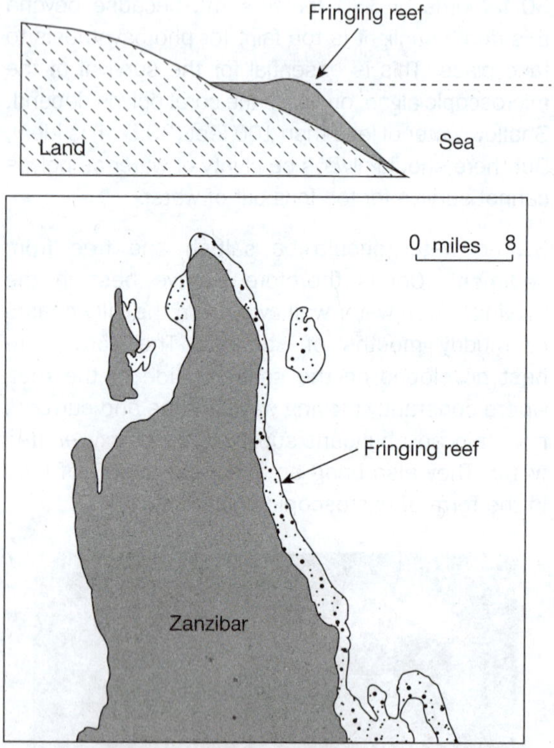

Fig. 99 Fringing reef

2. **Barrier reefs.** A barrier reef is separated from the coast by a much wider and deeper channel or lagoon (Fig. 100). The reef is partially submerged. Where it lies above the water level and sand can accumulate on it, a little vegetation is possible.

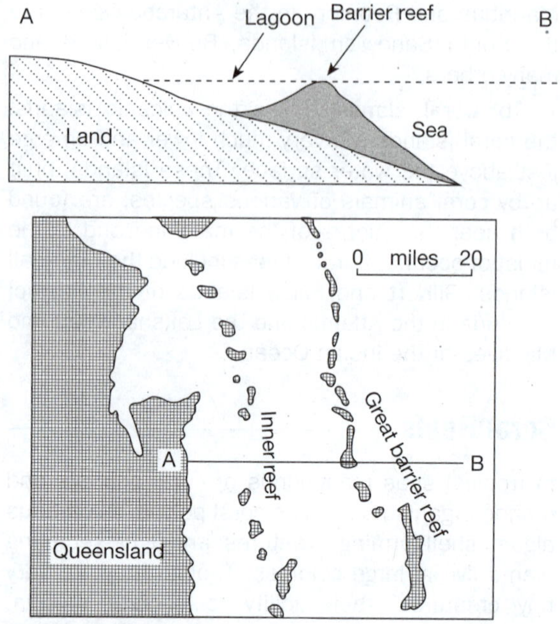

Fig. 100 Barrier reef

The barrier reefs have narrow gaps at several places to allow the water from the enclosed lagoon to return to the open ocean. Such gaps are very useful for shipping and provide the only entrances for ships to enter or leave the lagoon. The best known barrier reef is the Great Barrier Reef off the coast of Queensland, Australia. It is 1,200 miles (1,931 km) long, separated from the coast by a channel 100 miles (161 km) wide in places and over 200 feet (61 m) deep.

3. **Atolls.** Atolls are similar to barrier reefs except that they are circular in shape, enclosing a shallow lagoon without any land in the centre. The encircling ring is usually broken in a few places to allow the free flow of water (Fig. 101). On the inside of the reefs, sand and limestone debris collect and palm trees like coconuts may grow. Such palm trees thrive well in the brackish water of the lagoon. The nuts fall into the water and are distributed widely by floating from one coral island to another. The calm waters are useful for fishing and canoeing. Some of the large atolls, e.g. Suvadiva in the Maldives, west of Sri Lanka, have a lagoon over 40 miles (64 km) across. A number of them provide essential air bases for trans-Pacific aircraft.

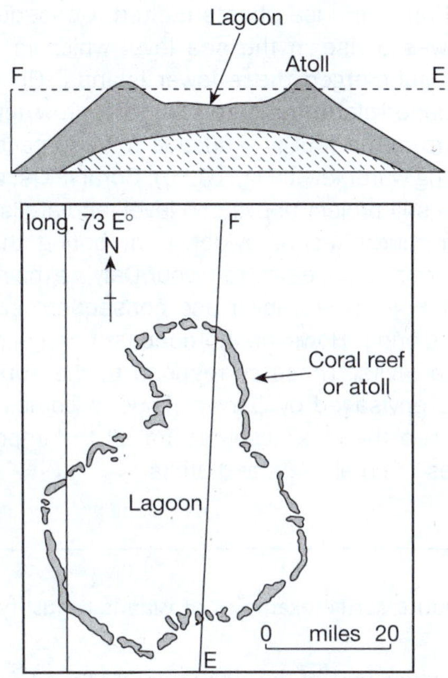

Fig. 101 Atoll

The Probable Origin of Coral Reefs

The subject of the origin of coral reefs has been studied and debated for over one and half centuries. Several theories have been suggested but none is universally accepted.

The most widely accepted theory is that put forward by the great scientist Charles Darwin, after his voyage to the Pacific islands in 1842. It is known as the subsidence theory. Darwin assumed that all coral reefs began as fringing reefs around an island or the topmost portions of extinct volcanoes that stood above the ocean bed. Due to a general downwarping of the earth's crust, the islands gradually subsided. The corals continued to grow upwards to keep pace with the subsidence. The growth was more vigorous at the outward edge than the landward edge because of the more favourable living conditions for corals, so the encircling reef widened. It then formed a barrier reef, with a lagoon between the island and the reef. Eventually, when the land completely submerged, only the outer rims of the reefs were seen, forming an atoll. The submerged island was covered by a layer of sediment so that the characteristic circular lagoon is generally shallow. Thus atolls mark the position of the former islands (Fig. 102 a). More recent researches by oceanographers have

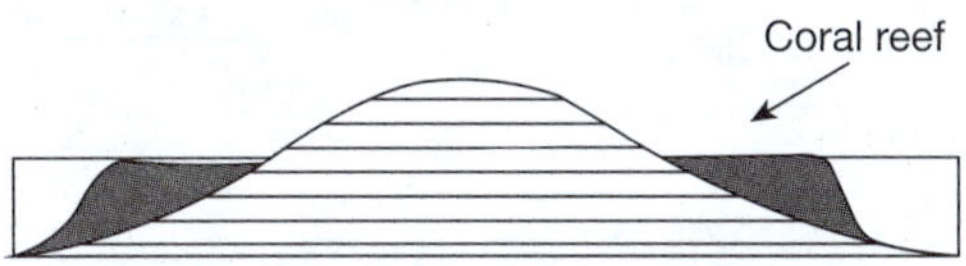

(i) A fringing reef

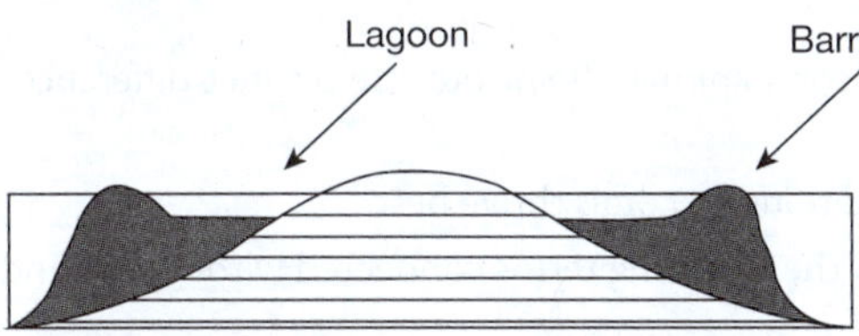

(ii) Subsidence of the land leads to a barrier reef developing.

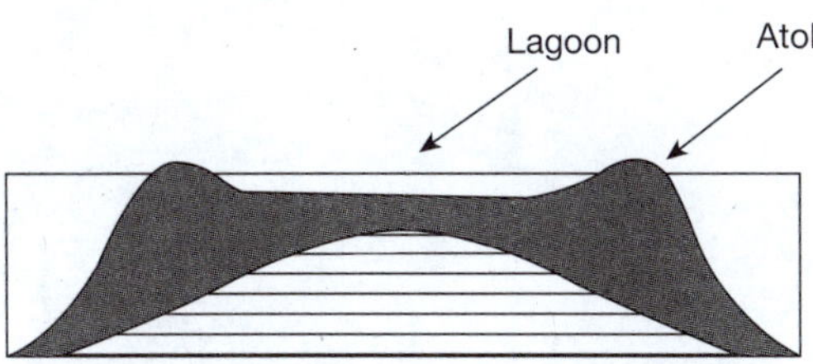

(iii) Further subsidence matched by the growth of coral leads to an atoll

Fig. 102 (a) Darwin's theory of subsidence (coral reef growing upwards and outwards to keep pace with subsiding island, passing from fringing reef, to barrier reef and eventually atoll)

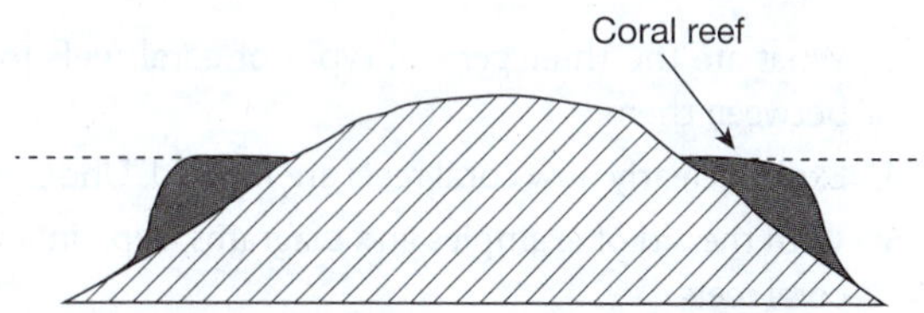

(i) A fringing reef

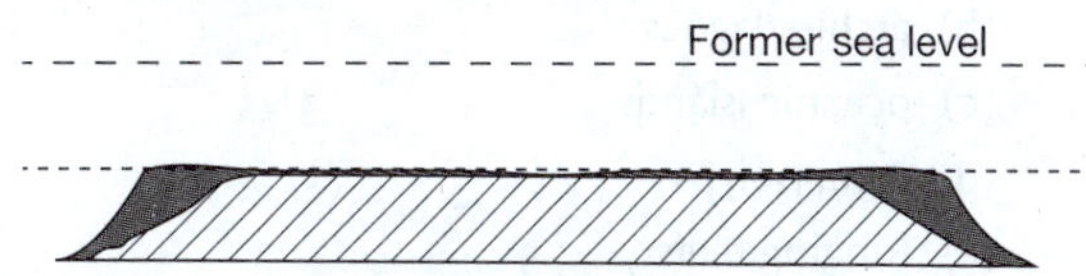

(ii) Island is planed when sea is at a lower level

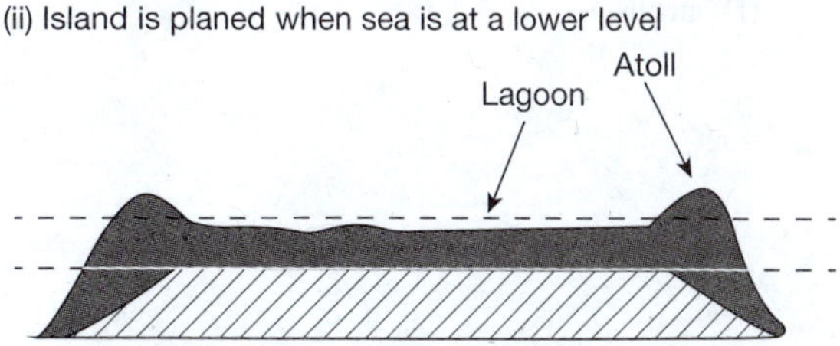

(iii) Sea level rises and corel grows upwards forming atoll

Fig. 102 (b) Daly's Glacial Control Theory

revealed that the ocean floor has, in fact, been subjected to subsidence especially in the Pacific. Darwin's explanation was therefore generally correct.

Amongst the other theories, perhaps the American geographer, R.A. Daly's glacial control theory put forward in 1910 is worth consideration. During his visit to Mauna Kea in Hawaii, he noticed the close relationship between glaciation and the development of coral reefs. He believed that during the height of the Ice Ages, the water was too cold for any coral growth to take place. With the absence of a coral barrier, marine erosion was able to attack and lower the islands. With the return of the warmer climate, the water that was locked up in the ice sheets melted. Consequently, there was a rise in the sea level which in some cases. submerged these lower islands. On these wave-planed platforms, corals began to grow upwards at the rate of a foot in a decade to keep pace with the rising water level (Fig. 102 b). Coral reefs, where islands still project above sea level, and atolls were thus formed. Recent evidence of boring through coral formations seems to favour Daly's explanation of a change in sea level and consequent erosion of the islands. However, the deepest borings reveal basaltic rocks. These correspond to the subsided islands envisaged by Darwin. Thus, a combination of the two theories accounts for all the important features of coral reefs and atolls.

QUESTIONS AND EXERCISES

1. Give a concise classification of the islands of the world. Quote actual examples of islands to justify your proposed classification.
2. The following are some of the islands of the world. State in which part of the globe they are found. For any *three* of them account for their probable origin.
   Sakhalin Island
   Andaman Islands
   Maldives
   St. Helena
   Hawaiian Islands
   Crete
3. What are the three general types of coral reefs formed by coral animals. Point out the distinct differences between them.
4. Explain clearly how coral reefs are formed. Under what conditions do corals thrive best?
5. With the aid of examples and diagrams, explain any *three* of the following terms connected with islands and coral reefs.
   (a) continental islands
   (b) archipelagoes
   (c) oceanic islands
   (d) coral polyps
   (e) fringing reefs
   (f) atolls

12 The Oceans

Exploring the Oceans

The oceans, comprising more than 70 per cent or 139 million square miles or 361 million square kilometres of the earth's surface, have tremendous potential waiting to be developed. Besides being a source of food – fish, mammals, reptiles, salt and other marine foodstuffs – the tides can be harnessed to provide power. Formal oceanographic investigation began only with the British expedition of the *Challenger* (1873–1876), the first successful world-wide deep-sea expedition.

Oceanography, the science of the oceans, has become such an important subject in recent years that researches into the deep seas have been conducted by many institutions, universities, government ministries and other international organizations. The most famous international oceanographic research centre is the International Council for the Exploration of the Sea with its headquarters in Copenhagen. Ocean exploration for the observation and recording of oceanographic data is a very expensive matter. It involves the operation and maintenance of specially equipped vessels in mid-ocean for long periods, and large-scale oceanographic researches are thus best undertaken by international bodies. The older echo-sounding techniques have now been replaced by radar sounding and electrical echo devices to find the precise depths of ocean floors and map the relief of the oceans. Trained frogmen equipped with modern breathing apparatus are employed to gather valuable information from great depths. Deep sea core samples are obtained by boring for the study of the oceanic deposits – the various kinds of oozes, muds and clays. Automatic-recording thermometers and other sensitive instruments can be lowered to any required depth by stationary vessels with laboratory facilities for processing any required data. For the observation

Only five per cent of the oceans have been explored till date

and measurement of current flow, various kinds of current meters using propellers, vanes or pendulums have been designed. Sealed bottles and other floating objects containing instructions for reporting their precise time and place of discovery are released in large numbers to compute the rate and direction of drift and current flow. With all these modern techniques at the disposal of the oceanographers, our knowledge of the mysteries of the oceans is greatly increased. But there is still much to be discovered.

The Relief of the Ocean

The ocean basins are in many ways similar to the land surface. There are submarine ridges, plateaux, canyons, plains and trenches. A section drawn across an ocean (Fig. 103) illustrates the typical submarine relief features.

1. **The continental shelf.** This is, in fact, the seaward extension of the continent from the shoreline to the continental edge marked, approximately, by the 100 fathom (600 feet or 183 m) *isobath* (isobaths are contours marking depths below sea level). The continental shelf is thus a shallow platform whose width varies greatly, from a few miles in the North Pacific off the continent of North America, to over 100 miles (161 km) off north-west Europe. In some places where the coasts are extremely mountainous, such as the Rocky Mountain and Andean coasts, the continental shelf may be entirely absent. Off broad lowland coasts like those of Arctic Siberia, a maximum width of 750 miles (1,207 km) has been recorded! A width of 20 to 100 miles (32 to 161 km) is generally encountered. The angle of the slope is also variable, and is normally least where the continental shelf is widest. A gradient of 1 in 500 is common to most continental shelves.

Many regard the continental shelf as part of the continent submerged due to a rise in sea level, e.g. at the close of the Ice Age, when the ice in the temperate latitudes melted and raised the sea level by several hundred feet. Some smaller continental shelves could have been caused by wave erosion where the land is being eroded by the sea as shown in Fig. 104. Conversely such shelves might have been formed by the deposition of land-derived or river-borne materials on the offshore terrace as in Fig. 105.

The continental shelves are of great geographical significance for the following reasons.

(a) Their *shallowness* enables sunlight to penetrate through the water, which encourages the growth of minute plants and other microscopic organisms. They are thus rich in plankton on which millions of surface and bottom-feeding fishes thrive. The continental shelves are therefore the richest fishing grounds in the world, e.g. the Grand Banks off Newfoundland, the North Sea and the Sunda Shelf.

(b) Their limited depth and gentle slope keep out cold undercurrents and increase the height of tides. This sometimes hinders shipping and other marine activities since ships can only enter and leave port on the tide. Most of the world's greatest seaports

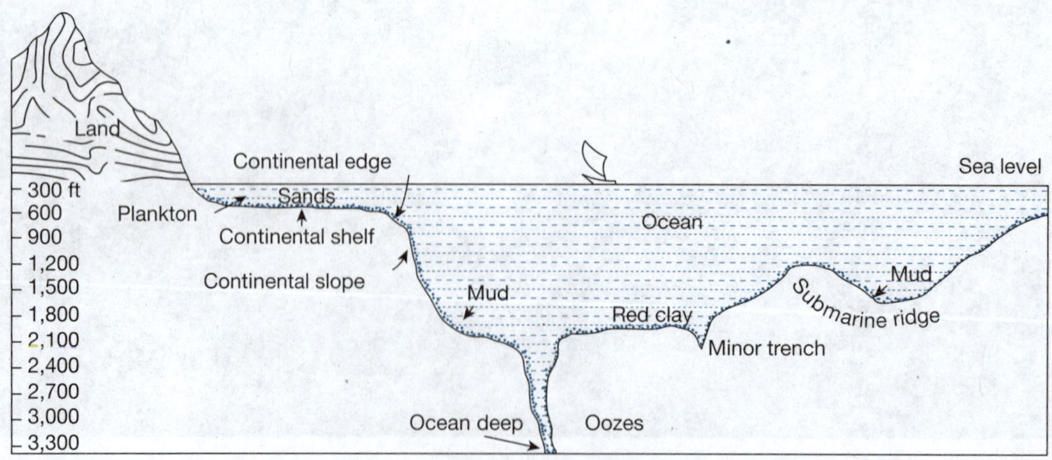

Fig. 103 The relief of the ocean basin (a typical section) with oceanic deposits — mud, clay and oozes.

including Southampton, London, Hamburg, Rotterdam, Hong Kong and Singapore are located on continental shelves.

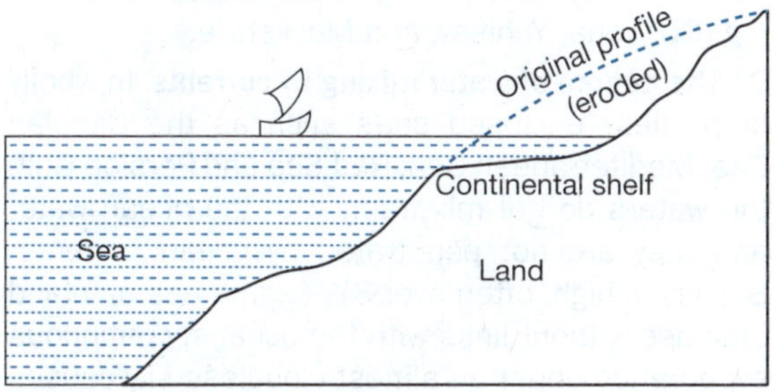

Fig. 104 Continental shelf formed by processes of erosion

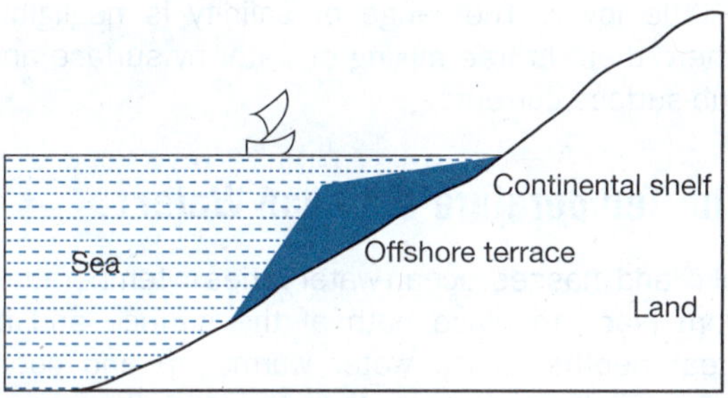

Fig. 105 Continental shelf formed by processes of deposition

2. **The continental slope.** At the edge of the continental shelf, there is an abrupt change of gradient to about 1 in 20, forming the continental slope.

3. **The deep-sea plain.** This is the undulating plain lying two to three miles below sea level, and covering two-thirds of the ocean floor, generally termed the abyssal plain. It was once thought to be featureless, but modern sounding devices reveal that the abyssal plain is far from being level. It has extensive submarine plateaux, ridges, trenches, basins, and oceanic islands that rise above sea level in the midst of oceans, e.g. the Azores, Ascension Island.

4. **The ocean deeps.** These are the long, narrow trenches that plunge as great ocean deep to a depth of 5,000 fathoms or 30,000 feet or 9,144 metres! Contrary to our expectations, most of the deepest trenches are not located in the midst of oceans. They are more often found close to the continents, particularly in the Pacific Ocean, where several deep trenches have been sounded. The greatest known ocean deep is the Mariana Trench near Guam Island, which is more than 36,000 feet (10,973 m) deep. We can see from this that ocean trenches are greater in magnitude than the highest mountains on land, for the highest peak Mt. Everest is only 29,031.69 feet (8,848.86 m). Other notable ocean deeps include the Mindanao Deep (35,000 feet or 10,668 metres), the Tonga Trench (31,000 feet or 9,449 metres) and the Japanese Trench (28,000 feet or 8,534 metres), all in the Pacific Ocean.

The Oceanic Deposits of the Ocean Floor

Materials eroded from the earth which are not deposited by rivers or at the coast are eventually dropped on the ocean floor. The dominant process is slow sedimentation where the eroded particles very slowly filter through the ocean water and settle upon one another in layers. The thickness of the layer of sediments is still unknown. Its rate of accumulation is equally uncertain. Generally speaking, we may classify all the oceanic deposits as either muds, oozes or clays.

1. **The muds.** These are terrigenous deposits because they are derived from land and are mainly deposited on the continental shelves. The muds are referred to as blue, green or red muds; their colouring depends upon their chemical content.

2. **The oozes.** These are pelagic deposits because they are derived from the oceans. They are made of the shelly and skeletal remains of marine microorganisms with calcareous or siliceous parts. Oozes have a very fine, flour-like texture and either occur as accumulated deposits or float about in suspension.

3. **The clays.** These occur mainly as red clays in the deeper parts of the ocean basins, and are particularly abundant in the Pacific Ocean. Red clay is believed to be an accumulation of volcanic dust blown out from volcanoes during volcanic eruptions.

Salinity of the Ocean

Almost every known chemical element can be found in varying proportions in the oceans whose most characteristic feature is their salinity, in contrast to the fresh water of lakes and streams. All sea water contains large amounts of dissolved mineral matter of which sodium chloride or common salt alone constitutes more than 77 per cent. The other more important compounds include magnesium, calcium and potassium, while the rest are distinguishable only in traces of very minute quantities. Due to the free movement of ocean water, the proportions of different salts, remain remarkably constant in all oceans and even to great depths. But the degree of concentration of the salt solution in oceans does vary appreciably in different areas. This is expressed as salinity, the degree of saltness of water, either as a percentage or more often in parts per thousand. Variations are shown in salinity distribution maps by isohalines, lines joining places having an equal degree of salinity.

Generally speaking, the average salinity of the oceans is 35.2 ‰, about 35 parts of salt in 1,000 parts of water. In the Baltic Sea, where there is much dilution by fresh water and melting ice, the salinity is much lower, only about 7 ‰ In the Red Sea where there is much surface evaporation and fewer rivers to bring in fresh water, the average salinity increases to 39 ‰. In enclosed seas, which are areas of inland drainage, such as the Caspian Sea, the salinity is very high, 180 ‰, and in the Dead Sea of Palestine, a salinity of 250 ‰ has been recorded. The highest salinity is perhaps, that of Lake Van, in Asia Minor, with 330 ‰. It is a salt lake, and salts are collected from its shores. The density of the water is so high that in Lake Van or the Dead Sea, it is almost impossible to sink. Beginner-swimmers will find it much easier to float here than anywhere else! The variation of salinity in the various seas and oceans is affected by the following factors.

1. **The rate of evaporation.** The waters fringing the High Pressure Belts of the Trade Wind Deserts, between 20° and 30°N and S, have high salinity because of the high rate of evaporation caused by high temperature and low humidity. The temperate oceans have lower salinity due to the lower temperature and a lower rate of evaporation.

2. **The amount of fresh water added by precipitation, streams and icebergs.** Salinity is lower than the average 35 ‰ in equatorial waters because of the heavy daily rainfall and high relative humidity. Oceans into which huge rivers like the Amazon, Congo, Ganges, Irrawaddy and Mekong drain, have much of their saltness diluted and have a lower salinity. The Baltic, Arctic and Antarctic waters have a salinity of less than 32 ‰ because of the colder climate with little evaporation and because much fresh water is added from the melting of icebergs, as well as by several large poleward-bound rivers, e.g. Ob, Lena, Yenisey, and Mackenzie.

3. **The degree of water mixing by currents.** In wholly or partially enclosed seas such as the Caspian Sea, Mediterranean Sea, Red Sea and Persian Gulf, the waters do not mix freely with the ocean water and they are not penetrated by ocean currents. Salinity is high, often over 37 ‰. In areas of inland drainage without links with the oceans, continuous evaporation under an almost cloudless sky causes the accumulation of salts around the shores. In the open oceans where currents freely flow, salinity tends to be near the average 35 ‰ or even a little lower. The range of salinity is negligible where there is free mixing of water by surface and sub-surface currents.

The Temperature of Ocean Water

Like land masses, ocean water varies in temperature from place to place both at the surface and at great depths. Since water warms up and cools down much more slowly than the land, the annual range of temperature in any part of the ocean is very much smaller. It is less than 10°F (–12°C) for most of the open seas. Generally, the mean annual temperature of the surface ocean water decreases from about 70°F (21°C) in equatorial areas to 55°F (13°C) at latitudes 45°N and S, and drops almost to freezing-point at the poles. The reduction of temperature with latitude is however never constant, because of the interference by warm and cold currents winds and air masses. Unlike the solid earth, ocean water is mobile and variations in the temperature between different parts of the oceans can be expected. Water flowing out from the Arctic and Antarctic as cold currents, such as the Labrador Current off north-east Canada, tends to reduce the surface-water temperature. Ports of eastern Canada even at 45°N are thus icebound for almost half the year. In the same way, coasts warmed by warm currents, such as the North Atlantic Drift, have their surface temperature raised. The Norwegian coast, even at latitudes 60° to 70°N is ice-free throughout the year!

The highest water temperatures are found in enclosed seas in the tropics, e.g. the Red Sea which records a temperature of 85° to 100°F.

The Arctic and Antarctic waters are so cold that their surface is permanently frozen as pack-ice down to a depth of several feet. In the warmer summer, parts of the ice break off as icebergs that both dilute the water and lower the surface temperature of surrounding ice-free seas.

The temperature of the oceans also varies vertically with increasing depth. It decreases rapidly for the first 200 fathoms (366 m), at the rate of 1°F for every 10 fathoms (18 m), and then more slowly until a depth of 500 fathoms (914 m) is reached. Beyond this, the drop is scarcely noticeable, less than 1°F for every 100 fathoms (183 m). In the ocean deeps below 2,000 fathoms (12,000 feet or 3,657 m), the water is uniformly cold, just a little above freezing-point. It is interesting to note that even in the deepest ocean trenches, more than 6 miles (9.65 km) below the surface, the water never freezes. It is estimated that over 80 per cent of all ocean waters have a temperature between 35° and 40°F (1.66° and 4.44°C).

The Movements of Ocean Currents

Ocean currents are large masses of surface water that circulate in regular patterns around the oceans, as shown in the world map in Fig. 106. Those that flow from equatorial regions polewards have a higher surface temperature and are warm currents. Those that flow from polar regions equator wards have a lower surface temperature and are cold currents. Their direction of movement is indicated by the arrows. But why should they follow such a pattern? Some of the underlying factors are explained below.

1. **The planetary winds.** Between the equator and the tropics blow the Trade Winds which move equatorial waters polewards and westwards and warm the eastern coasts of continents. For example, the North-East Trade Winds move the North Equatorial Current and its derivatives, the Florida Current and the Gulf Stream Drift to warm the southern and eastern coasts of USA. Similarly, the South-East Trade Winds drive the South Equatorial Current which warms the eastern coast of Brazil as the warm Brazilian Current.

In the temperate latitudes blow the Westerlies. Though they are less reliable than the Trade Winds, they result in a north-easterly flow of water in the northern hemisphere, so that the warm Gulf Stream is driven to the western coast of Europe as the North Atlantic Drift. In a similar manner, the Westerlies of the southern hemisphere, drive the West Wind Drift equatorwards as the Peruvian Current off South America and the Benguela Current off southern Africa. The planetary winds are probably the dominant influence on the flow of ocean currents. The strongest evidence of prevailing winds on current flows is seen in the North Indian Ocean. Here the direction of the currents changes completely with the direction of the monsoon winds which come from the north-east in winter and south-west in summer.

2. **Temperatures.** There is much difference in the temperature of ocean waters at the equator and at the poles. As warm water is lighter and rises, and cold water is denser and sinks, warm equatorial waters move slowly along the surface polewards, while the heavier cold waters of the polar regions creep slowly along the bottom of the sea equatorwards.

3. **Salinity.** The salinity of ocean water varies from place to place. Waters of high salinity are denser than waters of low salinity. Hence waters of low salinity flow on the surface of waters of high salinity while waters of high salinity flow at the bottom towards waters of low salinity. For example, in the Mediterranean region, there is great difference in salinity between the waters of the open Atlantic and those of the partially enclosed Mediterranean Sea. The less saline water of the Atlantic flows on the surface into the Mediterranean, and this is compensated for by an outflow of denser bottom water from the Mediterranean.

4. **The earth's rotation.** The earth's rotation deflects freely moving objects, including ocean currents, to the right. In the northern hemisphere this is a clockwise direction (e.g. the circulation of the Gulf Stream Drift and the Canaries Current). In the southern hemisphere it is an anti-clockwise direction (e.g. the Brazilian Current and the West Wind Drift).

5. **Land.** A land mass always obstructs and diverts a current. For instance, the tip of southern Chile diverts part of the West Wind Drift northwards as the Peruvian Current. Similarly the 'shoulder' of Brazil at Cape Sao Roque, divides the west-flowing equatorial currents into the Cayenne Current which flows north-westwards and the Brazilian Current which flows south-westwards.

The Circulation of the Atlantic Ocean

Let us now study more closely the circulation of ocean currents in the Atlantic Ocean. We shall begin with the North and South Equatorial Current at the equator. The steady Trade Winds constantly drift two streams of water from east to west. At the 'shoulder' of north-east Brazil, the protruding land mass splits the South Equatorial Current into the Cayenne Current which flows along the Guiana coast, and the Brazilian Current which flows southwards along the east coast of Brazil.

In the North Atlantic Ocean, the Cayenne Current is joined and reinforced by the North Equatorial Current and heads north-westwards as a large mass of equatorial water into the Caribbean Sea. Part of the current enters the Gulf of Mexico and emerges from the Florida Strait between Florida and Cuba as the Florida Current. The rest of the equatorial water flows northwards east of the Antilles to join the Gulf Stream off the south-eastern USA. The Gulf Stream Drift is one of the strongest ocean currents, 35 to 100 miles (56 to 161 km) wide, 2,000 feet (610 m) deep and with a velocity of three miles or 5 kilometres an hour approximately. The current hugs the coast of America as far as Cape Hatteras (latitude 35°N.), where it is *deflected eastwards* under the combined influence of the *Westerlies* and the *rotation* of the earth. It reaches Europe as the North Atlantic Drift. This current, flowing at 10 miles (16 km) per day, carries the warm equatorial water for over a thousand miles to the coasts of Europe. From the North Atlantic, it fans out in three directions, eastwards to Britain, northwards to the Arctic and southwards along the Iberian coast, as the cool Canaries Current. Oceanographic researches show that almost two-thirds of the water brought by the Gulf Stream to the Arctic regions is returned annually to the tropical latitudes by dense, cold polar water that creeps southwards in the ocean depths. The Canaries Current flowing southwards eventually merges with the North Equatorial Current, completing the clockwise circuit in the North Atlantic Ocean.

Within this ring of currents, an area in the middle of the Atlantic has no perceptible current. A large amount of floating seaweed gathers and the area is called the Sargasso Sea.

Apart from the clockwise circulation of the currents, there are also currents that enter the North Atlantic from the Arctic regions. These cold waters are blown south by the outflowing polar winds. The Irminger Current or East Greenland Current flows between Iceland and Greenland and cools the North Atlantic Drift at the point of convergence. The cold Labrador Current drifts south-eastwards between West Greenland and Baffin Island to meet the warm Gulf Stream off Newfoundland, as far south as 50°N where the icebergs carried south by the Labrador Current melt.

The South Atlantic Ocean follows the same pattern of circulation as the North Atlantic Ocean. The major differences are that the circuit is anti-clockwise and the collection of seaweed in the still waters of the mid-South Atlantic is not so distinctive.

Where the South Equatorial Current is split at Cape Sao Roque, one branch turns south as the warm Brazilian Current. Its deep blue waters are easily distinguishable from the yellow, muddy waters carried hundreds of miles out to sea by the Amazon further north. At about 40°S the influence of the prevailing Westerlies and the rotation of the earth propel the current eastwards to merge with the cold West Wind Drift as the South Atlantic Current. On reaching the west coast of Africa the current is diverted northwards as the cold Benguela Current (the counterpart of the Canaries Current). It brings the cold polar waters of the West Wind Drift into tropical latitudes. Driven by the regular South-East Trade Winds, the Benguela Current surges equatorwards in a north-westerly direction to join the South Equatorial Current. This completes the circulation of the currents in the South Atlantic. Between the North and South Equatorial Currents is the east-flowing Equatorial Counter Current.

The Circulation of the Pacific Ocean

The pattern of circulation in the Pacific is similar to that of the Atlantic except in modifications which can be expected from the greater size and the more open nature of the Pacific. The circulation can be easily followed in Fig. 106. Try to correlate it with the currents in the Atlantic.

The North Equatorial Current flows westwards with a compensating Equatorial Counter Current running in the opposite direction. Due to the greater expanse of the Pacific and the absence of an obstructing land mass the volume of water is very much greater than that of the Atlantic equatorial current. The North-East Trade Winds

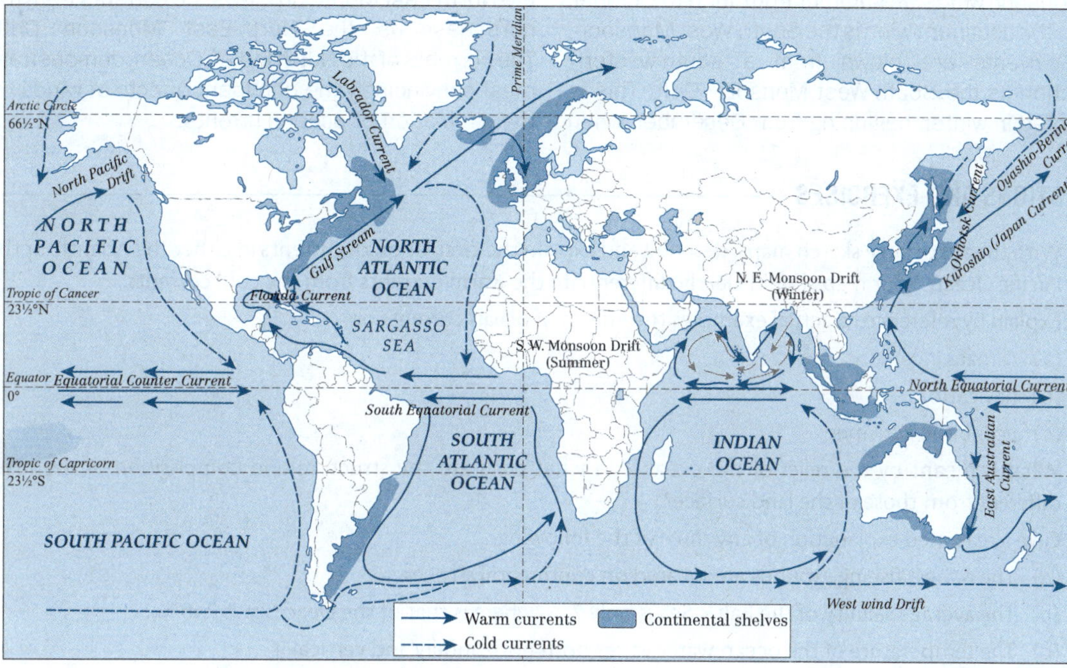

Fig. 106 Ocean currents of the world

blow the North Equatorial Current off the coasts of the Philippines and Formosa into the East China Sea as the Kuroshio or Kuro Siwo or Japan Current. Its warm waters are carried polewards as the North Pacific Drift, keeping the ports of the Alaskan coast ice-free in winter. The cold Bering Current or Alaskan Current creeps southwards from the narrow Bering Strait and is joined by the Okhotsk Current to meet the warm Japan Current as the Oyashio, off Hokkaido. The cold water eventually sinks beneath the warmer waters of the North Pacific Drift. Part of it drifts eastwards as the cool Californian Current along the coasts of the western USA and coalesces with the North Equatorial Current to complete the clockwise circulation.

The current system of the South Pacific is the same as that of the South Atlantic. The South Equatorial Current, driven by the South-East Trade winds, flows southwards along the coast of Queensland as the East Australian Current, bringing warm equatorial waters into temperate waters. The current turns eastwards towards New Zealand under the full force of the Westerlies in the Tasman Sea and merges with part of the cold West Wind Drift as the South Pacific Current. Obstructed by the tip of southern Chile, the current turns northwards along the western coast of South America as the cold Humboldt or Peruvian Current. The cold water chills any wind that blows onshore so that the Chilean and Peruvian coasts are practically rainless. The region is rich in microscopic marine plants and animals that attract huge shoals of fish. Consequently, millions of seabirds gather here to feed on the fish. Their droppings completely whiten the coastal cliffs and islands, forming thick deposits of *guano,* a valuable source of fertilizer. The Peruvian Current eventually links up with the South Equatorial Current and completes the cycle of currents in the South Pacific.

The Indian Ocean Circulation

As in the other oceans as illustrated in Fig. 106, the currents of the South Indian Ocean form a circuit. The Equatorial Current, turning southwards past Madagascar as the Agulhas or Mozambique Current merges with the West Wind Drift, flowing eastwards and turns equatorwards as the West Australian Current.

In the North Indian Ocean, there is a complete reversal of the direction of currents between summer and winter, due to the changes of monsoon winds. In summer from June to October, when the dominant wind is the South-West Monsoon, the currents are blown from a south-westerly direction as the South-West Monsoon Drift. This is reversed in winter, beginning from December, when the North-East Monsoon blows the currents from the north-east as the North-East Monsoon Drift. The currents of the North Indian Ocean, demonstrate most convincingly the dominant effects of winds on the circulation of ocean currents.

QUESTIONS AND EXERCISES

1. With the aid of large sketch maps, describe and explain the circulation of currents in either the Atlantic or the Pacific Ocean. Your map should clearly differentiate the warm currents from the cold currents.
2. Explain by reference to actual examples the effects of ocean currents on:
   (a) climate
   (b) navigation
   (c) economic activities
3. What is meant by the relief of the oceans? In what ways are the structure and composition of the relief different from those of the land surface?
4. Give a reasoned explanation of any *three* of the following.
   (a) The richest fishing grounds are located on continental shelves.
   (b) The average salinity of the Baltic Sea is only 7 ‰ whereas that of the Dead Sea is 240 ‰.
   (c) The temperature of the ocean water varies both horizontally and vertically.
   (d) The dominant influence on the circulation of ocean currents is wind.
5. Write brief notes on any *three* of the following terms associated with the oceans.
   (a) deep sea core samples
   (b) Mariana Trench
   (c) isohalines
   (d) Gulf Stream Drift
   (e) Sargasso Sea
6. *Either* (a) In each of *two* continents name:
   i. a volcano.
   ii. a rift valley.
   You need not select i. and ii. from the same continent.
   (b) With the aid of diagrams, describe the physical features and method of formation of *one* of the volcanoes and *one* of the rift valleys you have named in (a).
   Or Choose *three* of the following landforms: fjord, barrier reef, delta, lagoon. For each:
   i. With the aid of diagrams, describe its main features and suggest how the landforms may have been formed.
   ii. Name an example and locate it by means of a sketch map.
7. (a) With the aid of diagrams and by reference to actual examples, explain how lakes are caused by any *two* of the following:
   i. movement of the earth's crust.
   ii. glaciation.
   iii. the action of man.
   (b) Describe *three* ways in which lakes are useful to man.

13 Weather

The Difference Between Weather and Climate

The term weather should not be confused with climate, though they are very closely related to each other in the study of meteorology and climatology. We don't hear people saying that the climate of the day is warm or cold, but we do talk of warm weather, a cold morning, a sunny afternoon, a rainy day or a chilly night. Any casual remarks about the atmospheric conditions of a certain place at a certain time are about weather. It is never static, and thus cannot be generalized. In the same country, even over a small area, the weather can vary tremendously. It may be sunny in one part of the district, but raining heavily a few miles away. Strong gales may be experienced along the coasts while the interior may be relatively calm. It is important to realize that any place can be subjected to haphazard changes in weather at any time.

When we speak of climate we mean the average atmospheric conditions of an area over a considerable time. For climatic averages, a minimum period of 35 years is desirable. This involves the systematic observation, recording and processing of the various elements of climate such as rainfall, temperature, humidity, air pressure, winds, clouds and sunshine before any standardization of the climatic means or averages can be arrived at. The climate of Malaysia is described as *hot, wet, equatorial climate* which is a summing up of the average everyday climate of the country throughout the year.

The degree of variability in the climate or weather of a country also differs. Generally speaking, the climate of temperate latitudes is far more variable than that of the tropics. The climate of the British Isles is so changeable that many people have commented that 'Britain has no climate, only weather'. Conversely, the climate of Egypt is so static that it makes a good deal of sense when people say that 'Egypt has no weather, only climate'.

The Importance of Climate and Weather

The profound influence of climate and weather over man's activities can be seen from his everyday life. Forces of nature have regulated to a very great extent the sort of food we eat, what we wear, how we live and work. Our mental alertness, our physical characteristics and even our racial differences when closely examined have at least some relationship with climate. The direction of winds once controlled the pattern of trading routes. The safety of modern air communications is closely tied to accurate meteorological reports from the ground stations. Despite the advances made in science and technology, farmers and their crops are still at the mercy of the climate and the weather. Conditions of temperature, precipitation and humidity may promote or discourage the growth of fungus and diseases which may be injurious to both men and crops. Death rates are normally high in tropical countries and low in deserts, because germs are not transmitted readily in regions of high temperature and low humidity. Cool, fresh mountain air is always good for health.

Weather Bureaux or *Meteorological Stations* are scattered all over the globe, including the oceans, using some of the most up-to-date weather instruments to gather a wide range of data as raw materials for the construction of weather maps or synoptic charts. Though men are still unable to tame the forces of nature such as floods, droughts, typhoons or hurricanes, a sound knowledge of the trends or the weather systems can often help to avoid or reduce the seriousness of the calamities. Professional meteorologists are able to forecast the weather fairly accurately from local observations. A fall in the barometer, a change of cloud types, a bright sunset or even a whisper of the wind can be very useful tips to a weather forecaster in detecting what is going to happen next. A casual glance at the sky will be sufficient for a weather expert to sum up the conditions of the atmosphere.

Today farmers are becoming more and more dependent upon *meteorological services*. A knowledge of the likely weather of a place will be useful for a farmer to plan his work for the season or the year. Frequent *agricultural bulletins* issued by the Meteorological Office will assist farmers to take due precautions against frosts, hail, heavy snowfall or a period of possible drought. Sailors at sea are warned promptly of any oncoming gale or typhoon. Modern air transport, military operations, geographical expeditions, even important games and outings, often take due consideration of meteorological reports. A fair knowledge of the weather is not only useful but often essential.

The Elements of Weather and Climate —

To collect various climatic data and to prepare maps and charts of them, the following elements of climate are normally observed and measured by weather instruments.

1. **Rainfall.** Rainfall including other forms of precipitation (snow, sleet and hail) is always measured by a metal instrument called a rain gauge (Fig. 107 a). It consists of a copper cylinder with a metal funnel either 5 inches or 8 inches in diameter, which leads into a smaller copper container or a glass bottle. The hole in the funnel that leads down to the container is very small so that evaporation of the collected rain is minimized. The gauge should be at least one foot above the ground and firmly fastened, to avoid splashing. The instrument should be sited well away from tall buildings, high trees and other objects which would shelter it.

The *measurement* of the rainfall is done by removing the funnel, emptying the rain in the container into a graduated cylinder with a 1½ diameter (Fig. 107 b). The reading should be done at eye-level and to an accuracy of 0·01 inch. For greater accuracy, a special kind of taper measure as shown in Fig. 107 (c) which tapers at the bottom may be used. It gives an accuracy up to 0·005 inch. An inch of rainfall means the amount of water that would cover the ground to a depth of 1 inch, provided none evaporated, drained off or percolated away. For meteorological recordings, a *rain-day* is reckoned as a period of 24 hours with at least 0·01 inch or more rain being recorded. If the amount exceeds 0–04 inch, it is considered a wet day. For general reckoning, the average rainfall for Malaysia is less than 0–3 inch a day. Only a torrential downpour can account for more than an inch of rainfall in a day. The rain gauge must be examined every day. In temperate regions, snowfall

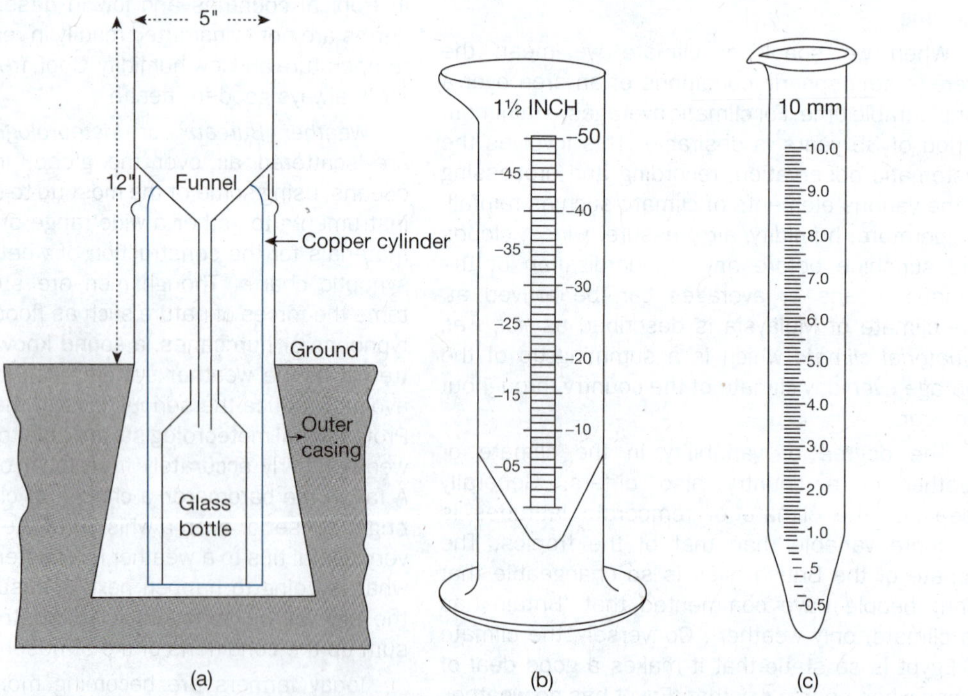

Fig. 107 (a) A rain gauge; (b) Ordinary measuring cylinder; (c) A calibrated taper measure

is carefully melted by warming the funnel and then measured. For all practical purposes 10 to 12 inches of snow may be considered as equivalent to 1 inch of rain.

The daily records of rainfall will be added at the end of the month to find the total rainfall for that month. The total for each month is again added at the end of the year to find the *annual rainfall.* The mean annual rainfall is obtained from the averages of annual rainfall taken over a long period of say 35 years. For plotting in rainfall maps, places having the same mean annual rainfall are joined by a line called an isohyet, as shown in many atlases. Rainfall can also be graphically depicted as shaded rainfall columns, one for each month of the year as in Fig. 108 or in dispersal diagrams, one dot for each year for as many years as possible as in Fig. 109. The former illustrates the monthly rainfall regime over a year and the latter shows at a glance the range of dry and wet years for 35 years.

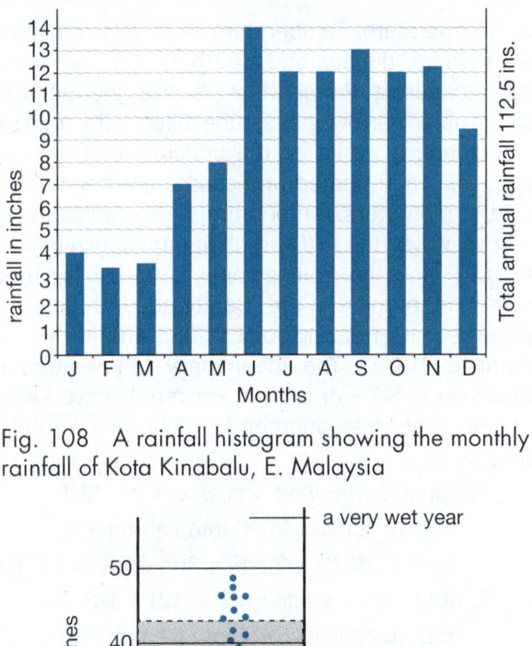

Fig. 108 A rainfall histogram showing the monthly rainfall of Kota Kinabalu, E. Malaysia

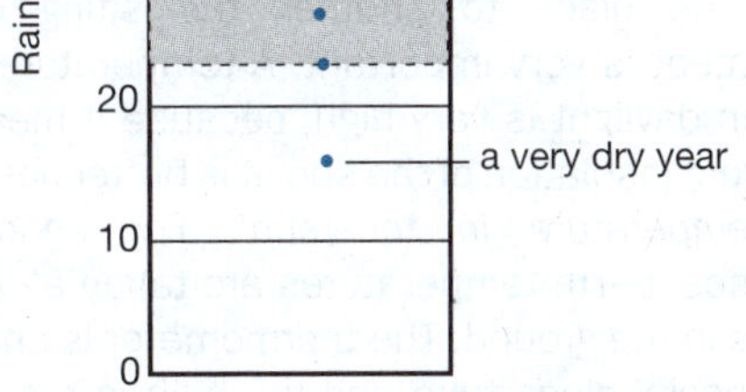

Fig. 109 A rainfall dispersal diagram for Gibraltar for 35 years

2. **Pressure.** Air is made up of a number of mixed gases and has *weight.* It therefore exerts a pressure on the earth's surface which varies from place to place and from time to time. This force that presses on the surface of any object can be fairly accurately measured. The instrument for measuring pressure is a barometer, as shown in Fig. 110, invented by the scientist Galileo and his assistant Torricelli in 1643. The ordinary mercury barometer consists of a long glass tube, sealed at the upper and open at the lower end. The lower end is inverted in a bowl of mercury, whose surface is exposed to the air. Variations in the atmospheric pressure on the mercury surface are balanced by the column of mercury in the glass tube. This gives the pressure of the air and can be read off quickly from the scale on the glass tube. Any liquid could be used for this purpose, but mercury has been chosen because it is the heaviest liquid known. If ordinary water were used, the corresponding column for normal atmospheric pressure would be 34 feet! At sea level, the mercury column is 29.9 inches, or 760 mm. If the pressure increases,

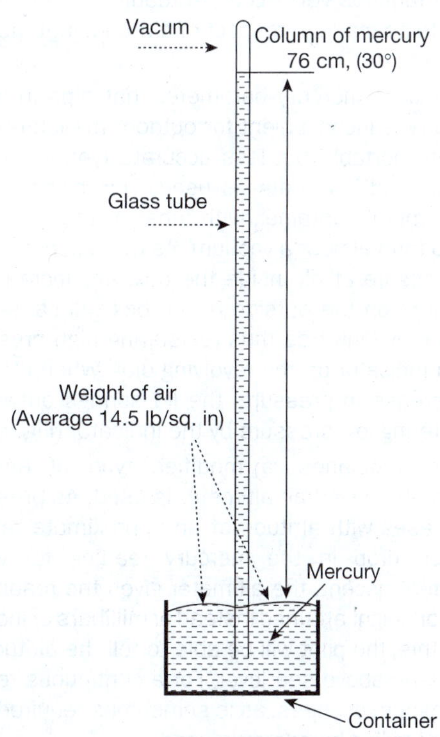

Fig. 110 A mercury barometer

the air pressing on the surface will force up the mercury column to about 31 inches (high pressure). When the pressure decreases, as less air presses on the surface, the mercury column will drop about 28 inches (low pressure). As pressure is a force, it is more appropriate to measure it in terms of a unit of force. A new unit known as the millibar (mb) was adopted by meteorological stations in 1914. A normal atmospheric pressure equivalent to 14·7 lb. per square inch in weight or a reading of 29·9 inches of mercury in the column is 1013 millibars. On maps places of equal pressure are joined by lines called isobars. In temperate latitudes, pressure changes are very rapid in the formation of cyclones and anticyclones. In normal circumstances, they vary from 960 mb. to 1,040 mb.

Pressure readings vary with a number of factors. A *sea-level* reading of 30 inches will be halved on *mountainous* regions of 3·5 miles above sea level. This is because as one ascends there is less air above and so the weight, or pressure is less. The barometer is also sensitive to gravitational forces at different latitudes. The mercury itself also expands with an increase in temperature. Therefore, for professional meteorological work which requires very accurate readings, corrections have to be made in respect of altitude, latitude and temperature.

Since a mercury barometer that dips in liquid mercury is inconvenient for outdoor measurement, a more portable but less accurate type known as the aneroid barometer is used. This comprises a small metal container, with most of the air driven out to form almost a vacuum. As there is practically no pressure at all inside the box, any increase in pressure on the outside of the box will cause the lid to move inwards thus registering high pressure by an indicator on the revolving dial. When there is a decrease in pressure, the lid springs outwards, registering low pressure by the indicator (Fig. 111).

In aeroplanes, a modified type of aneroid barometer called an altimeter is used. As pressure decreases with altitude at an approximate rate of 1 inch drop in the mercury reading for every 900 feet ascent, the altimeter gives the reading in feet for height attained instead of millibars or inches. With this, the pilot will be able to tell the altitude of the plane above sea level. For a continuous record of pressure changes, as is sometimes required, the self-recording barogram is used.

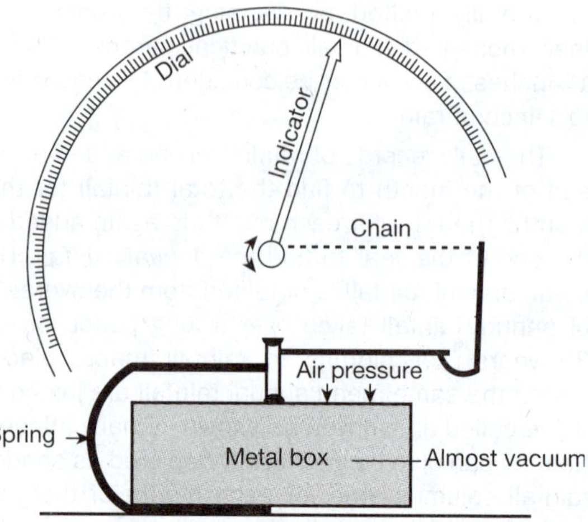

Fig. 111 An aneroid barometer

3. **Temperature.** Temperature is a very important element of climate and weather. The instrument for measuring temperature is the thermometer which is a narrow glass tube filled with mercury or alcohol. It works on the principle that mercury *expands* when heated and *contracts* when cooled. On thermometers, temperatures are marked in one of two ways. In °F (Fahrenheit) the freezing-point is 32°F and the boiling-point is 212°F for most scientific purposes the Centigrade °C scale is preferred. Its freezing-point is 0°C and its boiling-point is 100°C. The mean daily temperature of Malaysia is 80°F or 26.7°C For rapid conversation of one scale into another, the following formulae may be used.

To obtain *Fahrenheit* = (1·8 × °C) + 32°F

e.g. to convert 20°C into Fahrenheit:

(1·8 × 20°C) + 32°F- = 36° + 32° = 68°F

To obtain *Centigrade* = (°F – 32) ÷ 1·8

e.g. to convert 59°F into Centigrade:

(59° – 32°) ÷ 1·8 = 27 ÷ 1·8 = 15°C

As the degree of 'hotness' varies tremendously from one place to another, the siting of the instrument is very important. A temperature taken in open daylight is very high, because it measures the direct insolation of the sun. It is better described as *'temperature in the sun'*. For agricultural purposes, earth temperatures are taken at various depths in the ground. The thermometer is enclosed in a special glass tube and the bulb is embedded in paraffin wax, so that they are less sensitive

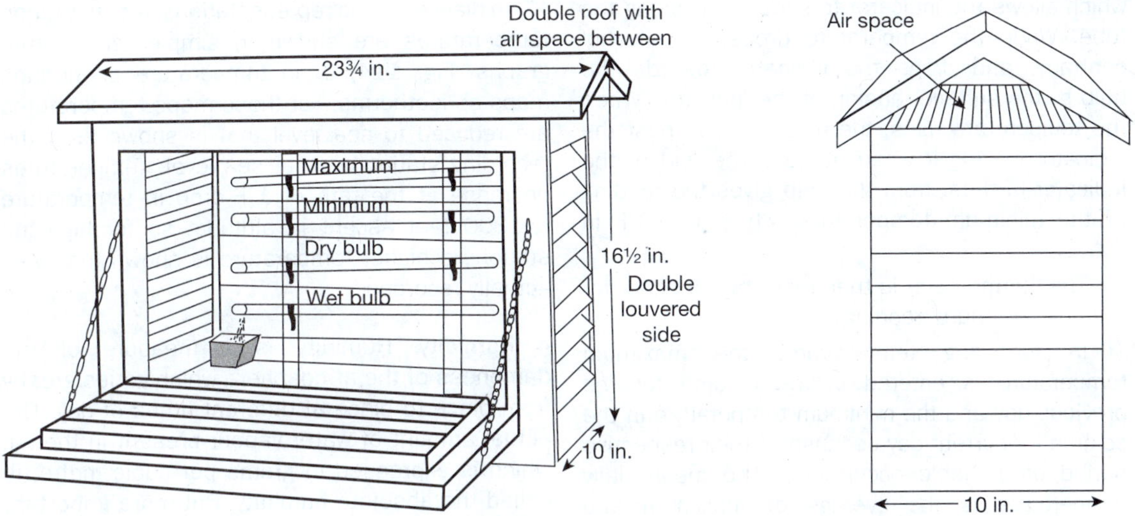

Fig. 112 A Stevenson Screen

to abrupt temperature changes. To assess the possible damages done by ground frosts to crops in temperate latitudes, grass temperatures are also taken.

But the temperatures that we are so accustomed to in climatic graphs are shade temperatures, that is the temperatures of the air. Precautions therefore must be taken to exclude the intensity of the sun's radiant heat. This is done by placing the thermometers in a standard: meteorological shelter known as the Stevenson Screen (Fig. 112). It consists of a white wooden box raised 4 feet above the ground on stilts. The roof is double-layered with an intervening air space to exclude much of the direct rays of the sun. The sides of the box are louvred like 'venetian blinds' to allow free circulation of the air. One side of the screen is hinged to serve as a door which can be opened and closed to give access to the instruments kept inside. The floor of the screen is also louvred. The Stevenson Screen normally carries maximum and minimum thermometers, dry and wet bulb thermometers. Larger ones may also contain a self-recording thermogram and hygrogram.

Maximum and minimum temperatures are measured by the maximum and minimum thermometers. They are either in the form of separate thermometers or joined in a U-shaped glass tube as in the *Six's thermometer.* The maximum thermometer records the highest temperature reached during the day. The mercury in the closed glass tube expands when the temperature rises. It pushes a metal indicator up the tube and this stays at the maximum level when the temperature drops. The end of the indicator nearest the mercury, as indicated in Fig. 113, gives the reading of the maximum temperature, which is 87°F in this case. To reset the mercury for the next day's reading, swing it hard or draw the indicator back by a magnet.

The minimum thermometer records the lowest temperature reached during the day; it probably occurs in the middle of the night or early in the morning. The glass tube is filled with alcohol

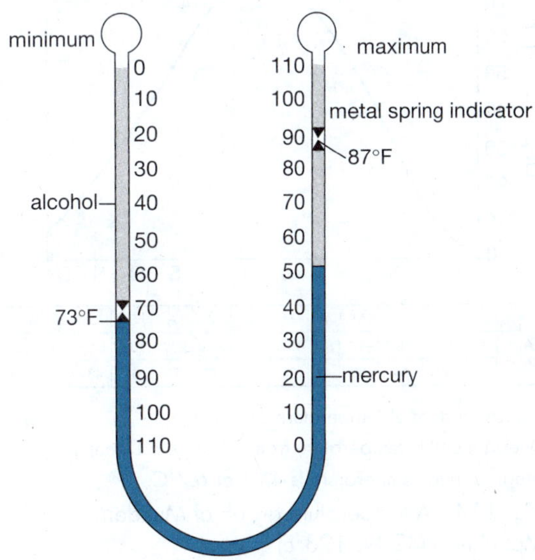

Fig. 113 Maximum and minimum thermometers

which allows the indicator to slide freely along the tube. When the temperature drops, the alcohol contracts and drags the indicator towards the bulb by the surface tension of the indicator. When the temperature rises, the alcohol flows past the indicator leaving it where it was. The end of the indicator farthest from the bulb gives the reading of the minimum temperature, which is 73°F in Fig. 113.

The thermometer is then reset by a magnet for the next 24 hours' reading.

In recording temperature, the maximum temperature is entered in the column for the previous day and the minimum temperature in the column for current day because of their respective period of probable occurrence. The mean daily temperature is the average of maximum and minimum, e.g. (87°F + 73°F) ÷ 2 = 80°F But an accurate mean should be the average of 24 readings taken at hourly intervals during the whole day. In practice this is almost impossible except with a self-recording instrument. The difference between the maximum and minimum temperatures of a day gives the diurnal range of temperature. The difference between the hottest month (i.e. July in the northern hemisphere) and the coldest month (i.e. January in the northern hemisphere) gives the annual range of temperature.

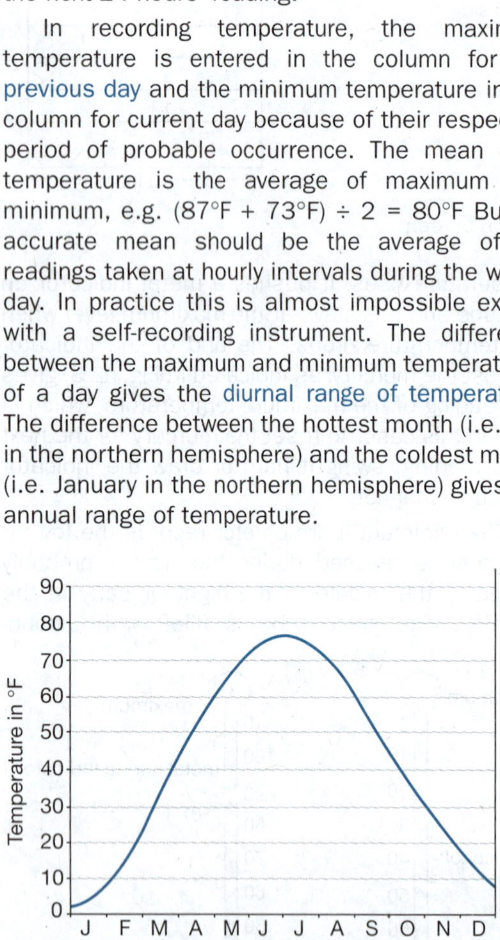

		J	F	M	A	M	J	J	A	S	O	N	D
Avg. Temp.	°C	-13.3	-10.0	-1.1	8.3	15.5	21.6	25.0	23.8	16.1	8.9	-1.7	-10.0
	°F	8	14	30	47	60	71	77	75	61	48	29	14

Statistical data of temperature of Mukden
(Mean monthly temperature from January to December)
Mean annual temperature is 44°F or 6.7°C

Fig. 114 A temperature graph of Mukden, Manchuria (42°N, 123°E)

In diagrammatic representations, monthly mean temperatures are shown in simple temperature graphs (Fig. 114) or in temperature distribution maps as isotherms. For these maps temperatures are reduced to sea level that is shown as if the recording station were at sea level. Temperatures decrease at the rate of 1°F drop in temperature for 300 feet ascent in altitude, so for highland stations a higher temperature is shown than was actually recorded.

4. **Humidity.** Humidity is a measure of the dampness of the atmosphere which varies greatly from place to place at different times of day. The actual amount of water vapour present in the air, which is expressed in grams per cubic metre, is called the absolute humidity. But more important from the point of view of weather studies is the relative humidity. This is the ratio between the actual amount of water vapour and the total amount the air can hold at a given temperature, expressed as a percentage. Warm air can hold more water vapour than cold air, so if it contains only half the amount it *could* carry, the relative humidity is 50 per cent. In the equatorial regions, over 80 per cent is common in the morning, which means the air contains four-fifths as much water vapour as it can carry. When the relative humidity reaches 100 per cent, the air is completely saturated. The air temperature is said to be at dewpoint. Further cooling will condense the water vapour into clouds or rain. It is thus clear that when relative humidity is high the air is moist, as in the equatorial regions; when it is low, the air is dry as in the deserts.

The instrument for measuring relative humidity is the hygrometer, which comprises wet and dry-bulb thermometers placed side by side in the Stevenson Screen (Fig. 115). The dry bulb is, in fact, the ordinary thermometer that measures the shade temperature mentioned earlier. The wet bulb is kept wet by a wick that dips into a reservoir of distilled water. When the air is not saturated evaporation, which produces a cooling effect, takes place from the moist wick. The wet bulb therefore always shows a lower reading than the dry bulb. With reference to prepared tables for calculating relative humidity, under the difference column of the dry and wet bulb reading, the relative humidity can be obtained as a percentage. Normally a

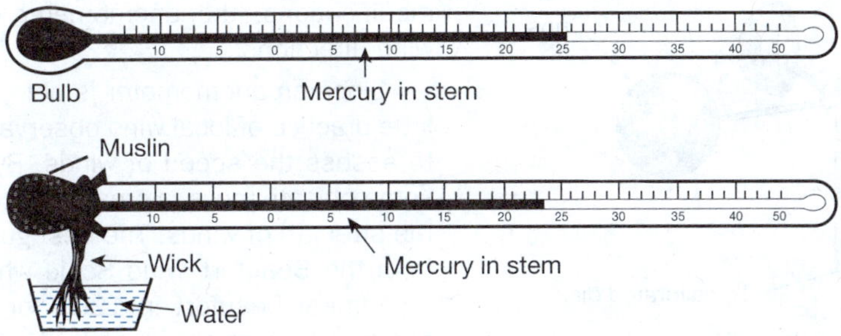

Fig. 115 The hygrometer consisting of wet and dry bulb thermometers

large difference indicates a low R.H. and a small difference a high R.H. If both have the same reading, R.H. is 100 per cent; the air is saturated.

5. **Winds.** Wind is air in motion and has both direction and speed. Unlike other elements in climate such as rain, snow or sleet, winds are made up of a series of gusts and eddies that can only be felt but not seen. When leaves fall, trees sway and dust particles move, we realize that the wind is blowing. But there is nothing tangible that we can show or measure unless we make use of some conventional instruments.

The instrument widely used for measuring wind direction is a wind vane or weather cock. As wind direction is always blocked by trees and tall buildings, weather cocks and wind vanes need to be erected in an exposed position, to get a true direction. It is made up of two parts as shown in Fig. 116 (a) and (b). One part is an arrow or vane on the top, which is free to move with the prevailing wind. The other part with the four compass points is stationary and shows in which direction the wind is moving. Winds are always named from the direction they blow; an east wind is one that blows from east to west and a south-west wind is one that blows from the south-west.

Most of the weather cocks that we see on church spires and country buildings seldom give a correct indication of wind directions. They are either too low or are blocked by taller structures nearby. The direction of smoke-drift or flag movements in fairly open spaces provides the most reliable indication of wind direction. Sometimes a piece of *wovencloth* with a tail is fixed to the top of a high pole and drifts freely in mid-air. This is another way of indicating wind direction.

The speed of wind is usually measured by an anemometer (Fig. 117). It consists of three or four semi-circular cups attached to the ends of horizontal spokes mounted on a high vertical spindle. As the concave sides of the cups offer greater resistance to the winds, the horizontal spokes will rotate, moving a central rod which transmits the velocity (speed) of the wind in miles per hour to an electrically operated dial. But the speed recorded is not absolutely accurate because after the winds have abated, the rotation continues due to its own momentum. With some

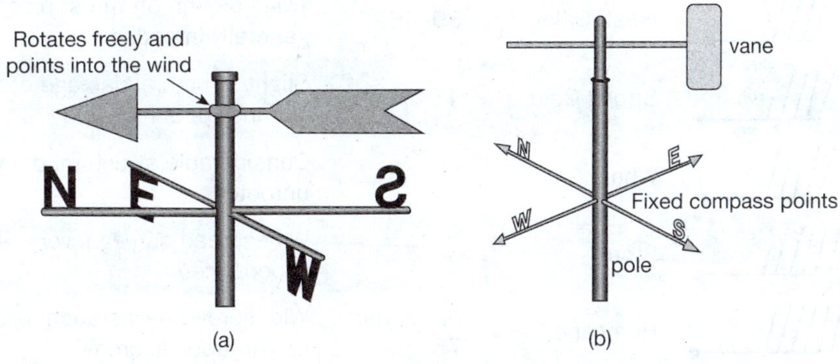

Fig. 116 Wind Vanes

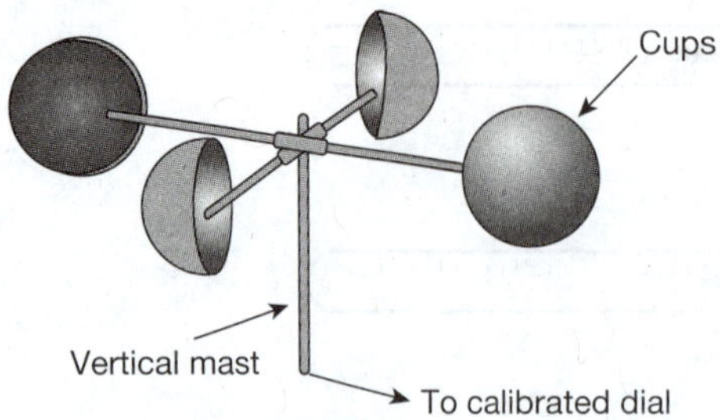

Fig. 117 Simplified sketch to illustrate the main features of a wind anemometer

modifications, the anemometer can also record wind directions.

Since an anemometer is not easily available, a little practice of local wind observations will help us to assess the speed of winds. By seeing the way some objects move, a great deal can be said about the strength of winds. The best guide is obtainable from the Beaufort Wind Scale which was devised by Admiral Beaufort in 1805 for estimating wind speed. Frequent reference to the table in your free time will help you to learn it quickly.

The Beaufort Wind Scale

Beaufort Scale No.	Arrow Indication	Wind Description	Speed (m.p.h.)	Effects (a guide to observation)
0		Calm	Less than 1	Smoke rises vertically
1		Light air	1–3	Wind direction shown by smoke-drift but not by wind-vanes
2	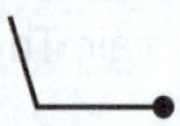	Slight Breeze	4–7	Wind felt on face; leaves rustle; vanes moved by wind
3	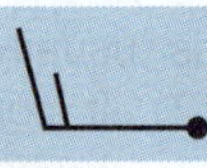	Gentle Breeze	8–12	Leaves and twigs in constant motion; winds extend light flags
4	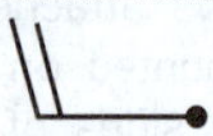	Moderate Breeze	13–18	Raises dust and loose paper; small branches moved
5		Fresh Breeze	19–24	Small trees in leaf begin to sway; crested wavelets form on inland water
6	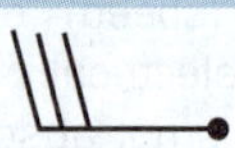	Strong Breeze	25–31	Large branches in motion; whistling heard in telegraph wires.
7	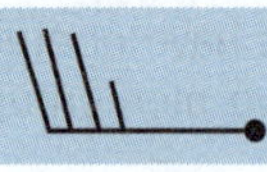	Moderate Gale	32–38	Whole tree in motion; walking inconvenienced
8		Fresh Gale	39–46	Twigs broken off trees; progress generally impeded
9		Strong Gale	47–54	Slight structural damage occurs, chimney pots removed
10	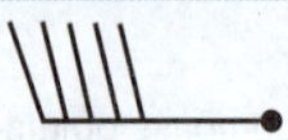	Whole Gale	55–63	Considerable structural damage, trees uprooted
11		Storm	64–75	Widespread damage, very rarely experienced
12		Hurricane	More than 75	Widespread devastation, experienced only in tropical areas

6. **Sunshine.** As mentioned in Chapter 1, the amount of sunshine a place receives, depends on the seasons, a factor determined by latitude and by the position of the earth in its revolution around the sun. Tourist resorts, particularly in the higher temperate latitudes, are most concerned about the numbers of hours of sunshine they receive. In the tropics, where sunshine is abundant people are less interested in the amount.

In the meteorological station, sunshine duration is recorded by a sundial, 4 inches in diameter, through which the sun's rays are focused upon a sensitized card, graduated in hours. A line is made on the card when it is sufficiently heated, but not when the rays are faint. On maps places with equal sunshine duration are joined by isohels.

7. **Clouds.** When air rises, it is cooled by expansion. After dew-point has been reached cooling leads to condensation of water vapour in the atmosphere. Tiny droplets of water vapour which are too small to fall as rain or snow (less than 0.001 cm, approximately 0.0005 inches in radius) will be suspended in the air and float as clouds. Their *form, shape, height and movements* tell us a great deal about the sky conditions and the weather we are likely to experience. It is fascinating and very rewarding to know something about the clouds which we see everyday. For meteorological purposes, the amount of cloud-cover in the sky is expressed in eighths or oktas (e.g. 2/8 ◔ is quarter covered; 4/8 ◑ is half covered; 6/8 ◕ is three-quarters obscured and 8/8 ● is completely overcast.) They are shown on weather maps by discs, shaded in the correct proportions. Details of cloud type are indicated in code figures which have been internationally accepted. On maps places with an equal degree of cloudiness are joined by lines known as isonephs. As clouds vary so quickly from time to time at any particular place, isoneph maps have little significance.

The classification of clouds is based on a combination of *form, height and appearance.* Four major cloud types and their variations can be recognized.

(a) **High Clouds:** mainly cirrus (Ci) of feathery form at 20–40,000 feet above ground.

i. **Cirrus (Ci)** This looks fibrous and appears like wisps in the blue sky; it is often called 'mares' tails'. It indicates fair weather, and often gives a brilliant sunset.

ii. **Cirrocumulus (Cc)** This appears as white globular masses, forming ripples in a 'mackerel sky'.

iii. **Cirrostratus (Cs)** This resembles a thin white sheet or veil; the sky looks milky and the sun or moon shines through it with a characteristic 'halo'

Cirrus cloud

Cirrocumulus cloud

Cirrostratus cloud

(b) **Medium Clouds:** mainly alto (Alt) or middle-height clouds at 7–20,000 feet.

iv. **Altocumulus (Alt-Cu)** These are woolly, bumpy clouds arranged in layers and appearing like waves in the blue sky. They normally indicate fine weather.

v. **Altostratus (Alt-St)** These are denser, greyish clouds with a 'watery' look. They have a fibrous or striated structure through which the sun's rays shine faintly.

(c) **Low Clouds** mainly stratus or sheet clouds below 7,000 feet.

vi. **Stratocumulus (St-Cu)** This is a rough, bumpy cloud with the waves more pronounced than in altocumulus. There is great contrast between the bright and shaded parts.

vii. **Stratus (St)** This is a very low cloud, uniformly grey and thick, which appears like a low ceiling or highland fog. It brings dull weather with light drizzle. It reduces the visibility of aircraft and is thus a danger.

viii. **Nimbostratus (Ni-St)** This is a dark, dull cloud, clearly layered, and is also known as a *rain cloud.* It brings continuous rain, snow or sleet.

(d) **Clouds with great vertical extent:** mainly cumulus or heap clouds with no definite height (2–30,000 feet).

ix. **Cumulus (Cu)** This is a vertical cloud with a rounded top and horizontal base, typical of humid tropical regions, associated with up-rising convectional currents. Its great white globular masses may look grey against the sun but it is a 'fair weather cloud'.

Cumulus cloud

x. **Cumulonimbus (Cu-Ni)** This is, in fact, an overgrown cumulus cloud, extending for a tremendous vertical height from a base of 2,000 feet to over 30,000 feet. Its black and white globular masses take a fantastic range of shapes. Its cauliflower top often spreads out like *an anvil.* This is frequently seen in tropical afternoons. It is also referred to as a *'thunder-cloud'* and brings convectional ram, accompanied by lightning and thunder.

8. **Other Elements pertaining to visibility.** Other elements affecting visibility include haze, mist and fog.

(a) **Haze** This is caused by smoke and dust particles in industrial areas or may be due to unequal refraction of light in air of different densities in the lower atmosphere. The term is usually used in connection with the reduction of visibility in regions of low humidity, less than 75 per cent. When visibility is less than 1¼ miles, haze is present.

Altocumulus cloud

Cumulonimbus cloud

(b) **Mist** The condensation of water vapour in the air causes small droplets of water to float about forming clouds at ground level called mist. It reduces visibility to about 1,000 metres or 1,100 yards. Unlike haze, mist occurs in wet air, when the relative humidity is over 75 per cent.

(c) **Fog** Ordinary fog is due to water condensing on dust and other particles like smoke from houses and factories. It only occurs in the lower strata of the atmosphere as a sort of dense *ground cloud.* The visibility in fog is even less than 1,000 metres. In industrial areas, like those of the Black Country and northern England, very thick smoky fog is formed, called smog. The visibility may be reduced to 220 yards or even less.

Fogs that occur on hills are called hill fogs. They are most common in the morning, even in the tropics, and disperse when the sun rises. In temperate lands, when days are hot and nights are clear and still, fogs may also result from cooling of the land surface by radiation. The lower layers of the air are chilled and water vapour in the atmosphere condenses to form radiation fog, or land fog. When the cooling surface is over the sea or when a damp air stream is brought into contact with a cold current as off Newfoundland, sea fog is formed. It varies in depth and thickness. Some sea fogs are so shallow and light that the masts of ships can be seen protruding above them.

Generally speaking fogs are more common over seas than lands, and are most prevalent over coastal areas. The dry interiors experience haze or mist. Dense fogs are more likely to occur in the high and middle latitudes rather than the tropics.

QUESTIONS AND EXERCISES

1. (a) What instruments are normally kept in the school weather station?
   (b) Why is it important that the times of observation and the method of recording should be uniform?
   (c) Explain what precautions you would take to ensure that your observations and records from the various instruments are accurate.
2. Name the instruments you would use to measure the following elements of climate.
   (a) relative humidity
   (b) atmospheric pressure
   (c) wind velocity
   For any *two* of the above, and with annotated diagrams, explain how the instruments work.
3. What weather elements are measured by the following apparatus?
   (a) a rain gauge
   (b) the Six's maximum and minimum thermometers
   (c) a wind vane
   Describe how the above apparatus function and state what special precautions must be taken when taking readings from them.
4. *Either:* Explain the following
   (a) Wind speed at 2,500 feet is greater than that at the surface.
   (b) Britain has no climate, only weather
   (c) Fog is, in fact, cloud at ground level
   Or: Distinguish between
   i. mist and fog
   ii. cirrus and stratus clouds
   iii. climate and weather
5. Define any *three* of the following terms or phrases, in their relation to weather studies.
   (a) mean annual rainfall
   (b) diurnal range of temperature
   (c) Beaufort Scale
   (d) synoptic charts
   (e) lapse rate

14 Climate

The Atmosphere

The atmosphere is made up of gases and vapour, and receives incoming *solar energy* from the sun giving rise to what we call climate. We actually live at the bottom of this indefinite layer of atmosphere where the air is densest. Higher up, the air thins out and it is still a matter of conjecture where the atmosphere ends. One estimate puts this limit at about 600 miles (965 km) above sea level. The lowest layer, in which the weather is confined, is known as the troposphere. It extends from the earth's surface for a height of 6 miles (9.65 km), and within it temperature normally falls with increasing altitude. The climatic elements such as temperature, precipitation, clouds, pressure and humidity within the troposphere account for the great variations in local climate and weather that play such a great part in our daily lives. From analyses taken in different parts of the globe, it is found that the lower part of the atmosphere contains a consistent proportion of certain gases: 78 per cent of nitrogen, 21 per cent of oxygen, 0.03 per cent of carbon dioxide and minute traces of argon, helium and other rare gases. In addition, it has an unpredictable proportion of water, existing either as a gas like water vapour, a liquid like rain, clouds and sleet or a solid like snow and hailstones, as well as other solid particles like smoke and dust. It is because of the *variable water content* of the atmosphere that we have such great contrasts in weather and climate over different parts of the world. If we were to live in a dry atmosphere, absolutely without water, there would be no weather and not even much climate.

Above the troposphere lies the stratosphere or the upper layer of the atmosphere. It extends upwards for another 50 miles or even more. It is not only very cold, but cloudless, with extremely thin air and without dust, smoke or water vapour but there are marked seasonal temperature changes. Beyond the stratosphere is the ionosphere which goes several hundred miles up. It has electrically conductive layers which make shortwave radio transmission possible over long distances. Modern artificial satellites, launched in the upper strata of the atmosphere, as well as balloons are used to transmit back to earth valuable information regarding the conditions of the atmosphere.

Insolation

The only source of energy for the earth's atmosphere comes from the sun which has a surface temperature of more than 10,800°F (5,982°C). This energy travels through space for a distance of 93 million miles (150 km) and reaches us as solar energy or radiant energy in the process called insolation. This radiation from the sun is made up of three parts, the visible 'white' light that we see when the sun shines and the less visible ultraviolet and infrared rays. The visible 'white' light is the most intense and has the greatest influence on our climate. The ultraviolet rays affect our skin and cause sunburn when our bare body is exposed to them for too long a period. The infrared rays can penetrate even dust and fog and are widely used in photography. Only that part of the sun's radiation which reaches the earth is called insolation.

What matters most is the effect of the atmosphere upon the incoming solar radiation. It is estimated that of the total radiation coming to us, 35 per cent reaches the atmosphere and is directly reflected back to space by dust, clouds and air molecules. It plays practically no part in heating the earth and its atmosphere. Another 14 per cent is absorbed by the water vapour, carbon dioxide and other gases. Its interception by the air causes it to be 'scattered' and 'diffused' so that the visible rays of the spectrum between the ultraviolet and infrared give rise to the characteristic blue sky that we see above us. The remaining 51 per cent reaches the earth and warms the surface. In turn the earth warms the layers of air above it by direct contact or conduction, and through the transmission of heat by upward movement of air currents or convection. This radiation of heat by the earth continues during the night, when insolation from the sun cannot replace it. The earth-surface therefore cools at night.

The rate of heating differs between land and water surfaces. Land gets heated up much more quickly than the water. Because water is transparent heat is absorbed more slowly and because it is always in motion, its absorbed heat is distributed over a greater depth and area. Thus any appreciable rise in temperature takes a much longer time. On the other hand the opaque nature of land allows greater absorption but all the radiant heat is concentrated at the surface, and temperature rises rapidly. Because of these differences between land and water surfaces land also cools more quickly than water.

Elements of Climate and Factors Affecting them

Of the various climatic elements, temperature, precipitation, pressure and winds are the most important because of their far-reaching global influences. These elements and their distribution, whether horizontal from equatorial to polar regions, or vertical from ground to atmosphere, are in one way or another affected by some or all of the climatic factors: latitude, altitude, continentality, ocean currents, insolation, prevailing winds, slope and aspect, natural vegetation and soil.

Temperature

The Importance of Temperature

1. Temperature influences the actual amount of water vapour present in the air and thus decides the moisture-carrying capacity of the air.

2. It decides the rate of evaporation and condensation, and therefore governs the degree of stability of the atmosphere.

3. As relative humidity is directly related to the temperature of the air, it affects the nature and types of cloud formation and precipitation.

Factors Influencing Temperature

1. **Latitude.** As explained in Chapter 1, due to the earth's inclination, the mid-day sun is almost overhead within the tropics but the sun's rays reach the earth at an angle outside the tropics. Temperature thus diminishes from equatorial regions to the poles. This is illustrated in Fig. 118. It shows two bands of rays coming from the sun to two different latitudes on the earth's surface. Band RI falls vertically over the equatorial latitudes on surface E. Band R2 falls obliquely over the temperate latitudes on surface T. RI travels through a *shorter distance* and its concentrated solar insolation heats up a smaller surface area; temperature is thus high. On the other hand, R2 travels through a *longer distance* and much of

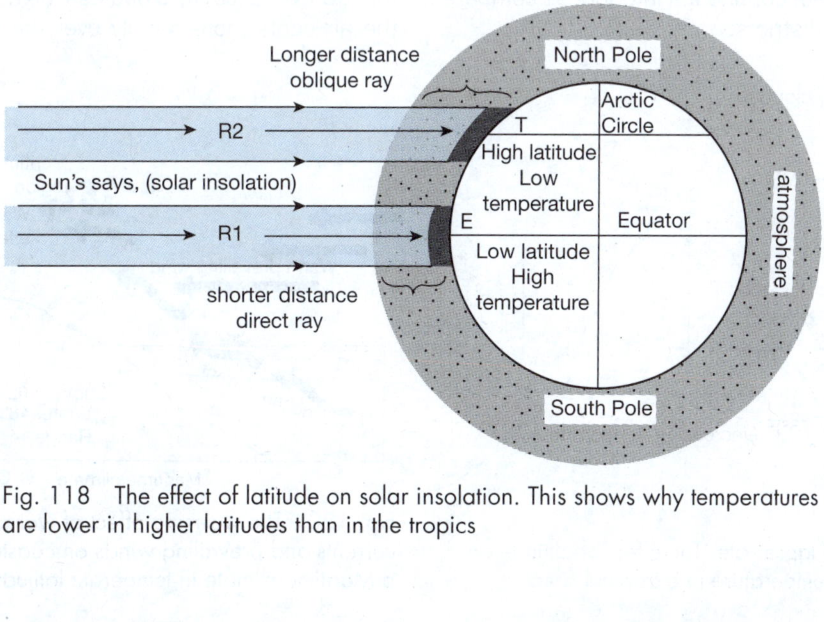

Fig. 118 The effect of latitude on solar insolation. This shows why temperatures are lower in higher latitudes than in the tropics

its heat is absorbed by clouds, water vapour and dust particles. Its oblique ray has to heat up a large area; temperature is therefore low.

2. **Altitude.** Since the atmosphere is mainly heated by conduction from the earth, it can be expected that places nearer to the earth's surface are warmer than those higher up. Thus temperature decreases with increasing height above sea level. This rate of decrease with altitude (lapse rate) is never constant, varying from place to place and from season to season. But for all practical purposes, it may be reckoned that a fall of 1°F occurs with an ascent of 300 feet or 0.6°C per 100 metres. It is usually more in summer than in winter. For example in temperate latitudes, in summer, an ascent of only 280 feet (85 m) will cause the temperature to drop by 1°F, whereas in winter it requires 400 feet (122 m). Similarly, the lapse rate is greater by day than at night, greater on elevated highlands than on level plains. In tropical countries where the sea level temperature is 80°F (26.6°C), a town that is located at a height of 4,500 feet or 1,372 metres (shown as X in Fig. 119) will record a mean temperature of 65°F (18.3°C).

3. **Continentality.** Land surfaces are heated more quickly than water surfaces, because of the higher specific heat of water. In other words, it requires only one-third as much energy to raise the temperature of a given volume of land by 1°F. as it does for an equal volume of water. This accounts for the warmer summers, colder winters and greater range of temperature of continental interiors as compared with maritime districts.

4. **Ocean currents and winds.** Both ocean currents and winds affect temperature by transporting their heat or coldness into adjacent regions (Fig. 120). Ocean currents like the Gulf Stream or the North Atlantic Drift warm the coastal districts of western Europe keeping their ports ice-free. Ports located in the same latitude but washed by cold currents, such as the cold Labrador Current off north-east Canada, are frozen for several months.

Cold currents also lower the summer temperature, particularly when they are carried landwards by onshore winds. On the other hand onshore Westerlies, convey much tropical warm air to temperate coasts, especially in winter. The Westerlies that come to Great Britain and Norway tend to be cool winds in summer and warm winds in winter and are most valuable in moderating the climate.

Local winds, e.g. Fohn, Chinook, Sirocco, Mistral, also produce marked changes in temperature.

5. **Slope, shelter and aspect.** A steep slope experiences a more rapid change in temperature than a gentle one. Mountain ranges that have an eastwest alignment like the Alps show a higher temperature on the *south-facing 'sunny slope'* than the north-facing 'sheltered slope'. The greater insolation of the southern slope is better suited for vine cultivation and has a more flourishing vegetative cover. Consequently, there are more settlements and it is better utilized than the 'shady slope' (Fig. 121). In hilly areas a hot day followed by a calm, cloudless night during which the air cools more rapidly over the higher ground

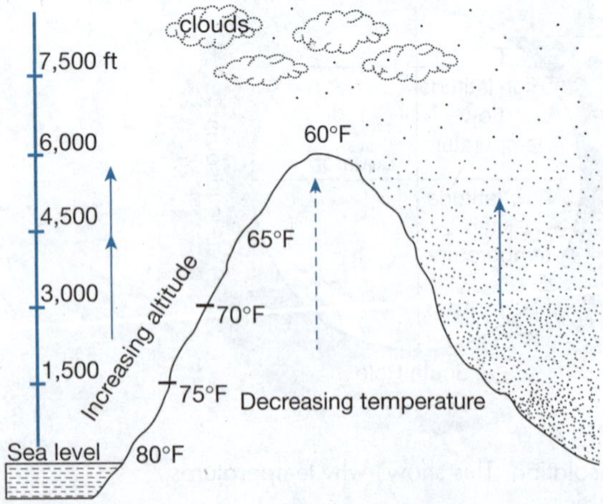

Fig. 119 The lapse rate. The effect of altitude on mean annual temperature in a tropical area

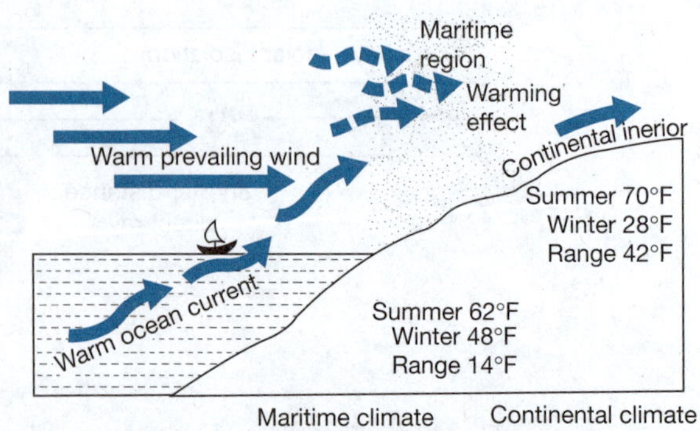

Fig. 120 The warming effect of warm ocean currents and prevailing winds on coastal regions with a Maritime climate in temperate latitudes

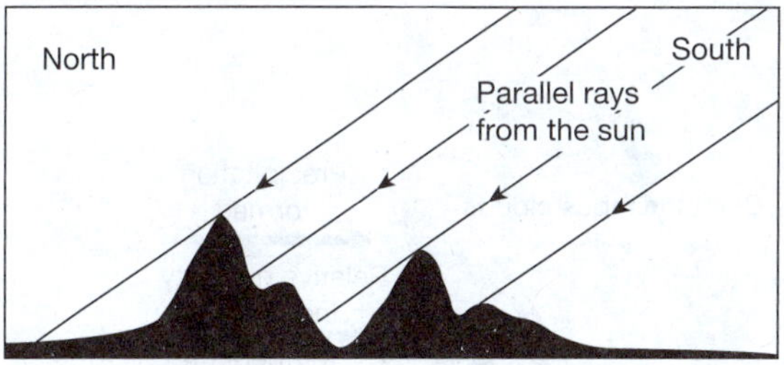

Fig. 121 South-facing slopes are more sunny

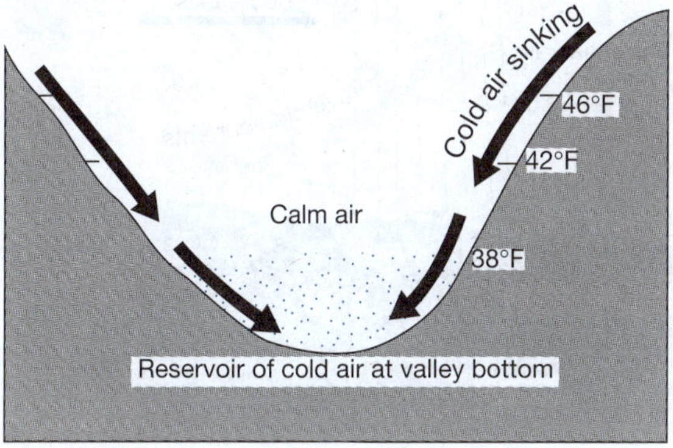

Fig. 122 Temperature inversion at valley bottom on a calm, still night e.g. an Alpine valley in spring

may induce cold, heavy air to flow down the slope and accumulate at the valley bottom pushing the warmer air upwards. The temperature may then be lower in the valley than higher up as the slopes as show in Fig. 122. A reversal of the lapse rate has taken place. This is called a temperature inversion.

6. **Natural vegetation and soil.** There is a definite difference in temperature between forested regions and open ground. The thick foliage of the Amazon jungle cuts off much of the incoming insolation and in many places sunlight never reaches the ground. It is, in fact, cool in the jungle and its shade temperature is a few degrees lower than that of open spaces in corresponding latitudes. During the day trees lose water by evapo-transpiration so that the air above is cooled. Relative humidity increases and mist and fog may form.

Light soils reflect more heat than darker soils which are better absorbers. Such soil differences may give rise to slight variations in the temperature of the region.

As a whole, dry soils like sands are very sensitive to temperature changes, whereas wet soils, like clay, retain much moisture and warm up or cool down more slowly.

Precipitation

Types of Precipitation. If air is sufficiently cooled below dew-point, tiny drops of water vapour will condense around dust particles. When they float about as masses of minute water droplets or ice crystals at a considerable height above sea level, they form clouds – cirrus, cumulus or stratus. When condensation occurs at ground level without necessarily resulting in rain, haze, mist or fog are formed. In higher latitudes or altitudes, where condensation of water vapour may take place in the atmosphere at temperatures below freezing-point, snow falls, either as feathery flakes or individual ice crystals. If the moist air ascends rapidly to the cooler layers of the atmosphere, the water droplets freeze into ice pellets and fall to the earth as hail or hailstones. As more and more super-cooled water drops accumulate around a hailstone, it increases steadily in size; some of them weigh as much as two pounds. In a severe hailstorm the hailstones do great damage to crops and buildings. Very often, the ice-pellets exist as frozen raindrops, melting and re-freezing on their way down; this forms sleet. It is only when the droplets in clouds coalesce into larger drops between 0.2 mm and 6 mm, that rain falls.

Rainfall

Types of Rainfall. There are three major types of rainfall.

1. **Convectional rainfall.** This type of rainfall is most common in regions that are intensely heated, either during the day, as in the tropics, or in the summer, as in temperate interiors. When the earth's surface is heated by conduction, moisture-laden vapour rises because heated air always expands, and becomes lighter. Air rises in a convection current after a prolonged period of intense heating (Fig. 123). In ascending, its water vapour condenses into cumulonimbus clouds with a great vertical extent. This probably reaches its maximum in the afternoon when the convectional system is well developed. Hot, rising air has great capacity for holding moisture, which is abundant in regions of high relative humidity. As the air rises it cools and when saturation point is reached torrential downpours occur, often accompanied by thunder and lightning. The summer showers in temperate regions are equally heavy with

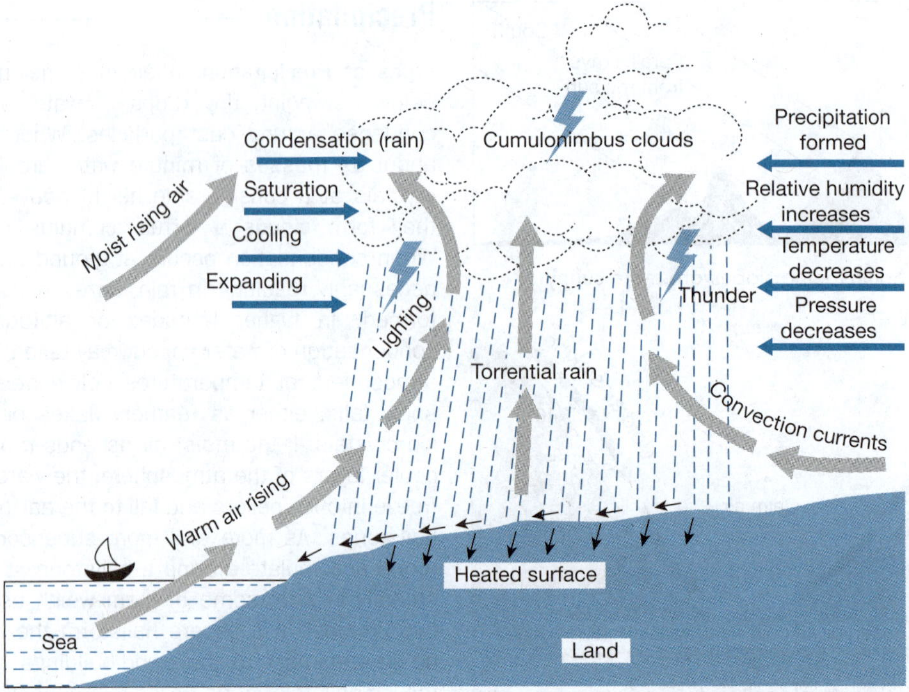

Fig. 123 Convection rainfall

occasional thunderstorms. These downpours may not be entirely useful for agriculture because the rain is so intense that it does not sink into the soil but is drained off almost immediately.

2. **Orographic or relief rain.** Unlike convectional rain which is caused by convection currents, orographic rain is formed wherever moist air is forced to ascend a mountain barrier. It is best developed on the windward slopes of mountains where the prevailing moisture-laden winds come from the sea. The air is compelled to rise as shown in Fig. 124, and is thereby cooled by expansion in the higher altitudes and the subsequent decrease in atmospheric pressure. Further ascent cools the air until the air is completely saturated (relative humidity is 100 per cent). Condensation takes place forming clouds and eventually rain. Since it is caused by the relief of the land, it is also known as relief rain. Much of the precipitation experienced on the windward slopes of the north-east of West Malaysia, western New Zealand, western Scotland and Wales and the Assam hills of the Indian sub-continent, is relief rain.

On descending the leeward slope, a decrease in altitude increases both the pressure and the temperature, the air is compressed and warmed. Consequently, the relative humidity will drop. There is evaporation and little or no precipitation. The area in the lee of the hills is termed the rain shadow area. The effects of rain shadow are felt on the Canterbury Plain of South Island, New Zealand and the western slopes of the Northern and Central Andes and in many other areas.

3. **Cyclonic or frontal rain.** This type of rainfall is independent of relief or convection. It is purely associated with cyclonic activity whether in the temperate regions (depressions) or tropical regions (cyclones). Basically it is due to the convergence (meeting) of two different air masses with different temperatures and other physical properties. As cold air is denser, it tends to remain close to the ground. The warm air is lighter and tends to rise over the cold air as shown in Fig. 125. In ascent, pressure decreases, the air expands and cools, condensation takes place and light showers called cyclonic or frontal rain occur. The heavier and colder air masses eventually pushes up the warmer and lighter air and the sky is clear again.

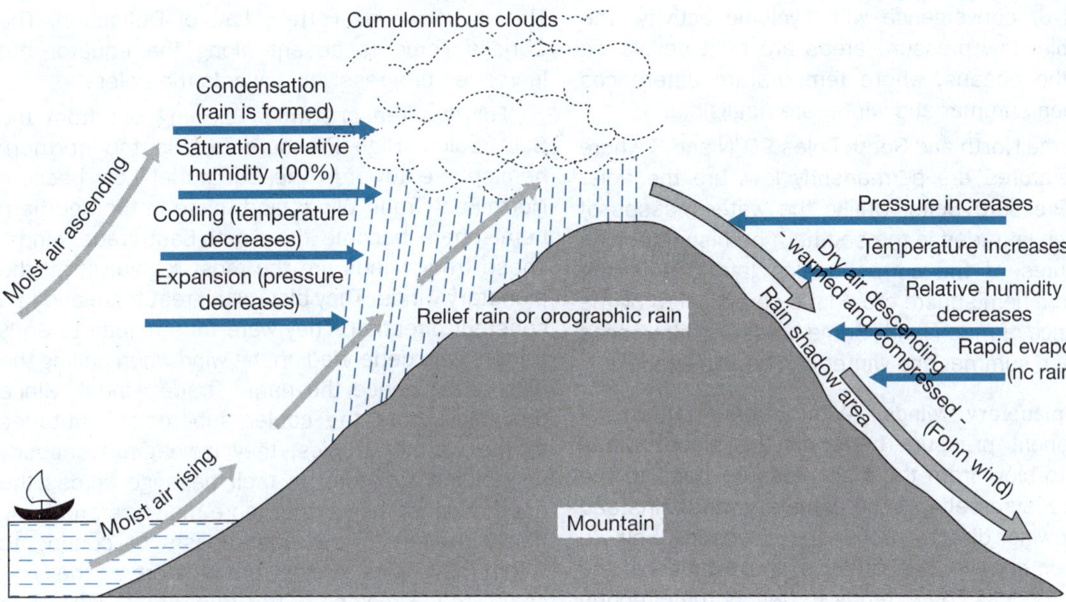

Fig. 124 Orographic or relief rain

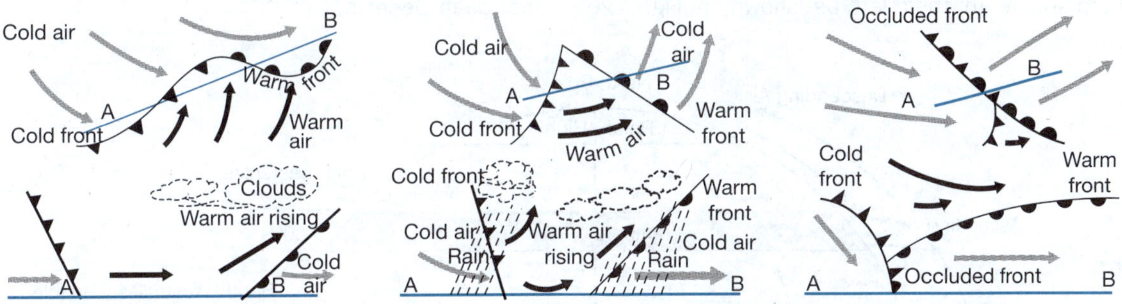

(a) The convergence of warm and cold air

(b) Warm air rises over cold air, cyclonic rain occurs

(c) Cold air eventually pushes up warm air and the sky is clear again

Fig. 125 Cyclonic or frontal rain (depression)

Pressure and Planetary Winds

World pressure belts. In Chapter 11 we studied the circulation of waters in the oceans and noted that they follow a regular pattern, flowing from the poles equatorwards and from the equator polewards. In the same way, there is also a circulation of air over the surface of the earth caused by the differences in pressure.

Along the equator and within 5 degrees north and south, is the Equatorial Low Pressure Belt, where there is intense heating, with expanding air and ascending convection currents. This equatorial belt is often termed the Doldrums, because sailors in the olden days often found themselves becalmed here. It is a zone of wind convergence.

About 30°N and S occur the Sub-Tropical High Pressure Belts where the air is comparatively dry and the winds are calm and light. It is a region of descending air currents or wind divergence and anticyclones. It is frequently referred to as the Horse Latitudes.

Around the latitudes 60°N and S are two Temperate Low Pressure Belts which are also zones of convergence with cyclonic activity. The sub-polar low pressure areas are best developed over the oceans, where temperature differences between summer and winter are negligible.

At the North and South Poles 90°N and S where temperatures are permanently low, are the Polar High Pressure Belts. Unlike the water masses of the high latitudes in the southern hemisphere, high pressures of the corresponding latitudes in the northern hemisphere are a little complicated by the presence of much land. Some pressure differences between summer and winter can be expected.

The planetary winds. Within this pattern of permanent pressure belts on the globe, winds tend to blow from the high pressure belts to the low pressure belts as the planetary winds. Instead of blowing directly from one pressure belt to another, however, the effect of the rotation of the earth (Coriolis Force) tends to deflect the direction of the winds. In the northern hemisphere, winds are deflected to their right, and in the southern hemisphere to their left as shown in Fig. 126. This is known as Ferrel's Law of Deflection. The Coriolis Force is absent along the equator but increases progressively towards the poles.

For this reason, winds blowing out from the Sub-Tropical High Pressure Belt in the northern hemisphere towards the Equatorial Low become North-East Trade Winds and those in the southern hemisphere become the South-East Trade winds. These trade winds are the most regular of all the planetary winds. They blow with great force and in a constant direction. They were thus helpful to early traders who depended on the wind when sailing the high seas; hence the name 'trade winds'. Since they blow from the cooler sub-tropical latitudes to the warmer tropics, they have great capacity for holding moisture: In their passage across the open oceans, they gather more moisture and bring heavy rainfall to the east coasts of continents within the tropics. As they are offshore on the west coast, these regions suffer from great aridity and form the Trade Wind Hot Deserts of the world, e.g. the Sahara, Kalahari, Atacama and the Great Australian Deserts.

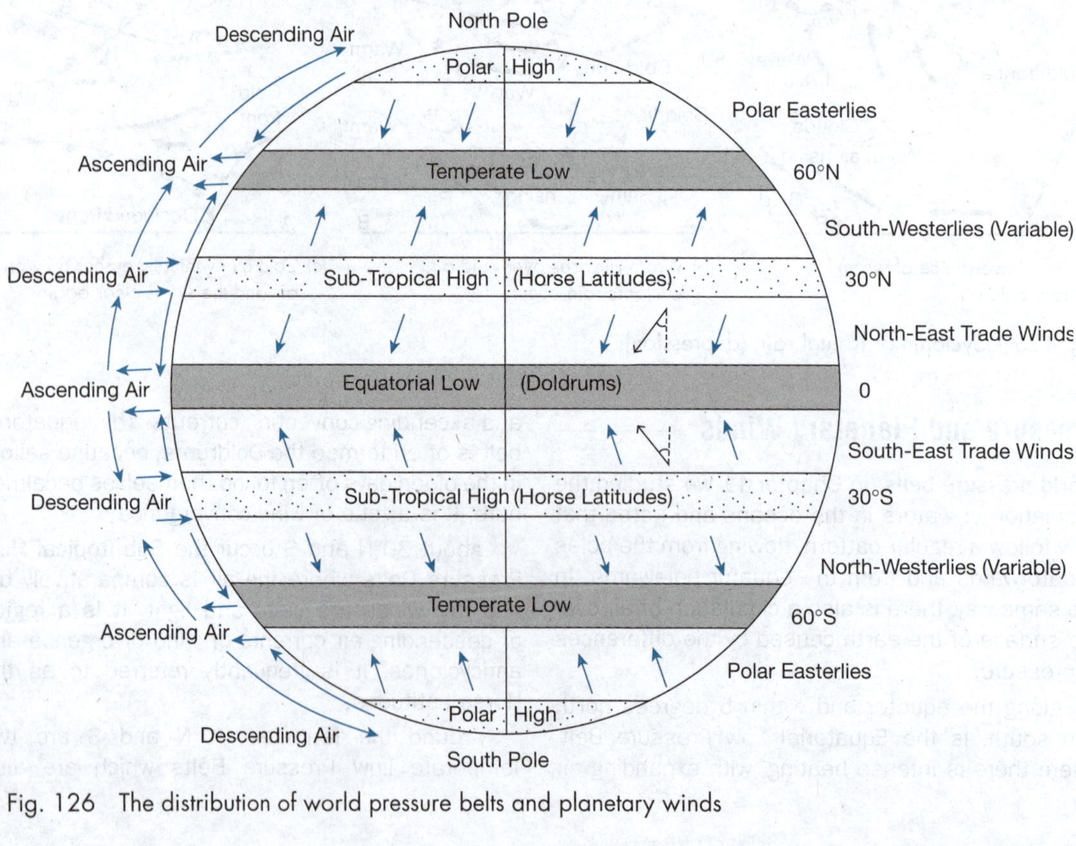

Fig. 126 The distribution of world pressure belts and planetary winds

From the Sub-Tropical High Pressure Belts, winds blow towards the Temperate Low Pressure Belts as the variable Westerlies. Under the effect of the Coriolis Force, they become the South-Westerlies in the northern hemisphere and the North-Westerlies in the southern hemisphere. They are more variable in the northern hemisphere, but they play a valuable role in carrying warm equatorial waters and winds to western coasts of temperate lands. This warming effect and other local pressure differences have resulted in a very variable climate in the temperate zones, dominated by the movements of cyclones and anticyclones. In the southern hemisphere where there is a large expanse of ocean, from 40°S to 60°S, Westerlies blow with much greater force and regularity throughout the year. They bring much precipitation to the western coasts of continents. The weather is damp and cloudy and the seas are violent and stormy. It is thus usual for seafarers to refer to the Westerlies as the *Roaring Forties, Furious Fifties* and *Shrieking or Stormy Sixties,* according to the varying degree of storminess in the latitudes in which they blow.

It must be pointed out that not all the western coasts of the temperate zone receive Westerlies throughout the year. Some of them like California, Iberia, central Chile, southern Africa and southwestern Australia receive Westerlies only in *winter.* This is caused by the *shifting of the wind belts* of such regions which lie approximately between the latitudes 30° and 40°N and S. Due to the earth's inclination, as explained in Chapter 1, the sun is overhead at midday in different parts of the earth at different seasons. The entire system of pressure and wind belts follows the movement of the midday sun. In June when the overhead sun is over the Tropic of Cancer, all the belts move about 5°–10° north of their average position. The 'Mediterranean' parts of the southern continents then come under the influence of the Westerlies and receive rain in June (winter in the southern hemisphere). In the same manner, when the sun is overhead at the Tropic of Capricorn in December, all the belts swing 5°–10° south of their average position. The 'Mediterranean' parts of Europe and California then come under the influence of the Westerlies and receive rain in December (winter in the northern hemisphere). This is illustrated in Fig. 127.

Lastly, mention must be made of the Polar Easterlies which blow out from the Polar High Pressure Belts towards the Temperate Low Pressure Belts. These are extremely cold winds as they come from the tundra and ice-cap regions. They are more regular in the south than in the north.

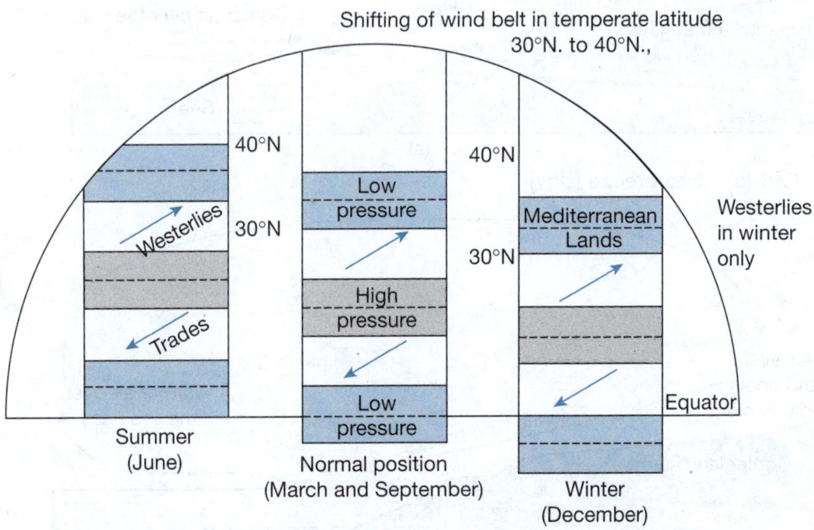

Fig. 127 The shifting of the pressure and wind belts in the northern hemisphere—showing their positions in summer and winter and at the equinoxes

Land and Sea Breezes and Monsoons

Land and sea breezes are, in fact, monsoons on a smaller scale. Both are basically caused by differential heating of land and sea, the former in a diurnal rhythm and the latter in a *seasonal* rhythm.

During the day, the land gets heated up much faster than the sea. Warm air rises forming a region of local low pressure. The sea remains comparatively cool with a higher pressure so a sea breeze blows in from sea to land. Its speed or strength is between 5–20 m.p.h. and it is generally stronger in tropical than temperate regions. Its influence does not normally exceed 15 miles from the coast. It is most deeply felt when one stands facing the sea in a coastal resort.

At night the reverse takes place. As the land cools down much faster than the sea, the cold and heavy air produces a region of local high pressure. The sea conserves its heat and remains quite warm. Its pressure is comparatively low. A land breeze thus blows out from land to sea. Fishermen in the tropics often take advantage of the outgoing land breeze and sail out with it. They return the next morning with the incoming sea breeze, complete with their catch. Land and sea breezes are illustrated in Fig. 128.

In the same way, monsoons are caused. Rapid heating in the hot summer over most parts of India for example induces heated air to rise. The *South-West Monsoon* from the surrounding ocean is attracted by the low pressure over the land and blows in, bringing torrential rain to the sub-continent.

Similarly, in winter when the land is cold, the surrounding seas remain comparatively warm. High pressure is created over Indo-Pakistan and the *North-East Monsoon* blows out from the continent into the Indian Ocean and the Bay of Bengal.

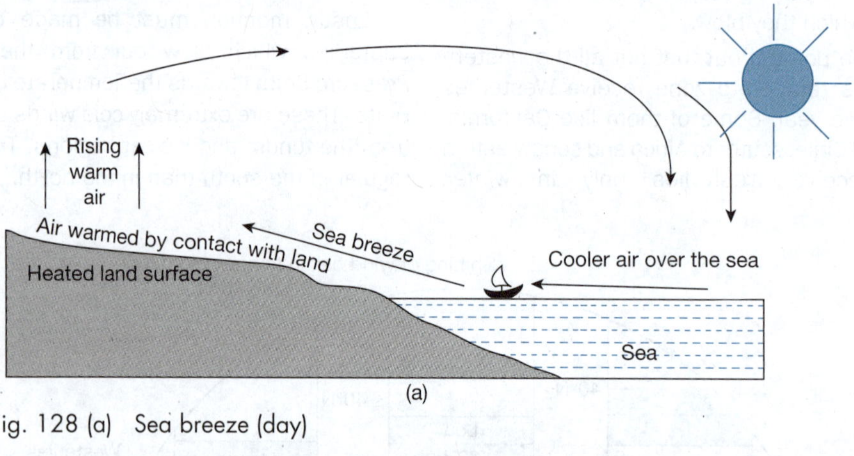

Fig. 128 (a) Sea breeze (day)

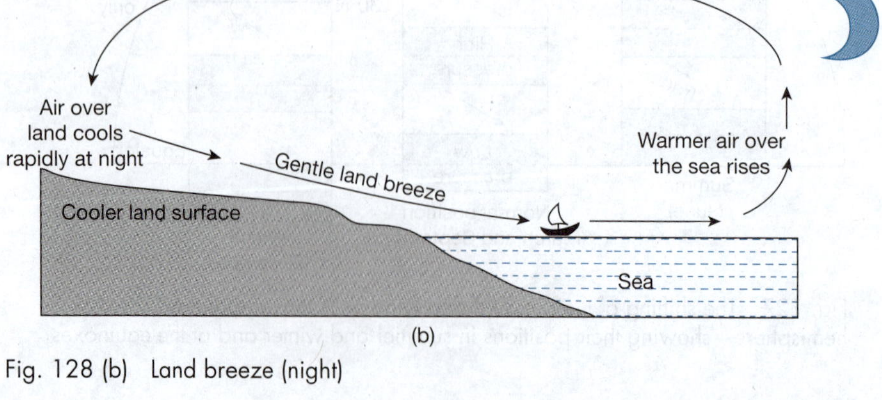

Fig. 128 (b) Land breeze (night)

Fohn Wind or Chinook Wind

Both the Fohn and Chinook winds are dry winds experienced on the leeward side of mountains when descending air becomes compressed with increased pressure. The Fohn wind is experienced in the valleys of the northern Alps, particularly in Switzerland in spring. Chinook winds are experienced on the eastern slopes of the Rockies in USA and Canada in winter.

As illustrated in Fig. 124 air ascending the southern slopes of the Alps expands and cools. Condensation takes place when the air is saturated. Rain and even snow fall on the higher slopes.

In descending the northern slope, the wind experiences an increase in pressure and temperature. The air is compressed and warmed. Most of its moisture is lost and the wind reaches the valley bottom as a dry, hot wind – the Fohn. It may raise the temperature by 15° to 30°F, within an hour! It melts snow and causes *avalanches.* In North America it is called Chinook, meaning *the snow-eater.* But it has its blessings too, it hastens the growth of crops and fruits and thaws the snow-covered pastures. In the Rockies, the Chinook has been known to raise temperature by 35°F within 15 minutes! The occurrence of frequent Chinooks means winter is mild.

Cyclonic Activity

Tropical cyclones, typhoons, hurricanes and tornadoes

All these are different kinds of tropical cyclones. They are well developed low pressure systems into which violent winds blow. Typhoons occur in the China Sea; tropical cyclones in the Indian Ocean; hurricanes in the West Indian islands in the Caribbean; tornadoes in the Guinea lands of West Africa, and the southern USA in which the local name of *Whirlwind* is often applied, and *willy-willies* occur in north-western Australia.

Typhoons occur mainly in regions between 6° and 20° north and south of the equator and are most frequent from July to October. In extent, they are smaller than temperate cyclones and have a diameter of only 50 to 200 miles, but they have a much steeper pressure gradient. Violent winds with a velocity of over 100 m.p.h. are common. The sky is overcast and the torrential downpour is accompanied by thunder and lightning. In the wake of the typhoon, damage is widespread, e.g. in 1922, a typhoon that hurled huge waves on to the Swatow coast drowned 50,000 people. In November 2013, Typhoon Haiyan struck South East Asia, especially the Philippines, causing devastating damage. It had winds reaching 195 miles (314 km) per hour, making it the most powerful typhoon ever recorded. 'Haiyan' is one of the deadliest typhoons in history, claiming the lives of at least 6,300 people in the Philippines alone. According to the Philippines government's report, some 8.7 million people were affected by the storm.

The other tropical cyclones have similar characteristics and differ, perhaps, only in intensity, duration and locality. Hurricanes have calm, rainless centres where the pressure is lowest (about 965 mb.) but around this 'eye', the wind strength exceeds force 12 of the Beaufort Scale (75 m.p.h.) (Fig. 129). Dense dark clouds gather and violent stormy weather lasts for several hours. A terrible hurricane struck Barbados in the West Indies in 1780, which nearly destroyed the whole island, tearing down buildings and uprooting trees. More than 20,000 inhabitants were reported dead. Hurricane Mitch was acknowledged as the second deadliest Atlantic hurricane ever recorded, following the Great Hurricane of 1780. In late October 1998, it brought devastating impacts to Central America, especially Honduras and Nicaragua. With peak wind speeds reaching 180 miles (290 km) per hour, the storm had a catastrophic impact. The

Typhoon Haiyan in November 2013 as it approaches Vietnam in the South China Sea

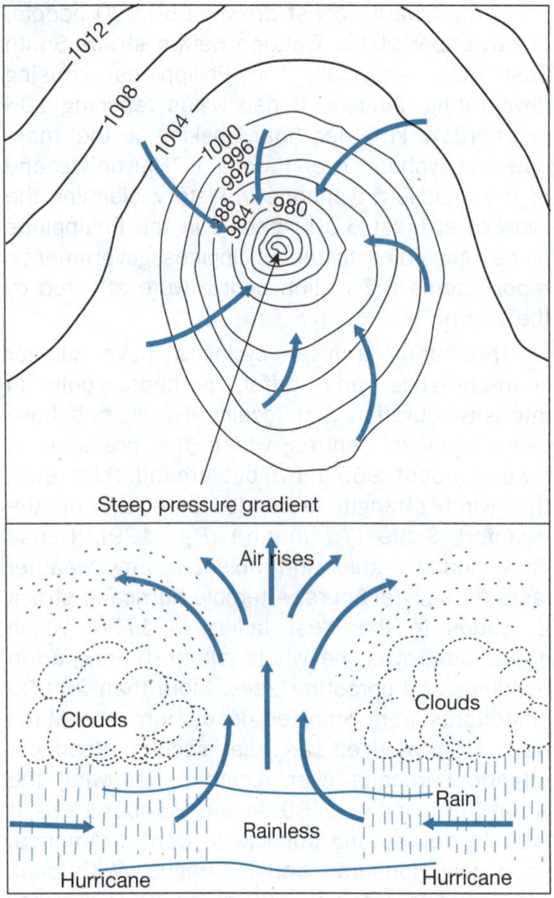

Fig. 129 A tropical cyclone—a hurricane in the West Indies

death toll surpassed 11,000 people, primarily affecting Honduras and Nicaragua, but also causing fatalities in Guatemala, El Salvador, Mexico, and Costa Rica. Additionally, thousands of individuals were reported missing after the hurricane's passage.

Tornadoes are small but very violent tropical and sub-tropical cyclones in which the air is spiraling at a tremendous speed of as much as 500 m.p.h.! A tornado appears as a dark funnel cloud 250 to 1,400 feet in diameter. As a tornado passes through a region, it writhes and twists, causing complete devastation within the limits of its passage. There is such a great difference in pressure that houses virtually explode. Tornadoes are most frequent in spring but can occur at almost any time. Fortunately they are not common in many countries and their destructive effects are confined to a small area. Tornadoes are most typical of the USA and occur mainly in the Mississippi basin.

Cyclones. These are better known as depressions and are confined to temperate latitudes. The lowest pressure is in the centre and the isobars, as shown in climatic charts, are close together. Depressions vary from 150 to 2,000 miles in extent. They remain quite stationary or move several hundred miles in a day. The approach of a cyclone is characterised by a fall in barometric reading, dull sky, oppressive air and strong winds. Rain or snow falls and the weather is generally bad. Winds blow inwards into regions of low pressure in the centre, circulating in anticlockwise direction in the northern hemisphere and clockwise in the southern hemisphere (Fig. 130 a).

Precipitation resulting from cyclonic activities is due to the convergence of warm tropical air and cold polar air. Fronts are developed and condensation takes place, forming either rain, snow or sleet.

Anticyclones. These are the opposite of cyclones, with high pressure in the centre and the isobars far apart. The pressure gradient is gentle and winds are light. Anticyclones normally herald fine weather. Skies are clear, the air is calm and temperatures are high in summer but cold in winter. In winter intense cooling of the lower atmosphere may result in thick fogs. Anticyclonic conditions may last for days or weeks and then fade out quietly. Winds in anticyclones blow outwards and are also subject to deflection, but they blow clockwise in the northern hemisphere and anticlockwise in the southern hemisphere (Fig. 130 b).

Chaos caused by a typhoon in Hong Kong

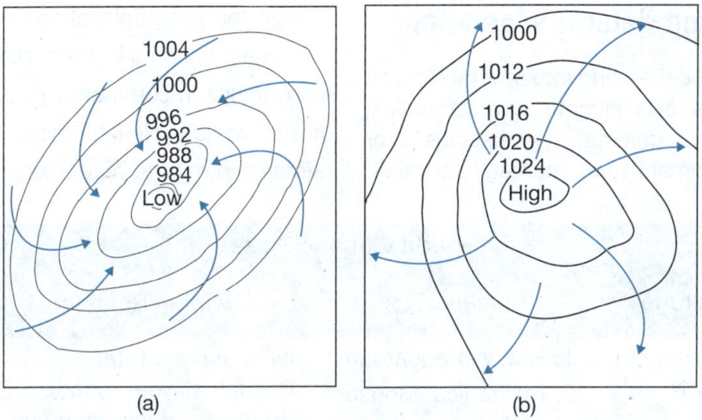

Fig. 130 (a) A cyclone in the northern hemisphere (close isobars, anticlockwise winds)
(b) An anticyclone in the northern hemisphere (well-spaced isobars, winds blow in clockwise direction)

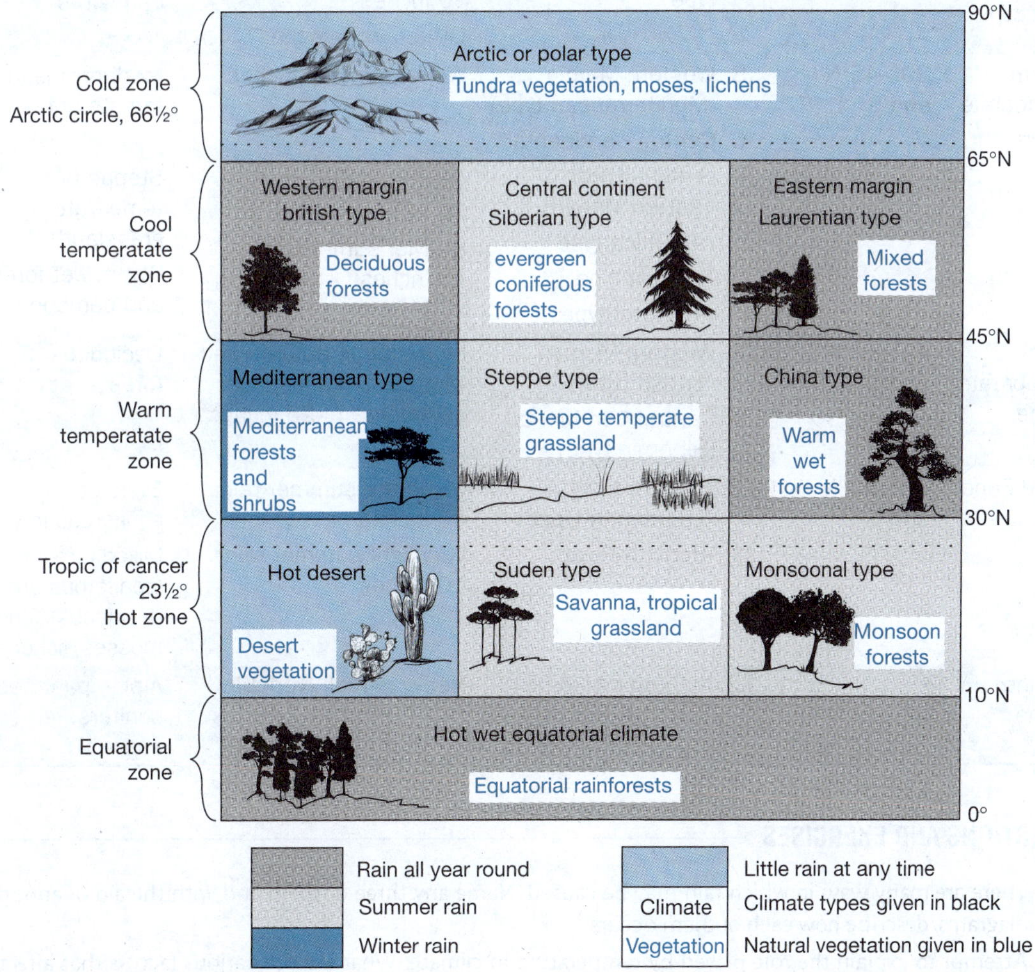

Fig. 131 Scheme of the world's climatic types (with seasonal rainfall and natural vegetation also indicated)

Climatic Types and Natural Vegetation —

It is necessary to divide the world into several climatic zones, each with its own climatic characteristics, natural vegetation (forests, grasslands or deserts), crops, animals and human activities. Though the geographical characteristics may not be absolutely uniform in each climatic type, they have many things in common. Fig. 131 gives the scheme of the world's climatic types with their seasonal rainfall and natural vegetation.

World Climatic Types

Climatic Zone	Latitude	Climatic Type	Rainfall Regime	Natural Vegetation
Equatorial Zone	(approximate) 0°–10°N and S	1. Hot, wet equatorial 2. (a) Tropical Monsoon (b) Tropical Marine	(with approx. total) Rainfall all year round: 80 inches Heavy summer rain: 60 inches	Equatorial rainforests Monsoon forests
Hot Zone	10°–30°N and S	3. Sudan Type 4. Desert: (a) Saharan type (b) Midlatitude type	Much summer rain: 70 inches Rain mainly in summer: 30 inches Little rain: 5 inches	Savanna (tropical grassland) Desert vegetation and scrub
Warm Temperate Zone	30°–45°N and S	5. Western Margin (Mediterranean type) 6. Central Continental (Steppe type) 7. Eastern Margin: (a) China type (b) Gulf type (c) Natal type	Winter rain: 35 inches Light summer rain: 20 inches Heavier summer rain: 45 inches	Mediterranean forests and shrub Steppe or temperate grassland Warm, wet forests and bamboo
Cool Temperate Zone	45°–65°N and S	8. Western Margin (British type) 9. Central Continental (Siberian type)	More rain in autumn and winter: 30 inches Light summer rain: 25 inches	Deciduous forests
Cold Zone	65°–90°N and S	10. Eastern Margin (Laurentian type) 11. Arctic or Polar	Moderate summer rain: 40 inches Very light summer rain: 10 inches	Evergreen coniferous forests Mixed forests (coniferous and deciduous) Tundra, mosses, lichens
Alpine Zone		12. Mountain climate	Heavy rainfall (variable)	Alpine pastures, conifers, fern, snow.

QUESTIONS AND EXERCISES

1. There are many ways in which rain may be caused. Name any three of them and with the aid of annotated diagrams, describe how each of them occurs.
2. Attempt to explain the role played by temperature in climate. What are the various factors that affect the distribution of temperature in the world?

3. Account for the occurrence of any three of the following. Make use of any relevant sketches.
   (a) the planetary winds
   (b) land and sea breezes
   (c) frontal rain
   (d) extremes of temperature in continental interiors
   (e) Horse Latitudes
4. Distinguish the differences between
   (a) troposphere and stratosphere
   (b) steady Trade Winds and variable Westerlies
   (c) insolation and radiation
   (d) tornado and hurricane
5. Explain any three of the following statements.
   (a) Anticyclones are more frequent in summer.
   (b) Without water vapour and dust in the atmosphere, there would be no weather.
   (c) Sleet is frozen rain.
   (d) Temperature decreases with increasing altitude.
   (e) Winds in the northern hemisphere are always deflected to their right.
6. (a) Name three different types of rainfall and, with the aid of diagrams, show clearly how the rainfall is caused in each case.
   (b) Describe the instrument used to measure the rainfall of a place, and the way in which the information so obtained is used to calculate the mean annual rainfall.
7. Give reasons for the following:
   (a) Fog at sea often experienced near the Californian coast.
   (b) Many of the hot deserts of the world lie on the west side of a continent either between 20°N and 30°N or between 20°S and 30°S.
   (c) The surface waters in the north-west Atlantic are cooler than surface waters in the north-east Atlantic.
8. With the aid of diagrams, and by reference to actual examples, describe *three* of the following and state clearly how *each* of the three has been caused:
   (a) land and sea breezes
   (b) a rain shadow area
   (c) Fohn (Chinook) winds
   (d) hurricanes (typhoons)

15 The Hot, Wet Equatorial Climate

Distribution

The equatorial, hot, wet climate is found between 5° and 10° north and south of the equator. Its greatest extent is found in the lowlands of the Amazon, the Congo, Malaysia and the East Indies. Further away from the equator, the influence of the onshore Trade Winds, gives rise to a modified type of equatorial climate with *monsoonal influences.* Within the tropics, the equatorial highlands have a distinctively cooler climate, modified by altitude, such as the Cameron Highlands in Malaysia, the Northern Andes, and the Kenyan Highlands in East Africa. Fig. 132 shows the regions of the world which experience the hot, wet equatorial climate.

Climate

Temperature. The most outstanding feature of the equatorial climate is its great uniformity of temperature throughout the year. The mean monthly temperatures are always around 80°F. with very little variation. There is no winter. Cloudiness and heavy precipitation help to moderate the daily temperature, so that even at the equator itself, the climate is not unbearable. In addition, regular land and sea breezes assist in maintaining a truly equable climate. The diurnal range of temperature is small, and so is the annual range.

Fig. 133 (a) and 133 (b) show the ryhthm of climate experienced in two different equatorial regions, one on a lowland (Kuala Lumpur) and the other on a highland (Bogota). The uniformity in temperature, is apparent at once. Kuala Lumpur has its hottest month with 80°F (26.6°C), and its coolest month with 78°F (25.5°C). The annual range is not more than 2°F or 1.1°C. The mean monthly temperatures for Bogota are comparatively low because of its altitudinal differences. It is located in the Andes, 8,730 feet (2,661 m) above sea level.

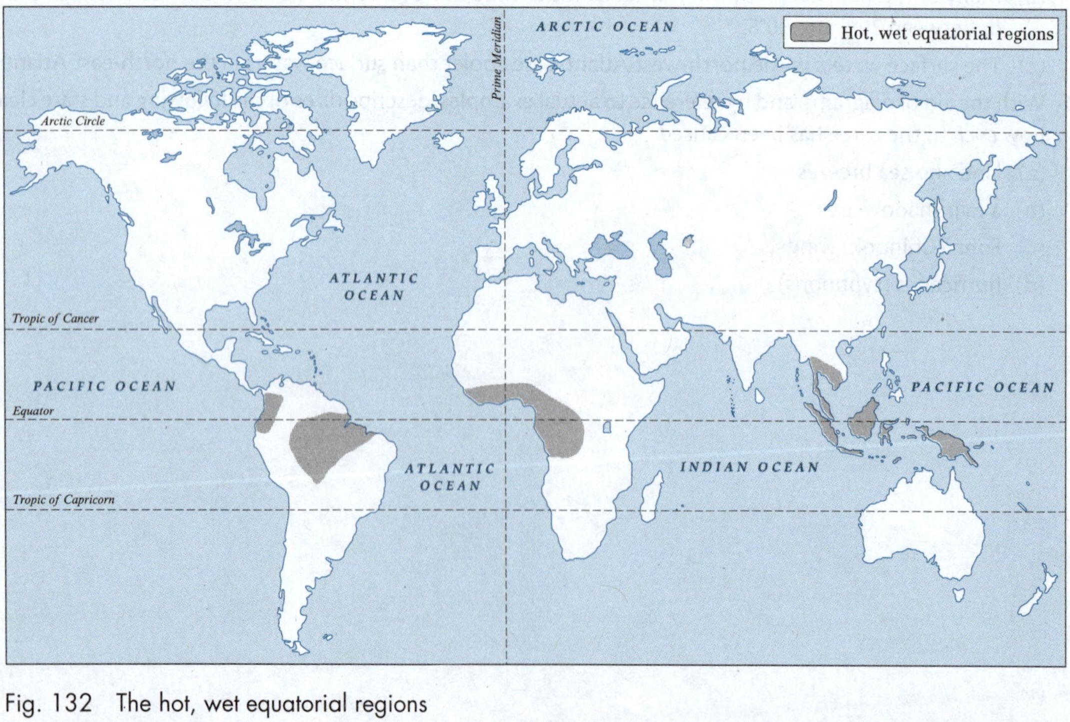

Fig. 132 The hot, wet equatorial regions

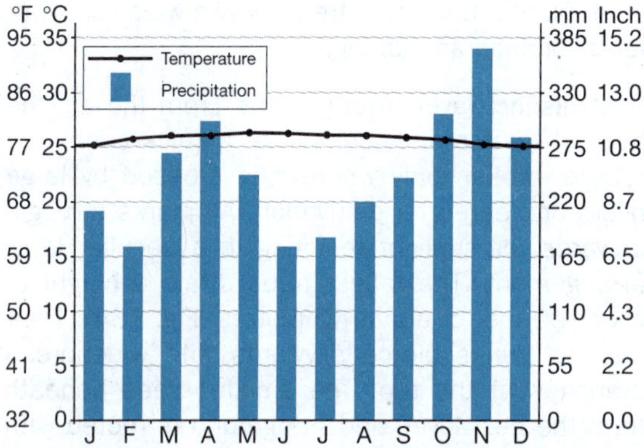

		J	F	M	A	M	J	J	A	S	O	N	D
Avg. Temp.	°C	25.1	25.7	26	26.1	26.3	26.2	26.1	26	25.8	25.7	25.2	25.1
	°F	77.2	78.3	78.8	78.9	79.3	79.2	78.9	78.8	78.5	78.2	77.4	77.2
Precip.	mm	209	174	268	300	246	174	183	219	243	305	373	284
	in	8	6	10	11	9	6	7	8	9	12	14	11

Data: 1991–2021

Place	Kuala Lumpur (3°N, 102°E)
Altitude	54 m or 177 feet
Annual precipitation	2,981 mm or 117.4 inch
Annual temperature range	2.1°F (79.3°F – 77.2°F) or 1.2°C (26.3°C – 25.1°C)

Fig. 133 (a) Equatorial Climate—a lowland station

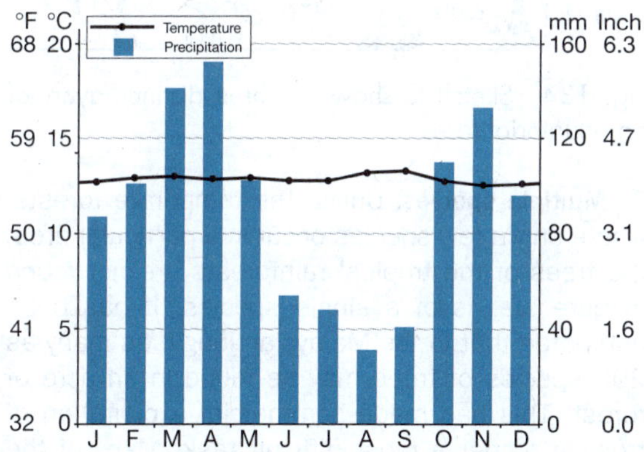

		J	F	M	A	M	J	J	A	S	O	N	D
Avg. Temp.	°C	12.7	12.9	13	12.9	12.9	12.8	12.8	13.2	13.3	12.7	12.5	12.6
	°F	54.9	55.3	55.4	55.2	55.2	55	55	55.8	56	54.9	54.6	54.7
Precip.	mm	81	101	141	152	103	54	48	31	41	110	133	96
	in	3	3	5	5	4	2	1	1	1	4	5	3

Data: 1991–2021

Place	Bogota (4°, 38′S, 74° 15′W)
Altitude	2,586 m or 8,485 feet
Annual precipitation	1,091 mm or 43.0 inch
Annual temperature range	1.4°F (56.0°F – 54.6°F) or 0.8°C (13.3°C – 12.5°C)

Fig. 133 (b) Equatorial Climate—a highland station

Its annual range is equally small, also 2°F or 1.1°C (59°F–57°F or 15°C–13.9°C). The dotted line in the temperature graph shows its temperature reduced to sea level. Statistics taken from the various equatorial stations indicate that the annual range of temperature is small: Singapore, 2.8°F or 1.6°C, Jakarta 2.7°F or 1.5°C, Quito 0.6°F or 1.1°C, Colombo 3.0°F or 1.7°C. Over the oceans, the range is even smaller, e.g. Majuro in the Marshall Islands in the Pacific Ocean records a range in temperature of only 0.6°F or 0.3°C.

Precipitation. Precipitation is heavy, between 60 inches and 100 inches, and well distributed throughout the year. There is no month without rain, and a distinct dry season like those of the Savanna or the Tropical Monsoon Climates, is absent. Instead, there are two periods of maximum rainfall, in April and October as shown in Fig. 133 (a) and 133 (b), which occur shortly after the equinoxes. Least rain falls at the June and December solstices. The double rainfall peaks coinciding with the equinoxes are a characteristic feature of equatorial climates not found in any other type of climate. But this simple pattern may be upset by local conditions, e.g. Kota Bharu, Kelantan (Malaysia) receives most of its rainfall from the North-East Monsoon at the end of the year and Yangon (Myanmar), from the South-West Monsoon between June and September. As one goes further north and south of the equator, particularly in coastal districts open to the influences of the trades, the tendency is towards a monsoonal pattern with the heaviest rainfall coming in the summer months, i.e. June, July and August in the northern hemisphere and December, January and February in the southern hemisphere.

Due to the great heat in the equatorial belt, mornings are bright and sunny. There is much evaporation and convectional air currents are set up, followed by heavy downpours of convectional rain in the afternoons from the towering cumulonimbus clouds (see Chapter 13). Thunder and lightning often accompany the *torrential showers* and the amount of rainfall recorded in one single afternoon may be as much as the deserts receive for the entire year! Besides the convectional rainfall, mountainous regions also experience much orographic or relief rain. In addition, there are some intermittent showers from cyclonic atmospheric disturbances caused by the convergence of air currents in the Doldrums.

Forested slopes of Mt. Kinabalu. The lower slopes have been cleared in places for cultivation and settlements. The vegetation on the higher slopes gradually changes in response to lower temperatures

The relative humidity is constantly high (over 80 per cent) making one feel 'sticky' and uncomfortable. The monotonous climate, oppressive and enervating, taxes one's mental alertness and physical capability, though along the coasts refreshing sea breezes do bring some relief. As a result, most of the white settlers, whose bodies are attuned to cooler and more varied conditions take to the cooler highlands whenever they can.

Equatorial Vegetation

High temperature and abundant rainfall in the equatorial regions support a luxuriant type of vegetation – the tropical rainforest. In the Amazon lowlands, the forest is so dense and so complete in its vegetational extravagance that a special term selvas is used. Unlike the temperate regions, the growing season here is all the year round – seeding, flowering, fruiting and decaying do not take place in a seasonal pattern, so some trees may be in flower while others only a few yards away may be bearing fruit. There is neither drought nor cold to check growth in any part of the year. The characteristic features of the equatorial vegetation may be summarized as follows.

1. **A great variety of vegetation.** The equatorial vegetation comprises a multitude of evergreen trees that yield tropical hardwood, e.g. mahogany, ebony, greenheart, cabinet woods and dyewoods. There are smaller palm trees, climbing plants like the lianas or rattan which may be hundreds of feet long and epiphytic and parasitic plants that live on other plants. Under the trees grow a wide variety of ferns, orchids and lalang.

2. **A distinct layer arrangement.** From the air, the tropical rainforest appears like a thick canopy of foliage, broken only where it is crossed by large rivers or cleared for cultivation. All plants struggle upwards for sunlight resulting in a peculiar layer arrangement. The tallest trees attain a height of over 150 feet or about 45 metres (Fig. 134). Their slender trunks pierce skywards with widespread branches at the top. The smaller trees beneath form the next layer, and the ground is rooted with ferns and *herbaceous* plants which can tolerate shade. Because the trees cut out most of the sunlight the undergrowth is not dense.

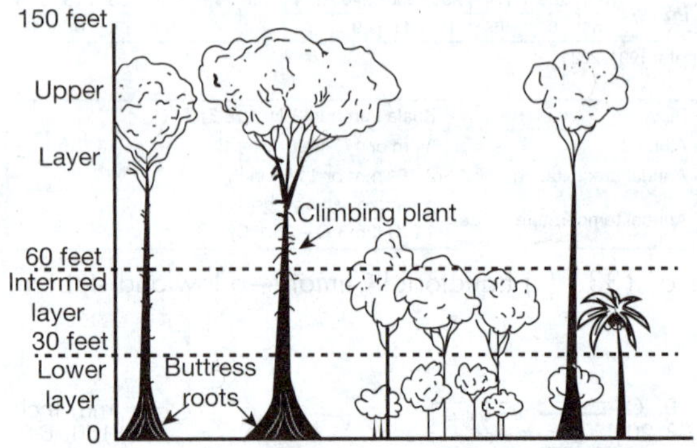

Fig. 134 Sketch to show the three distinct layers of an equatorial forest

3. **Multiple species.** Unlike the temperate forests, where only a few species occur in a particular area, the trees of the tropical rainforests are not *found in* pure stands of a single species. It has been estimated that in the Malaysian jungle as many as 200 species of trees may be found in an acre of forest. This has made commercial exploitation of tropical timber a most difficult task. Many of the tropical hardwoods do not float readily on water and this makes haulage an expensive matter. It is therefore not surprising that many tropical countries are net timber importers!

4. **Forest Clearings.** Many parts of the virgin tropical rainforests have been cleared either for *lumbering or shifting cultivation.* When these clearings are abandoned, less luxuriant secondary forests, called belukar in Malaysia, spring up. These are characterized by short trees and very dense undergrowth. In the coastal areas and brackish swamps, mangrove forest thrive.

Life and Development in the Equatorial Regions

The equatorial regions are generally sparsely populated. In the forests most primitive people live as *hunters and collectors* and the more advanced ones practice shifting cultivation. Food is so abundant in such a habitat that many people worry very little about the life of the next day. There are numerous animals, birds and reptiles that can be hunted to serve the needs of the community. The ever flowing rivers and streams provide an inexhaustible supply of fish that the people spear or trap. From the forest, they gather leaves, fruits, nuts and other forest products. In the Amazon basin the Indian tribes collect wild rubber, in the Congo Basin the Pygmies gather nuts and in the jungles of Malaysia the Orang Asli make all sorts of cane products and sell them to people in villages and towns. In the clearings for shifting cultivation, crops like manioc (tapioca), yams, maize, bananas and groundnuts are grown. When the fertility is exhausted, the clearing is abandoned and they move on to a new plot. Such farming practices are becoming more and more widespread even among backward tribes.

With the coming of the Europeans, many large plantations have been established, especially in Java, Sumatra, Malaysia, West Africa and Central America. The climate has proved to be very favourable for the cultivation of certain crops that are highly valued in the industrial West. The most outstanding is natural rubber, called *hevea brasiliensis.* Though it was first discovered in its wild state as *Para rubber* in the Amazon basin, it has since been transplanted to other parts of the equatorial lands and is grown very profitably on large estates. Malaysia and Indonesia are the leading producers, each accounting for more than a third of the world production. The home country, Brazil exports practically no natural rubber. The problems of tree diseases and the lack of commercial organization of the Indians in the Amazon lowlands have brought about this unexpected 'shift' of rubber cultivation.

Another tropical crop that has achieved an amazing success is cocoa. It is most extensively cultivated in West Africa, bordering the Gulf of Guinea. The two most important producers are Ghana and Nigeria. There is a keen demand for the crop and acreages are rapidly on the increase. Most of the crop leaves West Africa for Europe or North America for the cocoa and chocolate industry. From the same area another crop, oil palm, has done equally well and many countries outside Africa have now taken to its cultivation. Other crops that have been found suitable for the hot, wet equatorial climate and are extensively cultivated are coconuts, sugar, coffee, tea, tobacco, spices, cinchona, bananas, pineapples and sago.

Harvesting oil palm fruits in Malaysia

Factors Affecting the Development of Equatorial Regions

1. **Equatorial climate and health.** Under conditions of excessive heat and high humidity, people are subject to serious physical and mental handicaps. They perspire profusely and lose vigour and energy in such an enervating environment. They expose themselves to such dangers as sunstroke and to such diseases as malaria and yellow fever. Consequently, their capacity for active work is greatly reduced and their resistance to diseases is much weakened. Unless there is adequate provision for satisfactory sanitation, physical and mental health are bound to be affected. Nowadays malaria eradication schemes are in progress in most tropical areas and vaccines have been developed to counteract other diseases.

2. **Prevalence of bacteria and insect pests.** The hot, wet climate which stimulates rapid plant growth, also encourages the spread of insects and pests. As germs and bacteria are more easily transmitted through moist air, equatorial conditions are ideal for the survival of such organisms. Insects and pests not only spread diseases but are injurious to crops. They plague both men and animals.

Market gardening in Malaysia. In many parts of the equatorial zone intensive farming, to supply city-dwellers with vegetables, is profitable.

3. **Jungle hinders development and maintenance.** The jungle is so luxuriant that it is quite a problem to clear a small patch of it and even more difficult to maintain it. Lalang (tall grass) and thick undergrowth spring up as soon as the shade trees are cut and unless they are weeded at regular intervals, they may *choke crops* and overwhelm estates. In the same way, roads and railways constructed through the equatorial lands have to cut through forests, dense thickets and swamps and those who build and maintain them encounter wild animals, poisonous snakes and insects. Once completed, they have to be maintained at a *high cost*. Many remote parts of the Amazon basin, the Congo and Borneo are without modern communication lines. The rivers form the only natural highways.

4. **Rapid deterioration of tropical soil.** It is a misconception that tropical soils are rich. In its virgin, untouched state, due to heavy leaf-fall and the decomposition of leaves by bacteria, a thick mantle of humus makes the soil fairly fertile. This is clear from the shifting cultivators' heavy croppings in their newly cleared ladangs. But once the humus is used and the natural vegetative cover is removed, the torrential downpours soon wash out most of the soil nutrients. The soil deteriorates rapidly with subsequent soil erosion and soil impoverishment One may quote the Indonesian island of Java as an exception, because of its rich volcanic ashes and the energetic local people. In Malaysia, Singapore and eastern Brazil much progress has also been made in the development of the tropical lands through systematic planning and the will of the people to succeed.

Difficulties in lumbering and livestock farming. As mentioned earlier, though the tropics have great potential in timber resources, commercial extraction is difficult. The trees do not occur in homogenous stands, there are no frozen surfaces to facilitate logging and the tropical hardwoods are sometimes too heavy to float in the rivers, even if these flow in the desired directions.

Livestock farming is greatly handicapped by an absence of meadow grass, even on the highlands. The few animals like bullocks or buffaloes are kept mainly as beasts of burden. Their yield in milk or beef is well below those of the cattle in the temperate grasslands. The grass is so tall and coarse that it is not nutritious. In Africa, domesticated animals are attacked by tsetse flies that cause *ngana*, a deadly disease.

QUESTIONS AND EXERCISES

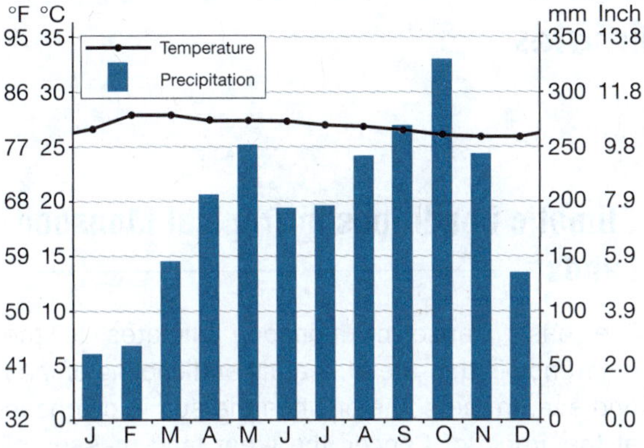

(a) Alor Setar

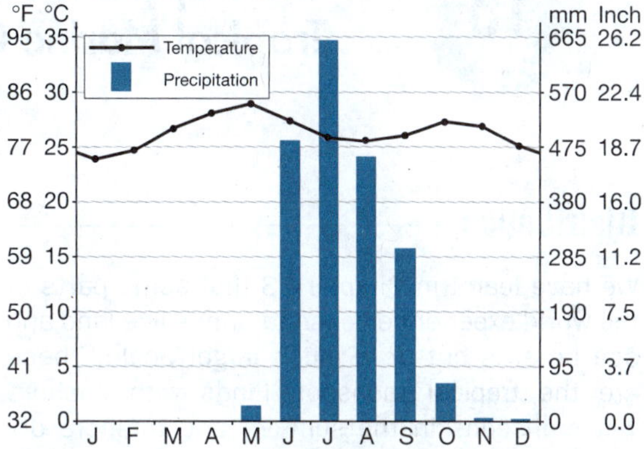

(b) Mumbai

1. The above two graphs taken from two different stations, Alor Setar in West Malaysia and Mumbai in India, show two different types of climate.
   (a) Name the type of climate experienced in each of the stations.
   (b) Describe the major differences in temperature and precipitation between the two stations.
   (c) In what ways are the rainfall of the two stations similar?
2. What type of climate is characterized by two periods of maximum rainfall? Explain why this is so. What local conditions may upset this normal pattern?
3. Outline the characteristics of the equatorial climate and vegetation and for any *one* equatorial region describe how the inhabitants overcome some of the difficulties posed by the environment.
4. Write brief notes on any *three* of the following statements about the equatorial regions.
   (a) Cloudiness and heavy precipitation moderate the temperature of the equatorial regions.
   (b) The most prominent feature of the tropical rainforest is its layer arrangement.
   (c) Large-scale livestock farming is unknown in the hot, wet equatorial areas.
   (d) The greatest single drawback to commercial lumbering in equatorial regions is inaccessibility.
   (e) The equatorial environment is best suited to plantation agriculture.
5. On the map of the world, locate the hot, wet equatorial forests. Relate their vegetational characteristics to the climate of the regions.

16 The Tropical Monsoon and Tropical Marine Climates

Distribution

We have learnt in Chapter 13 that some parts of the world experience seasonal winds like land and sea breezes but on a much larger scale. These are the tropical monsoon lands with onshore wet monsoons in the summer and offshore dry monsoons in the winter. They are best developed in the Indian sub-continent, Myanmar, Thailand, Laos, Cambodia, parts of Vietnam and south China and northern Australia. Outside this zone, the climate is modified by the influence of the onshore Trade Winds all the year round, and has a more evenly distributed rainfall. Such a climate, better termed the Tropical Marine Climate, is experienced in Central America. West Indies, north-eastern Australia, the Philippines, parts of East Africa, Madagascar, the Guinea Coast and eastern Brazil (Fig. 135).

Climatic Conditions in Tropical Monsoon Lands

The basic cause of monsoon climates is the difference in the rate of heating and cooling of land and sea. In the summer when the sun is overhead at the Tropic of Cancer, the great land masses of the northern hemisphere are heated. Central Asia, backed by the lofty Himalayan ranges, is more than 15°F hotter than its normal temperature and a region of intense low pressure is set up. The seas, which warm up much slower, remain comparatively cool. At the same time, the southern hemisphere experiences winter, and a region of high pressure is set up in the continental interior of Australia. Winds blow outwards as the South-east monsoon, to Java, and after crossing the equator are drawn towards the continental low pressure area reaching the

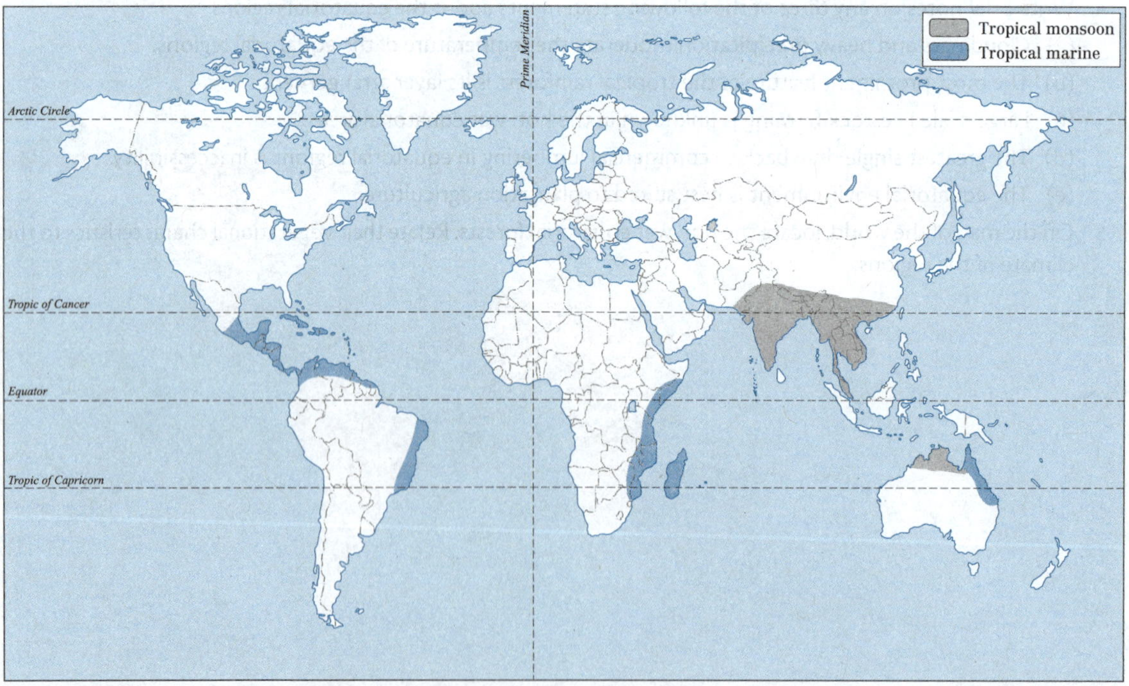

Fig. 135 The tropical monsoon and marine regions

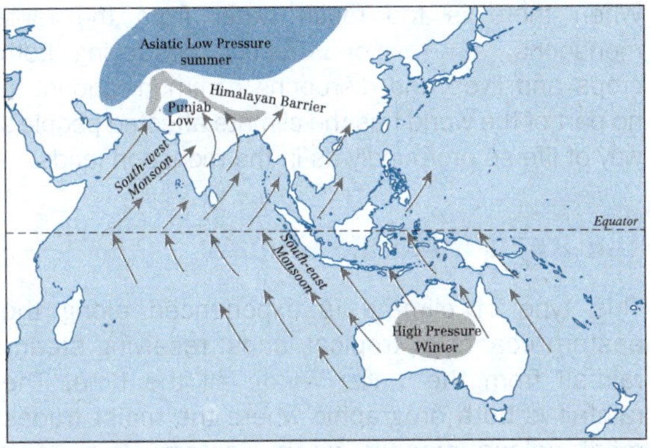

Fig. 136 (a) Summer conditions in Asia—South-west monsoon in Indo-Pakistan is onshore in the rainy season (July)

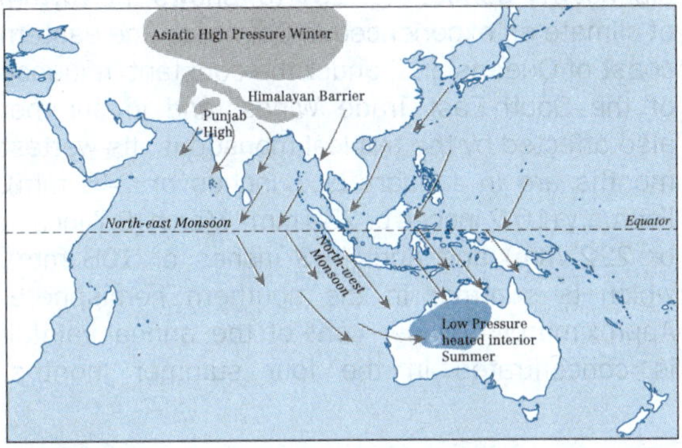

Fig. 136 (b) Winter conditions in Asia—North-east monsoon in Indo-Pakistan is offshore in the cool, dry season (January)

Indian sub-continent as the South-west monsoon, as shown in Fig. 136 (a).

In the winter, conditions are reversed. The sun is overhead at the Tropic of Capricorn, central Asia is extremely cold, resulting in rapid cooling of the land. A region of high pressure is created with outblowing winds – the North-east monsoon. On crossing the equator, the winds are attracted to the low pressure centre in Australia and arrive in northern Australia as the North-west monsoon (Fig. 136 (b)). In other parts of the world which experience a tropical monsoon climate a similar seasonal reversal of wind directions occurs.

The Seasons of Tropical Monsoon Climate

In regions like the Indian sub-continent which have a true Tropical Monsoon Climate, *three* distinct seasons are distinguishable, as illustrated in Fig. 137 (a).

1. **The cool, dry season (October to February).** Temperatures are low 76°F (24.4°C) in Mumbai and only 50°F (10°C) in Punjab, with heavy sinking air. Frosts may occur at night in the colder north. The centre of high pressure is over the Punjab. Outblowing dry winds, the North-east monsoon, bring little or no rain to the Indian sub-continent. However, a small amount of rain falls in Punjab from cyclonic sources and this is vital for the survival of winter cereals. Where the North-east monsoon blows over the Bay of Bengal it acquires moisture and thus brings rain to the south-eastern tip of the peninsula at this time of the year. For instance, in Chennai 50 inches (1,270 mm) of rain falls during October and November, accounting for half its annual rainfall.

2. **The hot dry season (March to mid-June).** As can be seen from Fig. 137 (a), the temperature rises sharply with the sun's northward shift to the Tropic of Cancer. Mumbai has a mean May temperature of 84°F (29°C) which is considered moderate, for many parts of India are even hotter. The heat is so great that schools and colleges are closed. The stifling heat and the low relative humidity make

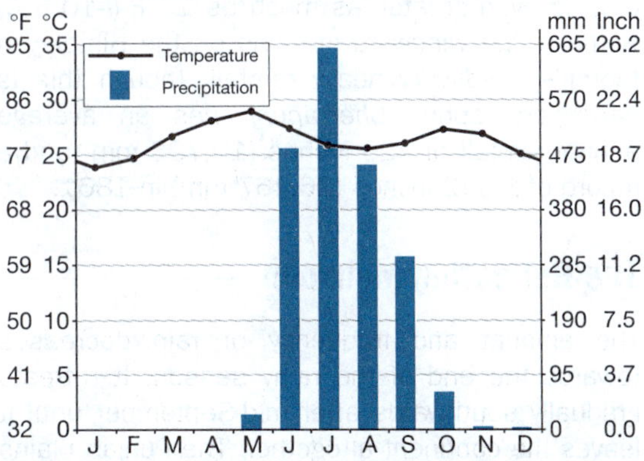

		J	F	M	A	M	J	J	A	S	O	N	D
Avg. Temp.	°C	23.9	24.7	26.7	28.2	29	27.4	25.9	25.6	26.1	27.3	27	25.1
	°F	75.1	76.5	80.1	82.7	84.2	81.3	78.6	78.2	79	81.2	80.6	77.2
Precip.	mm	0	1	0	0	27	487	661	459	300	66	6	5
	in	0	0	0	0	1	19	26	18	11	2	0	0

Data: 1991–2021

Place	Mumbai, India (18° 55′N, 73°E)
Altitude	12 m or 39 feet
Annual precipitation	2,012 mm or 79.2 inch
Annual temperature range	9.1°F (84.2°F – 75.1°F) or 5.1°C (29.0°C – 23.9°C)

Fig. 137 (a) Tropical Monsoon Climate

outdoor life almost unbearable. Day temperatures of 95°F (35°C) are usual in central India and the mean temperature in Sindh, Pakistan may be as high as 110°F (43°C). Coastal districts are a little relieved by sea breezes. There is practically no rain anywhere. By May, the temperature is so high that an intense low pressure zone is set up in north-west India. *Duststorms* are frequent, followed by long awaited rainstorms that 'break' by the middle of June. The transitional period between 'no rain' and 'plenty of rain' is over.

3. **The rainy season (mid-June to September).** With the 'burst' of the South-west monsoon in mid-June, *torrential downpours* sweep across the country to the delight of everybody. Almost all the rain for the year falls within this rainy season. For example, in Mumbai 19 inches (487 mm) are recorded in June, 26 inches (661 mm) in July, 18 inches (459 mm) in August and a further 11 inches (300 mm) in September. As much as 95 per cent of the annual rainfall is concentrated within four months. This pattern of concentrated heavy rainfall in summer is a characteristic feature of the Tropical Monsoon Climate. The torrential downpours have an immediate impact on the local temperature. They lower the temperature considerably. The mean temperature for Mumbai is 84.2°F or 29°C in May but only 78.6°F or 25.9°C in July. In the north the drop is even greater, as much as 13°F (–10.5°C) Some of the windward stations on the Himalayan foothills have very heavy rainfall, though this is partly orographic. *Cherrapunji* has an average annual rainfall of 425 inches (10,795 mm) and a record of 1,042 inches (26,467 mm) in 1861.

The Retreating Monsoon

The amount and frequency of rain decreases towards the end of the rainy season. It retreats gradually southwards after mid-September until it leaves the continent altogether. The Punjab plains which receive the south-west monsoon earliest are the first to see the withdrawal of the monsoon. The skies are clear again and the cool, dry season returns in October, with the outblowing North-east monsoon.

The role of monsoons in India is vital in its economy. A late monsoon or one that ends far too early will condemn large stretches of agricultural land to drought. There will be widespread famine from crop failure and thousands will perish. When there is too much water from the rainy monsoons, severe floods occur, destroying both crops and lives and disrupting communications. In no part of the world has the climate affected people's way of life so profoundly as in the monsoon lands.

The Tropical Marine Climate

This type of climate is experienced along the eastern coasts of tropical lands, receiving steady rainfall from the Trade Winds all the time. The rainfall is both orographic where the moist trades meet upland masses as in eastern Brazil, and convectional due to intense heating during the day and in summer. Its tendency is towards a summer maximum as in monsoon lands, but without any distinct dry period. Fig. 137 (b) shows the rhythm of climate as experienced in Cairns, on the eastern coast of Queensland, under the constant influence of the South-East Trade Winds, and in summer also affected by the tropical monsoons. Its wettest months are in January (9.7 inches or 246 mm), February (10.2 inches or 259 mm), March (8.7 inches or 222 mm) and April (4.3 inches or 108 mm), which is summer in the southern hemisphere. Approximately 70 per cent of the annual rainfall is concentrated in the four summer months.

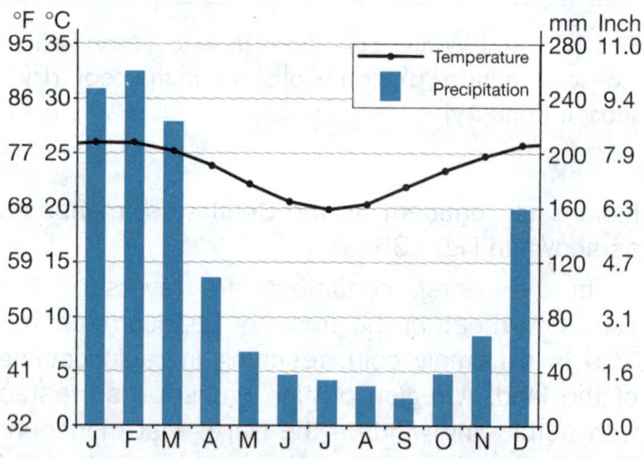

		J	F	M	A	M	J	J	A	S	O	N	D
Avg. Temp.	°C	25.9	25.9	25.1	23.8	22.1	20.5	19.7	20.2	21.8	23.3	24.6	25.6
	°F	78.6	78.6	77.2	74.8	71.8	68.9	67.5	68.4	71.2	73.9	76.3	78.1
Precip.	mm	246	259	222	108	54	37	33	29	20	38	66	159
	in	9	10	8	4	2	1	1	1	0	1	2	6

Data: 1991–2021

Place	Cairns, Australia (17°S, 145° 42′E)
Altitude	coastal lowland (about 7 m or 22 feet)
Annual precipitation	1,271 mm or 50.0 inches
Annual temperature range	11.1°F (78.6°F – 67.5°F) or 6.2°C (25.9°C – 19.7°C)

Fig. 137 (b) Tropical marine Climate

There is no month without any rainfall. The range of temperature is typical of the tropical latitudes with a maximum of 82°F (27.8°C) in January and a minimum of 70°F (21.1°C) in July – a range of 12°F (6.7°C) for the year. Due to the steady influence of the trades, the Tropical Marine Climate is more favourable for habitation, but it is prone to severe tropical cyclones, hurricanes or typhoons, as mentioned in Chapter 13.

Tropical Monsoon Forests

The natural vegetation of tropical monsoon lands depends on the *amount of the summer rainfall.* Trees are normally deciduous, because of the marked dry period, during which they shed their leaves to withstand the drought. Where the rainfall is heavy, e.g. in southern Myanmar, peninsular India, northern Australia and coastal regions with a tropical marine climate, the resultant vegetation is forest. The forests are more open and less luxuriant than the equatorial jungle and there are far fewer species. Most of the forests yield valuable timber, and are prized for their durable hardwood. Amongst these teak is the best known. Myanmar alone accounts for as much as three quarters of the world's production. It is such a durable timber that it is extensively used for ship building, furniture and other constructional purposes. Other kinds of timber include sal, acacia and some varieties of eucalyptus in northern Australia. Together with the forests are bamboo thickets, which often grow to great heights (Fig. 138).

With a decrease in rainfall in summer, the forests thin out into thorny scrubland or savanna with scattered trees and tall grass. In parts of the Indian sub-continent, rainfall is so deficient

Fig. 138 Main features of a monsoon forest

that semi-desert conditions are found. Monsoonal vegetation is thus most varied, ranging from forests to thickets, and from savanna to scrubland.

Agricultural Development in the Monsoon Lands

Much of the monsoon forest has been cleared for agriculture to support the very dense population. The cultural landscape throughout the length and breadth of the monsoon lands deeply reflects the intensity of people's quest for subsistence. Wherever possible, crops are grown. The plains are ploughed, and the hills are terraced to provide farmland. Farms are small and the people are forever 'land hungry'. In their quest for land, they, have removed the natural vegetation, sometimes wantonly, resulting in acute soil erosion. This is particularly serious in the Indian sub-continent which has a very high density of population with a rapid rate of growth. But in the plains the same piece of land may have been tilled for generations with little or no replenishment, and yet able to yield fairly reasonable returns.

Tropical agriculture dependent on natural rainfall and a large labour force, reaches its greatest magnitude in the monsoon lands. The soil provides the basis for the livelihood of millions. Farming is not only the dominant occupation of the greater part of the people, but also forms the mainstay of the economy of the Indian sub-continent, China, South-East Asia, eastern Brazil and the West Indies. The following types of agriculture are recognisable.

1. **Wet padi cultivation.** Rice is the most important staple crop and is grown in tropical lowlands wherever the rain exceeds 70 inches (1,778 mm). It is perhaps the most characteristic crop of the monsoon lands and its total acreage far exceeds that of any other crop. In fact, very few areas outside the influence of the monsoons ever take to the cultivation of padi. There are two main varieties, the wet padi, which is mainly grown on lowlands in flooded fields or in terraced uplands, and the dry padi grown in regions of lower rainfall. A minimum of 50 inches (1,270 mm) of rainfall is required during the growing season. Droughts and floods that are almost inseparable from a monsoonal type of climate can be very detrimental to its cultivation. Irrigation water from rivers, canals, dams or wells is extensively used in the major rice

producing countries. Other food crops like maize, millet, sorghum, wheat, gram and beans are of subsidiary importance. They are cultivated in the drier or cooler areas where rice cannot be grown.

2. **Lowland cash crops.** A wide range of lowland tropical cash crops are cultivated for the export market, after local needs have been met. The most important crop in this category is sugar cane. As much as two-thirds of the world's sugar production comes from tropical countries. Sugar is either grown on plantations or on small holdings wherever rainfall and sunshine are abundant. Some of the major producers include India, Java, Taiwan, Cuba, Jamaica, Trinidad and Barbados. Jute is confined almost entirely to the Ganges-Brahmaputra delta, in India and Bangladesh. It has long been a leading hard fibre for the manufacture of sacks (gunny). Manila hemp (abaca) is a product of the Philippines, particularly of Mindanao. It is used to make high quality rope. Other crops include indigo, still cultivated in India and Java; cotton, a major export of the Indian sub-continent and bananas, coconuts and spices.

Harvesting sugar cane in Queensland, Australia

3. **Highland plantation crops.** The colonization of tropical lands by Europeans gave rise to a new form of cultivated landscape in the cooler monsoonal highlands. This is the cultivation of certain tree crops in tropical plantations. Thousands of acres of tropical upland forests were cleared to make way for *plantation agriculture* in which tea and coffee are the most important crops. These were luxuries in Europe in the eighteenth century and the products of the plantations were originally meant only for export to the mother countries where there was a great craze for the beverages. Later, the local people also got into the habit of drinking them and they fast became necessities. Both the beverages became so popular in and out of the tropics that there was great expansion in their acreages both in regions with a Tropical Monsoon Climate and the Tropical Marine Climate.

Coffee originated in Ethiopia and Arabia, where it is still grown, but *Brazil* now accounts for about 40 per cent of the world's production of coffee. It is mainly grown on the eastern slopes of the Brazilian plateau. The crop is also cultivated on the highland slopes between 2,000 feet (or about 600 m) and 4,500 feet (or about 1,400 m) in the Central American states, India and eastern Java.

Tea picking in a plantation in Sri Lanka

Tea originated in China and is still an important crop there, but as it requires moderate temperatures (about 60°F or about 15°C), heavy rainfall (over 60 inches or 1,500 mm) and well drained highland slopes it thrives well in the tropical monsoon zone, but preferably at a higher altitude. The best regions are thus the Himalayan foothills of India and Bangladesh, the central highlands of Sri Lanka and western Java, from all of which it is exported. In China tea is grown mostly for local consumption.

4. **Lumbering.** Wherever there are tropical forests which still have not been felled to make way for the plough, *lumbering* is undertaken in the more accessible areas. This is particularly important in continental South-East Asia. Of the tropical deciduous trees, teak, of which Myanmar is the leading producer, is perhaps the most sought after. It is valuable on account of its great durability, strength, immunity to shrinkage, fungus attack and insects. It is grown in hilly districts up to 3,000 feet (about 900 m) in altitude with a moderate rainfall. Under government supervision, teak trees which are cut have to be replaced. This is the only way

to ensure the steady supply of the timber which is the second greatest money-earner for Myanmar after rice. In northern Myanmar, in the region of the Chindwin River, there are large teak plantations. It takes as long as 100 years for a teak tree to mature into commercial timber. Green teak logs are so heavy that they will not float readily on water. It is therefore necessary to 'poison' the tree several years before actual felling, so that it is dry and light enough to be floated down the Chindwin and the Irrawaddy to reach the saw mills at Yangon. The individual logs are tied in rafts and guided downstream by crews of men and tugboats. Teak logs are also floated downstream and loaded on trucks to be transported to various destinations. In some places, elephants are still used for logging and carrying timber in the forests. It takes something like 18 months or another season for a log of teak to reach Yangon to be sawn into planks for export.

5. **Shifting Cultivation.** This most primitive form of farming is widely practised. Instead of rotating the crops in the same field to preserve fertility, the tribespeople move to a new clearing when their first field is exhausted. The clearing, or field, in the midst of the jungle is usually made by fire, which destroys practically everything in its way. After planting, little attention is paid to the field either in weeding or manuring. The crops are left entirely to the care of nature. The farmers use simple hoes and sticks for ploughing and seeding. Draught animals are unknown and labour is exclusively manual. Their needs are so basic that every farmer produces much the same range of crops as their neighbours. Maize or corn, dry padi, yams, tapioca, sweet potatoes and some beans are the most common crops. Farming is entirely for subsistence, i.e. everything is consumed by the farmer's family, it is not traded or sold.

As tropical soils are mainly latosolic, rapidly leached and easily exhausted, the first crop may be bountiful but the subsequent harvests deteriorate. A few years later, the field has to be abandoned and a new patch cleared elsewhere. This system of a short period of cultivation alternating with long periods of fallowing is probably the best way of using land in many parts of the tropics where manuring is unknown.

Shifting cultivation is so widely practised amongst indigenous peoples that different local names are used in different countries. For example, *ladang* in Malaysia, *taungya* in Myanmar, *tamrai* in Thailand, *caingin* in the Philippines, *humah* in Java, *chena* in Sri Lanka and *milpa* in Africa and Central America.

QUESTIONS AND EXERCISES

1. The climate of India is characterized by three distinct seasons. Explain why this is so.
2. With the aid of diagrams or sketch maps, explain any *three* of the following statements.
   (a) The east coasts of continents within the tropics have much heavier rainfall than the interiors or the west coasts.
   (b) The Tropical Monsoon Climate is, in fact, land and sea breezes on a continental scale.
   (c) Near the equatorial latitudes, the period of maximum rainfall is closely related to the movements of the overhead sun.
   (d) There is a marked difference in temperature between the east and west coasts of countries in latitudes 20° to 35°N.
3. In which parts of the monsoon lands has the natural vegetation been removed by men? Describe and explain the uses made of the cleared lands.
4. Name the types of climate which have
   (a) rain mainly in winter
   (b) rain only in summer
   (c) rain throughout the year
      i. Describe the characteristic climatic features of any *two* of the types you have named.
      ii. For any *one* of them account for its rainfall distribution.
5. Contrast the essential characteristics of plantation agriculture and shifting cultivation.

17 The Savanna or Sudan Climate

Distribution

The Savanna or Sudan Climate is a transitional type of climate found between the equatorial forests and the trade wind hot deserts. It is confined within the tropics and is best developed in the Sudan where the dry and wet seasons are most distinct, hence its name the Sudan Climate. The belt includes West African Sudan, and then curves southwards into East Africa and southern Africa north of the Tropic of Capricorn as shown in Fig. 139. In South America, there are two distinct regions of savanna north and south of the equator, namely the *llanos* of the Orinoco basin and the *campos* of the Brazilian Highlands. The Australian savanna is located south of the monsoon strip running from west to east north of the Tropic of Capricorn.

Climate of the Sudan Type

Rainfall. The Sudan type of climate is characterized by an alternate hot, rainy season and cool, dry season, as illustrated in Fig. 140 (a). In the northern hemisphere, the hot, rainy season normally begins in May and lasts until September, as in Kano, Nigeria. The rest of the year is cool and dry. The annual rainfall for Kano, which is located at a height of 1,588 feet (484 m) above sea level, is 26.5 inches (674 mm) and is almost entirely concentrated in the summer. But the amount varies from 48 inches (1,220 mm) at Banjul (earlier known as Bathurst), in Gambia on the coast to only 2.8 inches (70 mm) at Khartoum, in Sudan in the interior. Both the length of the rainy season and the annual total rainfall decrease appreciably from the equatorial region polewards towards the desert fringes. On the whole, the annual precipitation is

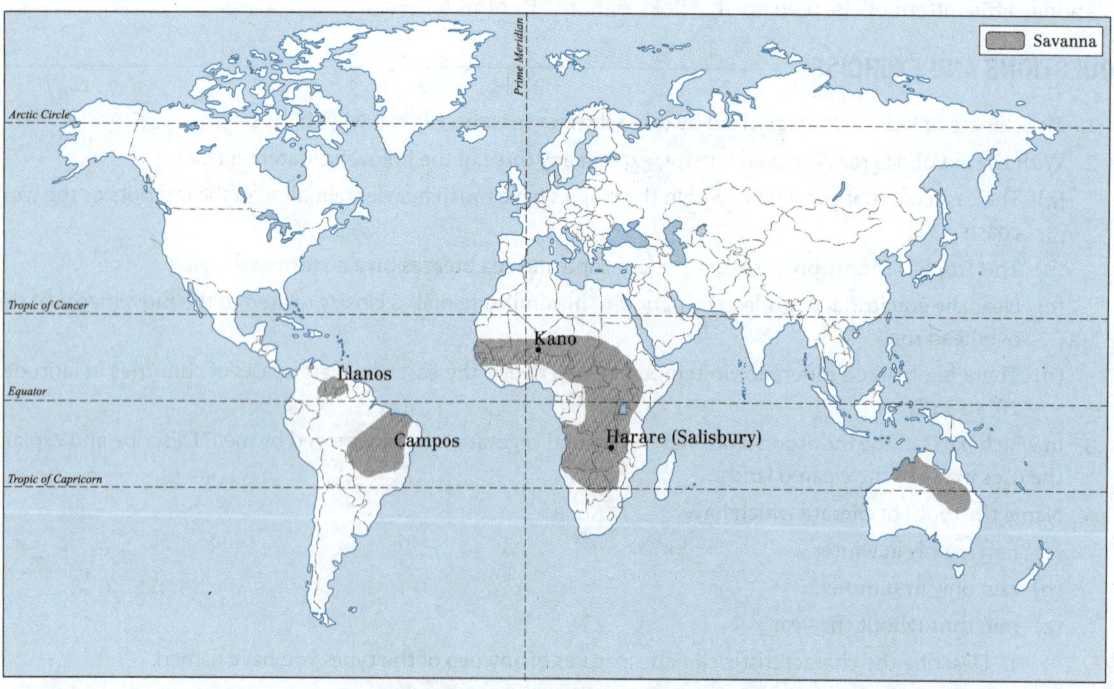

Fig. 139 Regions of Sudan Climate with savanna or tropical grasslands

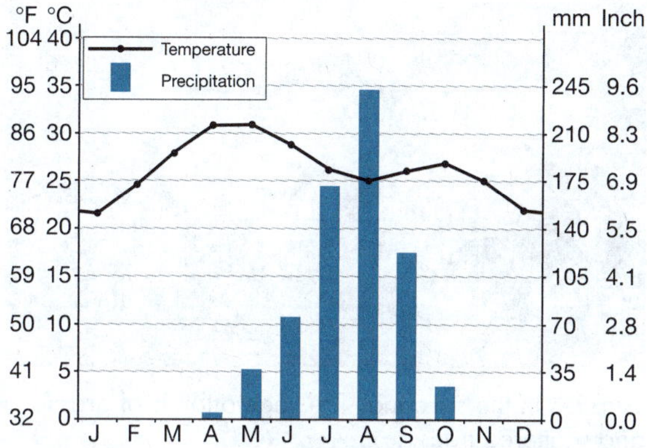

		J	F	M	A	M	J	J	A	S	O	N	D
Avg. Temp.	°C	21.6	24.6	28	30.9	30.9	28.8	26.2	25.1	26.1	26.9	25.1	22
	°F	70.9	76.3	82.4	87.5	87.7	83.9	79.1	77.1	79.1	80.4	77.2	71.6
Precip.	mm	0	0	0	4	36	75	171	242	122	24	0	0
	in	0	0	0	0	1	2	6	9	4	0	0	0

Data: 1991–2021

Place	Kano, Nigeria (11° 58′N, 8° 20′E)
Altitude	484 m or 1,588 feet
Annual precipitation	674 mm or 26.5 inches
Annual temperature range	16.8°F (87.7°F – 70.9°F) or 9.3°C (30.9°C – 21.6°C)

Fig. 140 (a) The Savanna or Sudan Climate in the northern hemisphere

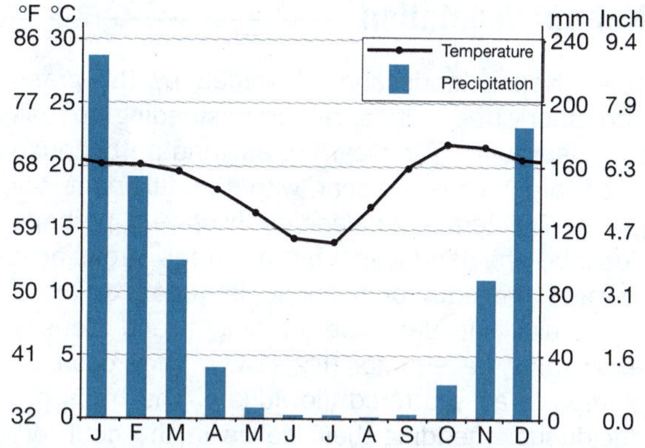

		J	F	M	A	M	J	J	A	S	O	N	D
Avg. Temp.	°C	20.2	20.1	19.6	18.1	16.3	14.3	13.9	16.6	19.9	21.8	21.5	20.6
	°F	68.3	68.2	67.3	64.6	61.4	57.7	57.1	61.9	67.8	71.2	70.8	69.1
Precip.	mm	229	153	100	32	7	2	2	1	3	22	88	185
	in	9	6	3	1	0	0	0	0	0	0	3	7

Data: 1991–2021

Place	Harare, Zimbabwe (17°45′S, 31°E)
Altitude	1,479 m or 4,852 feet
Annual precipitation	824 mm or 32.4 inches
Annual temperature range	14.1°F (71.2°F – 57.1°F) or 7.9°C (21.8°C – 13.9°C)

Fig. 140 (b) The Savanna or Sudan Climate in the southern hemisphere

less than that of the Tropical Monsoon Climate and the length of the wet and dry seasons differs with the locality. In the southern hemisphere, the rainy season is from October to March (the southern summer) as shown in Fig. 140 (b) of Harare (earlier known as Salisbury), in Zimbabwe (earlier known as Rhodesia). Its annual precipitation of 32.4 inches (824 mm) also varies much from year to year.

Temperature. The monthly temperature hovers between 70°F and 90°F (21°C–32°C) for lowland stations. An annual temperature range of 20°F (11°C) is typical, but the range increases as one moves further away from the equator. It is, however, interesting to note that the highest temperatures do not coincide with the period of the highest sun (e.g. June in the northern hemisphere) but occur just before the onset of the rainy season, i.e. April in Kano and October in Harare (earlier, Salisbury). There is also a distinct drop in temperature in the rainy period, due to the overcast sky and the cooler atmosphere.

Days are hot, and during the hot season, noon temperatures of over 100°F (about 37°C) are quite frequent. When night falls the clear sky which promotes intense heating during the day also causes rapid radiation in the night. Temperatures drop to well below 50°F (10°C) and night frosts are not uncommon at this time of the year. This extreme diurnal range of temperature is another characteristic feature of the Sudan type of climate.

Winds. The prevailing winds of the region are the Trade Winds which bring rain to the coastal districts. They are strongest in the summer but are relatively dry by the time they reach the continental interiors or the western coasts of the continents, so that grass and scattered short trees predominate. In West Africa, the North-East Trades, in fact, blow offshore from the Sahara Desert and reach the Guinea coast as a dry, dust-laden wind, called locally the Harmattan, meaning 'the doctor'. It is so dry that its relative humidity seldom exceeds 30 per cent. 'The doctor' provides a welcome relief from the damp air of the Guinea lands by increasing the rate of evaporation with resultant cooling effects, but it is such a dry dusty wind that, besides ruining the crops, it also stirs up a thick dusty haze and impedes inland river navigation.

Natural Vegetation

The savanna landscape is typified by tall grass and short trees. It is rather misleading to call the savanna 'tropical grassland', because trees are always present with the luxuriant tall grass. The terms *parkland* or *bush-veld* perhaps describe the landscape better. Trees grow best towards the equatorial humid latitudes or along riverbanks but decrease in height and density away from the equator (Fig. 141). They occur in clumps or as scattered individuals. The trees are deciduous, shedding their leaves in the cool, dry season to prevent excessive loss of water through transpiration, e.g. *acacias.* Others have broad trunks, with water-storing devices to survive through the prolonged drought such as *baobabs* and *bottle trees.* Trees are mostly hard, gnarled and thorny and may exude gum like *gum arabic.* Many trees are umbrella shaped, exposing only a narrow edge to the strong winds. Palms which cannot withstand the drought are confined to the wettest areas or along rivers. Vegetative luxuriance reaches its peak in the rainy season, when trees renew their foliage and flower.

In true savanna lands, the grass is tall and coarse, growing 6 to 12 feet (1.8–3.6 m) high. The elephant grass may attain a height of even 15 feet (4.5 m)! The grass tends to grow in compact *tufts* and has long roots which reach down in search of water. It appears greenish and well-nourished in the rainy season but turns yellow and dies down in the dry season that follows. The grass lies dormant throughout the long, rainless period and springs up again in the next rainy season. In between the tall grass are scattered short trees and low bushes. As the rainfall diminishes towards the deserts the savanna merges into thorny scrub. In Australia, this scrubland is particularly well represented by a number of species: *mallee, mulga, spinifex grass* and other bushes.

Giraffes in the savanna. The vegetation is of grass and scattered trees

Animal Life of the Savanna

The savanna, particularly in Africa, is the home of wild animals. It is known as the big game country and thousands of animals are trapped or killed each year by people from all over the world. Some of the animals are tracked down for their skins, horns, tusks, bones or hair, others are captured alive and sent out of Africa as zoo animals, laboratory specimens or pets. There is such a wealth of animal life in Africa that many of the animal films that we see at the cinema are actually taken in the savanna.

There are, in fact, two main groups of animals in the savanna, the grass-eating herbivorous animals and the flesh-eating carnivorous animals. The herbivorous animals are often very alert and move swiftly from place to place in search of green pastures. They are endowed with great speed to run away from the savage flesh-eaters that are always after them. The leaf and grass-eating animals include the zebra, antelope, giraffe, deer, gazelle, elephant and okapi. Many are well camouflaged species and their presence amongst the tall greenish-brown grass cannot be easily detected. The giraffe with such a long neck can locate its enemies a great distance away, while the

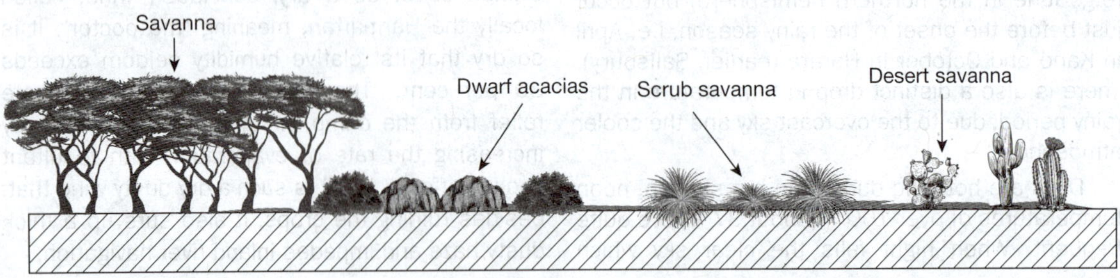

Fig. 141 Changes in vegetation from Savanna to desert

elephant is so huge and strong that few animals will venture to come near it. It is well equipped with tusks and trunk for defence.

The carnivorous animals like the lion, tiger, leopard, hyaena, panther, jaguar, jackal, lynx and puma have powerful jaws and teeth for attacking other animals. Their natural colourings of light yellowish-brown, often with stripes like the tiger or spots like the leopard, match perfectly with the tawny background of the savanna. They often hide themselves in shady spots up in the branches or amidst the tall bushes, and many wild animals, as well as hunters themselves, are caught unawares in this manner. Along rivers and in marshy lakes are numerous species of reptiles and mammals including crocodiles, alligators, monitors and giant lizards together with the larger rhinoceros and hippopotamus. In such an *animal paradise* there are many diverse species of birds, snakes, butterflies, moths and insects.

In many parts of East and South Africa, national parks have been set up which control the killing of animals. This is a necessity, if many of the rare species of animals are to be preserved and protected from wanton shooting. In Kenya there are large hotels and viewing towers, built in the heart of the savanna, with special transport arrangements to bring tourist in to see the animals in their natural settings. This is a progressive step made in conserving animal life of the savanna and should be encouraged.

Human Life in the Savanna

Within the savanna lands of the tropics live many different tribes who are either cattle pastoralists like the Maasai of the East African plateau or settled cultivators like the Hausa of northern Nigeria. We shall examine the life of these two groups of people more closely, and see how they adapt themselves to the savanna environment.

The Maasai, cattle pastoralists. The Maasai are a nomadic tribe who once wandered with their herds of cattle in the central highlands of East Africa – in Kenya, Tanzania and Uganda. At the height of their power, in the mid-nineteenth century, the Maasai occupied most of the Great Rift Valley and adjacent lands. In Kenya, the British evicted the Maasai with a treaty in 1904, followed by another treaty in 1911. This led to a cut down in Maasai lands by 60 per cent, thus confining them to Narok and Kajiado districts of the present-day. In the 1940s in Tanzania, the Maasai were forced to leave their fertile lands between Mount Kilimanjaro and Mount Meru, as well as areas close to the Ngorongoro. The Maasai also had to give up more grazing land for the creation of wildlife parks and national reserves. But today after a century's tribal clashes, epidemics, natural deaths and displacements, they are now mainly confined to the 15,000 square miles (38,850 sq. km) of Maasai reserves in Kenya and Tanzania. Their numbers are now estimated to be 900,000.

Their old grazing grounds in the Kenyan Highlands were taken over first by the immigrant white settlers for plantation agriculture (coffee, tea, cotton) and dairy farming and later, after independence, by African farmers. They now occupy the less favoured areas of savanna in which are grazed something like a million cattle and perhaps twice as many sheep and goats. On the lower slopes of the East African plateau, where rainfall is as low as 20 inches (508 mm) and there are long periods of drought, the grass seldom reaches a foot high and is not nutritious. When there is a drought the Maasai move upwards to the higher and cooler plateau regions in which their herds can graze on the better pastures. They build circular huts with sticks, bushes and mud for temporary shelter. The cattle are kept in a special enclosure at night and are protected from attack by wild animals by a strong fence.

The cattle kept by the Maasai are the zebu cattle with humps and long horns. They are treated with great respect and affection and are never slaughtered for food or for sale. The meat from cattle is only consumed when they die a natural death from old age or disease. They are never used as draught animals and are kept entirely for the supply of milk and blood. Milking is done by women before daybreak and at dusk. The yield is extremely low by any standard and usually not more than two pints are obtained at a single milking. The milk is drunk either fresh or sour. Cheese-making is still not known to the Maasai. Blood from both bulls and cows is drunk. This is obtained by tying a leather cord around the neck of an animal until the veins swell. A vein is then punctured by a special arrowhead and the blood gushes out and is collected and drunk fresh or clotted.

Traditional Maasai people's lifestyle concentrates on their cattle which make up the primary source of food.

Cattle are kept by every Maasai family. They are considered far more valuable than anything else, and are symbols of wealth. The richest man has the largest herds of cattle, leaving aside the sheep and goats which, to the Maasai tribes, are of little significance. Cattle are used in payment for wives, and when the father of a family dies, the mother divides the livestock among the sons. The Maasai will not slaughter the cattle for food, so from the agricultural tribes such as the Kikuyu of Kenya, they obtain a small amount of millet, bananas, groundnuts and vegetables.

Because the number of cattle is more important to the Maasai than their quality, the Maasai will not willingly sell their cattle. So, the large area of land which they occupy in East Africa is not used profitably. Great efforts are being made to get the Maasai to care for their animals properly and raise them for sale, keeping only as many animals as the pasture can support. Many Maasai are responding to modern techniques but the majority stubbornly continue in their old ways. Amongst most of the other African tribes, pastoralism exists side by side with agriculture.

The Hausa, settled cultivators. The Hausa are a tribe of settled cultivators who inhabit the savanna lands of the Bauchi Plateau of northern Nigeria. They number almost six million and have been organized in settled agricultural communities for hundreds of years. They are more advanced in their civilization and ways of life than many of the other African negroes.

The Hausa live in towns or villages. The ancient Hausa city of Kano, with a population of 135,000 has long been a focus of routes and trade. They do not practise shifting cultivation as many tribes do. Instead, they clear a piece of land and use it for several years, growing a wide range of crops like maize, millet, Guinea corn, groundnuts, bananas and beans. Some Hausa also cultivate non-food crops, e.g. cotton and tobacco. When the fertility of the plot declines, they plant a new field and allow the old one to lie *fallow*. This enables natural forces to act on it until fertility is restored. New crops are then sown in the old plot again and the harvests are good. In this manner, the Hausa rotate their crops between different fields at different parts of the year, which is a technique employed in advanced agricultural societies.

Besides cultivation, the Hausa also make use of domesticated animals. Herds of cattle and goats are kept for both milk and meat, but they are only subsidiary to crop cultivation. Though they do not contribute much to the income of the Hausa, because of their small numbers, their manure is used to fertilize the fields. Poultry are raised by the villagers and both eggs and chicken are consumed.

The farming year is very closely related to the season of rainfall. In Nigeria, the rainy season begins in May and lasts till September. The annual precipitation is about 40 inches (1,016 mm), falling entirely in summer. The Hausa sow the seeds in late April when sufficient rain has fallen. The seedlings sprout with the heavy rain and grow rapidly throughout the rainy season. Weeding with traditional hoes is done at regular intervals till the crops are ripened and harvested in September, the beginning of the cool, dry season. The tall brown bushes are burnt down by the farmers in preparation for new fields for the following year. Sometimes fires may be caused by the dry, dusty Harmattan.

Problems, Prospects and Development of the Savanna

There is little doubt that in years to come, world population pressure and the need for greater food production will necessitate greater economic development of the savanna. The deserts or the freezing tundra form climatic barriers too formidable for large-scale human intervention to take place. But the savanna lands with an annual rainfall of over 30 inches (762 mm) and without any severe cold, should be able to support a wide range of tropical crops. *Pioneer settlements* in central Africa, northern Australia and eastern Brazil have shown that the savannas have immense agricultural potential for plantation agriculture of cotton, cane sugar, coffee, oil palm, groundnuts and even tropical fruits. Tropical Queensland, despite its scarcity of labour force has been very successful in its attempts to develop its huge empty land. The newly independent states of Kenya, Uganda, Tanzania and Malawi have already taken to large-scale production of cotton and sisal hemp. Both crops thrive well in savanna conditions. In West Africa, the commercial cultivation of groundnuts, oil palm and cocoa have been gradually extended into the savanna lands. New drought-resistant varieties will have to be introduced into these newly emergent countries to increase their foreign earnings in such tropical raw materials. In the cooler highlands, temperate crops have been successfully raised.

But farming in the savanna land is not without natural hazards. *Droughts* may be long and trying, as rainfall is often unreliable. Unless countermeasures can be taken in the form of adequate provision for irrigation, improved crop varieties and scientific farming techniques suitable for the tropical grasslands, crop failures can be disastrous for the people, who have very little to fall back on. The Sudan Climate, with distinct wet-and-dry periods is also responsible for the rapid deterioration of soil fertility. During the rainy season, torrential downpours of heavy rain cause leaching, in which most of the plant nutrients, such as nitrates, phosphates and potash, are dissolved and washed away. During the dry season, intense heating and evaporation dry up most of the water. Many savanna areas therefore have poor lateritic soils which are incapable of supporting good crops. Unless the soil is properly conserved through regular manuring, weeding and careful maintenance, crop yields are bound to decline.

The savanna is said to be the natural cattle country and many of the native people are, in fact, herdsmen or pastoralists. Cattle are kept in large numbers and fed on the tall grass or the bushes. They provide the people with milk, blood and meat. Unfortunately, the native zebu cattle are bony and yield little meat or milk. They often fall victim to tropical diseases, e.g. the ngana or sleeping sickness carried by the tsetse fly in Africa. The export of either beef or milk from the tropical grasslands is so far not important.

It seems necessary to introduce temperate cattle such as the English Shorthorn, Friesian or Guernsey to *cross* with the tropical *zebu,* if cattle rearing is to be successful in the savanna. In fact, a start has already been made in tropical Queensland which has become Australia's largest cattle producing state. Both meat and milk are exported. In other regions such as the *campos and llanos* of South America, though cattle ranching has been carried out for centuries, little progress has been made so far. The quality of the grass needs to be improved and a better network of communications is essential. Above all cattle breeding and disease control must be carried out on a scientific basis. In the African savanna, the attitude of such native herdsmen as the Maasai who treat cattle as prestige animals, not for slaughtering, will pose many difficulties towards the commercialization of the cattle industry. But as an agricultural region, the savanna holds great promise for the future.

QUESTIONS AND EXERCISES

1. The following are brief descriptions of *three* different types of climate.
   (a) A very large temperature range, with summer rain.
   (b) Distinct wet and dry seasons with concentrated summer rain.
   (c) High uniform temperature with well distributed heavy rainfall.
      i. Name the type of climate.
      ii. For any *two* of them, give a fuller description of the climate and the factors which give rise to it.
2. Explain why
   (a) The savanna lands have a parkland type of natural vegetation.
   (b) The savanna is the natural home of cattle.
   (c) The savanna grass decreases in height and luxuriance further away from the equator.
   (d) Rainfall in the Sudan Climate is concentrated in the summer.
3. Write a descriptive account of
   Either: The Maasai, pastoralists of East Africa
   Or: The Hausa, food growers of northern Nigeria
   You should bear in mind the environmental influence on their mode of living
4. It is said that the savanna land holds great promise for the future. Do you think so? Why? Outline some of the probable difficulties that may be encountered in their development.
5. Write brief notes on the following.
   (a) The effects of Harmattan in West Africa.
   (b) The savanna is the 'Big Game Country'.
   (c) Tropical grasslands have great potential for the cultivation of tropical hot, crops, e.g. cotton, coffee, fruits.
   (d) The savanna is a transitional zone between the equatorial forests and the hot deserts.

18 The Hot Desert and Mid-Latitude Desert Climates

Distribution

Deserts are regions of scanty rainfall which may be hot like the hot deserts of the Saharan type; or temperate as are the mid-latitude deserts like the Gobi. The aridity of the hot deserts is mainly due to the effects of offshore Trade Winds, hence they are also called *Trade Wind Deserts.* The temperate deserts are rainless because of their interior location in the temperate latitudes, well away from the rain-bearing winds.

The major hot deserts of the world are located on the western coasts of continents between latitudes 15° and 30°N and S as shown in Fig. 142. They include the Sahara Desert, the largest single stretch of desert, which is 3,200 miles from east to west and at least 1,000 miles wide. Its total area of 3.5 million square miles is larger than all the 50 states of USA put together. The next biggest desert is the Great Australian Desert which covers almost half of the continent. The other hot deserts are the Arabian Desert, Iranian Desert, Thar Desert, Kalahari and Namib Deserts. In North America, the desert extends from Mexico into USA and is called by different names at different places, e.g. the Mohave. Sonoran, Californian and Mexican Deserts. In South America, the Atacama or Peruvian Desert is the driest of all deserts with less than 0.5 inches of rainfall annually.

Amongst the mid-latitude deserts, many are found on plateaux and are at a considerable distance from the sea. These are the Gobi, Turkestan and Patagonian Deserts. The Patagonian Desert is more due to its rain-shadow position on the leeward side of the lofty Andes than to continentality.

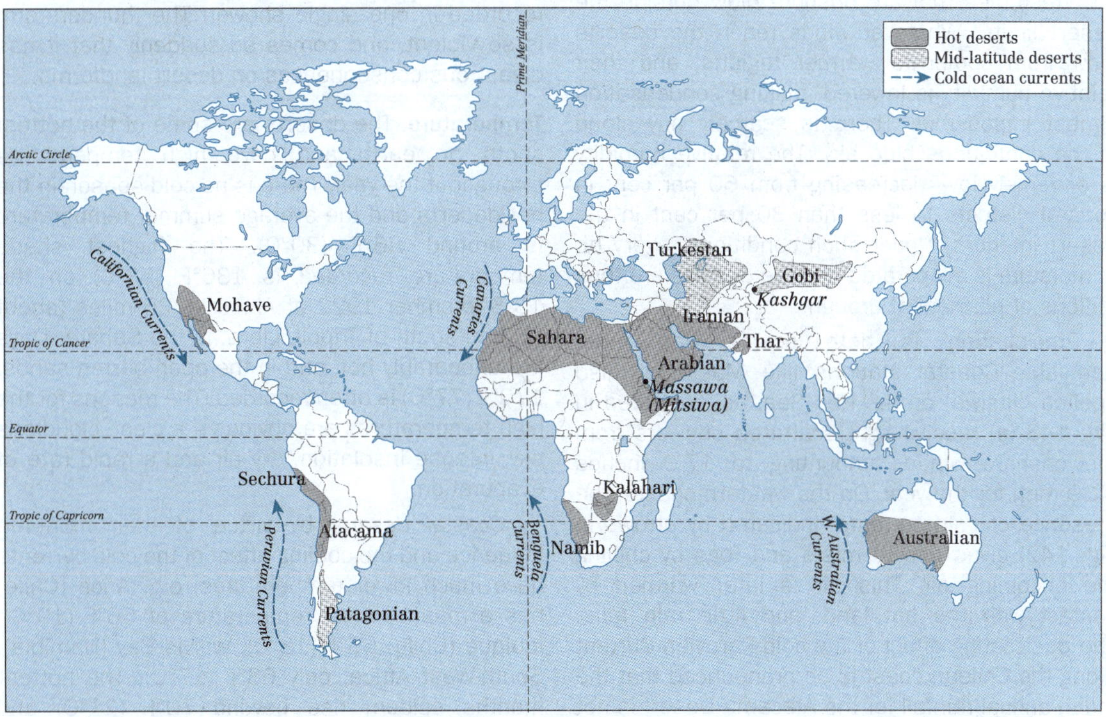

Fig. 142 The hot deserts and mid-latitude deserts of the world

Climate

Rainfall. Few deserts whether hot or mid-latitude have an annual precipitation of more than 10 inches (254 mm). For example, William Creek in Australia has 5.4 inches (137 mm), Jaisalmer in India has 6.9 inches (about 176 mm), whereas Kota in Rajasthan (India) has 28.4 inches (about 720 mm) of annual precipitation. Yuma, Arizona, USA has 3.3 inches (about 90 mm). In Salah (Algeria) in the mid-Sahara and Arica (Chile) in the mid-Atacama have practically no rain at all. In the latter, less than 0.02 inches (0.5 mm) fell within a period of 17 years in three light showers! In another station less than 150 miles (about 240 km) away at Iquique (Chile), not a single drop of rain was recorded for four years and then a torrential downpour suddenly came one afternoon in which 2.5 inches (63.5 mm) of rain fell! The aridity of deserts is the most outstanding feature of the desert climate. We shall examine more closely why they are so dry.

The hot deserts lie astride the Horse Latitudes or the Sub-Tropical High Pressure Belts where the air is descending, a condition least favourable for precipitation of any kind to take place. The rain-bearing Trade Winds blow offshore and the Westerlies that are onshore blow outside the desert limits. Whatever winds reach the deserts blow from cooler to warmer regions, and their relative humidity is lowered, making condensation almost impossible. There is scarcely any cloud in the continuous blue sky. The relative humidity is extremely low, decreasing from 60 per cent in coastal districts to less than 30 per cent in the desert interiors. Under such conditions, every bit of moisture is evaporated and the deserts are thus regions of permanent drought.

Precipitation is both scarce and most unreliable Coastal stations like Massawa (also spelled Mitsiwa) on the Red Sea, as illustrated in Fig. 143 (a) receive light scattered showers from the onshore winds, amounting to 17.3 inches (439 mm) for the year. On the western coasts, the presence of cold currents (indicated by arrows in Fig. 142) gives rise to mists and fogs by chilling the oncoming air. This air is later warmed by contact with the hot land, and little rain falls. The desiccating effect of the cold Peruvian Current along the Chilean coast is so pronounced that the mean annual rainfall for the Atacama Desert is not more than half an inch! Rain normally occurs as

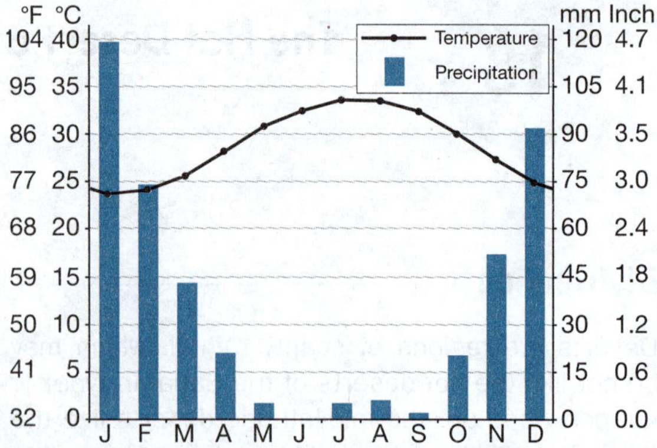

		J	F	M	A	M	J	J	A	S	O	N	D
Avg. Temp.	°C	24.5	25.0	27.0	29.0	31.0	33.5	35.0	34.0	33.04	30.5	27.5	26.0
	°F	76.1	77.0	80.6	84.2	87.8	92.3	95.0	93.2	91.4	86.9	81.5	78.8
Precip.	mm	33	25	8	8	4	0	9	11	4	16	33	33
	in	1.3	1.0	0.3	0.3	0.2	0	0.4	0.4	0.2	0.6	1.3	1.3

Data: 1991–2021

Place	Massawa (Mitsiwa), Eritrea (16°N, 39°E)
Altitude	6 m or 20 feet
Annual precipitation	182 mm or 7.2 inches
Annual temperature range	18.9°F (95.0°F – 76.1°F) or 10.5°C (35.0°C – 24.5°C)

Fig. 143 (a) The Hot Desert Climate

violent thunderstorms of the convectional type. It 'bursts' suddenly and pours continuously for a few hours over small areas. An inch or more may be recorded in one single shower! The thunderstorm is so violent, and comes so suddenly that it has disastrous consequences on desert landforms.

Temperature. The deserts are some of the hottest spots on earth and have high temperatures throughout the year. There is no cold season in the hot deserts and the average summer temperature is around 86°F (30°C). The highest shade temperature recorded is 136°F (58°C) on the 13 September 1922 at Al Azizia, 25 miles (about 25 km) south of Tripoli, Libya, in the Sahara. Days are unbearably hot, and in the open barren sands, 170°F (77°C) is often recorded. The reasons for the high temperatures are obvious – a clear, cloudless sky, intense insolation, dry air and a rapid rate of evaporation.

Coastal deserts by virtue of their maritime influence and the cooling effect of the cold currents have much lower temperatures, e.g. Arica (Chile) has a mean annual temperature of 66°F (19°C), Iquique (Chile) 65°F (18°C), Walvis Bay (Namibia), South-West Africa, only 63°F (17°C). The hottest months seldom rise beyond 70°F (21°C) and the annual temperature range is equally small, e.g. 16°F (or 9°C) in Arica, 10°F (or 6°C) in Iquique and 10°F (5°C) in Walvis Bay.

The desert interiors, however, experience much higher summer temperatures and the winter months are rather cold. For example, In Salah, in the Sahara, has a temperature of 99°F (37°C) in the hottest month but only 55°F (13°C) in the coldest month. The annual range is 44°F (or 24°C). The range for Yuma (Arizona, USA) is 36°F (or 21°C) and for Jacobabad (Sindh, Pakistan) is 41°F (or 22°C). In comparison, the station Massawa, illustrated in Fig. 143 (a), located near the coast, facing the Red Sea has only a moderate range of 19°F. Its hottest month is July (95°F or 35°C) and its coldest month is January (76°F or 24.5°C).

The diurnal range of temperature in the deserts is very great. Intense insolation by day in a region of dry air and no clouds causes the temperature to rise with the sun. The barren ground is so intensely heated that, by noon, particularly in summer, a reading of 120°F (about 48–49°C) is common. But as soon as the sun sets, the land loses heat very quickly by radiation, and the mercury column in the thermometer drops to well below the mean temperature. A daily temperature range of 30° to 40°F (20 to 25°C). is common, though in the Death Valley of California, an exceptionally great diurnal range of 74°F (about 30–35°C) has been recorded. Frosts may occur at night in winter. These extremes of temperature make desert living most trying. This explains why the desert people wear thick gowns all day long, to protect themselves from the glaring heat by day and chilling frost by night, not to mention the sand grains that are carried by the wind.

Climatic Conditions in the Mid-Latitude Deserts

The climatic conditions of the mid-latitude deserts are in many ways similar to those of the hot deserts. Aridity is the keynote. These inland basins lie hundreds of miles from the sea, and are sheltered by the high mountains all around them. As a result they are cut off from the rain-bearing winds. Occasionally depressions may penetrate the Asiatic continental mass and bring light rainfall in winter, or unexpected convectional storms may bless the parched lands with brief showers in summer. For example, Kashgar (Xinjiang) in western China in the Gobi Desert, as illustrated in

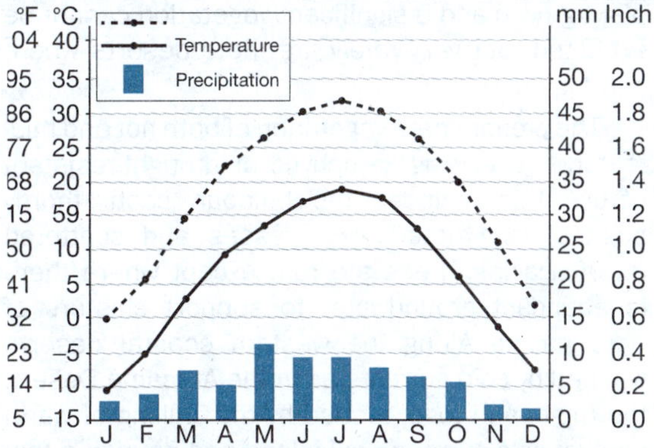

Month		J	F	M	A	M	J	J	A	S	O	N	D	Y
Avg. Temp.	°C	–5.2	0.4	8.8	15.9	20	23.7	25.5	24.1	19.8	13.1	5	–2.7	12.4
	°F	22.6	32.6	47.9	60.5	68.1	74.7	77.8	75.4	67.6	55.6	41	27.1	54.5
Precip.	mm	3	4	7	5	11	9	9	8	6	6	2	2	70
	in	0.1	0.1	0.3	0.2	0.4	0.4	0.4	0.3	0.2	0.2	0.1	0.1	2.8

Data: 1991–2021

Place	Kashgar (Xinjiang) China (39°N, 76°E)
Altitude	1,300 m or 4,265 feet
Annual precipitation	70 mm or 2.8 inches
Annual temperature range	55.2°F (77.8°F – 22.6°F) or 30.7°C (25.5°C – -5.2°C)

Fig. 143 (b) The Mid-Latitude Desert Climate

Fig. 143 (b), has most of its 3.5 inches of annual precipitation in the summer. Due to their coldness and elevation, snow falls in winter.

From Fig. 143 (b), it is clear that summers are very hot (77.8°F or 25.5°C) in July at Kashgar and winters are extremely cold with two months below freezing point. The annual range of temperature is 55.2°F or 30.7°C, much greater than that of the hot deserts. Continentality accounts for these extremes in temperature. Winters are often severe, freezing lakes and rivers, and strong cold winds blow all the time. When the ice thaws in early summer, floods occur in many places. The greatest inhibiting factors to settlement are the winter cold and the permanent aridity, besides remoteness from the sea.

Desert Vegetation

All deserts have some form of vegetation such as grass, scrub, herbs, weeds, roots or bulbs. Though they may not appear green and fresh all the time, they lie dormant in the soil awaiting rain which comes at irregular intervals or once in many years. The environment, so lacking in moisture and so excessive in heat, is most unfavourable for plant growth and a significant vegetation cannot be expected. But *very rarely* are there deserts where *nothing grows.*

The predominant vegetation of both hot and mid-latitude deserts is xerophytic or drought-resistant scrub. This includes the bulbous cacti, thorny bushes, long-rooted wiry grasses and scattered dwarf acacias. Trees are rare except where there is abundant groundwater to support clusters of date palms. Along the western coastal deserts washed by cold currents as in the Atacama Desert, the mists and fogs, formed by the chilling of warm air over cold currents, roll inland and nourish a thin cover of vegetation.

Plants that exist in deserts have highly specialized means of adapting themselves to the arid environment. Intense evaporation increases the salinity of the soil so that the dissolved salts tend to accumulate on the surface forming hard pans. Absence of moisture retards the rate of decomposition and desert soils are very deficient in humus. Plants, whether annuals or perennials must struggle for survival against both aridity and poor soil.

Most desert shrubs have long roots and are well spaced out to gather moisture, and search for groundwater. Plants have few or no leaves and the foliage is either waxy, leathery, hairy or needle-shaped to reduce the loss of water through transpiration. Some of them are entirely leafless, with pricks or thorns. Others like the cacti have thick succulent stems to store up water for long droughts. There are still others that shed their leaves during droughts. The seeds of many species of grasses and herbs have thick, tough skins to protect them while they lie dormant. They germinate at once when their seeds are moistened by the next rain. In short, all plants must adapt themselves to survive in such an inhospitable region as the desert.

Desert plants in Arizona (USA)

Life in the Deserts

Despite its inhospitality, the desert has always been peopled by different groups of inhabitants. They struggle against an environment deficient in water, food and other means of livelihood. Some, like the Egyptians have attained a high level of civilization, others like the Bedouin Arabs have fared quite well with their flocks of sheep, goats, camels and horses. The Bushmen of the Kalahari and the Bindibu of Australia remain so primitive in their mode of living that they barely survive. They are, in fact, a relic of the Old Stone Age in the modern world. The desert inhabitants may be grouped under the following categories.

1. **The primitive hunters and collectors.** Of the primitive tribes, the Bushmen and the Bindibu are the best known. Both the tribes are *nomadic hunters and food gatherers,* growing no crops and domesticating no animals. The Bushmen roam the Kalahari Desert with their bows and poisoned arrows, spears, traps and snares. They are not only skilful and strong but also have great endurance. In order to capture their prey, they have to be very patient and if necessary run many miles to track down the wounded animals. In this way, they hunt antelope, and other smaller animals. The women and children collect insects, rodents and lizards, and gather honey, roots, grass and grubs. Great skill is required in obtaining water in the desert. Dew is carefully gathered from leaves early in the morning and stored in ostrich shells. Very often, it is necessary to dig a hole in damp sand and suck the water up from the ground through a hollow reed. This is often a very slow process. Bushmen either wear a loin cloth or go virtually naked. They travel in small family groups, and live together in open *sherms.* This is a hollow dug beneath a thorn tree, surrounded by bushes. At night a fire is lit to keep the family warm.

The Bindibu or Aborigines of Australia live in very much the same way as the Bushmen. They are lean and dark but healthy. They are skilled trackers and some of them use wooden throwing sticks or *boomerangs* and spears. They also domesticate the *dingo,* a wild dog that assists them in tracking down kangaroos, rabbits and birds. The women gather grass, roots, seeds, berries, moles and insects, to supplement their diet. Like the wandering Bushmen, the Bindibu move in family groups in search of fresh hunting grounds. But one distinct difference is that they always stay close to a water supply as they still have not devised a means of tapping and storing water. They live in *wurlies,* simple shelters made of branches and tufts and grass.

2. **The nomadic herdsmen.** These people represent a more advanced group of desert dwellers who pursue a livestock economy. They ride on animals instead of walking and are heavily clad against the blazing sun, the stormy winds and the chilly nights. The Bedouin of Arabia ride on horses and live in tents; the Tuaregs of the Sahara are camel riders and dwell in grass *zeriba,* while the Gobi Mongols ride on horses to herd their yaks and live in portable *yurts* (a kind of tent). The Bedouin are the best examples of a desert group who have fared well as nomadic herdsmen. Besides keeping large flocks of animals, they are also engaged in trade with the caravan merchants and the oases people. All round the year, the Bedouin wander with their herds in search of water and green pastures. Their wealth is their animals: sheep, goats, camels and perhaps a few horses. The animals provide them with all that they require, daily milk and cheese and on occasions meat as well. Their skin is used for hides or leather, for making tents, clothing, belts, footwear and water bags. From the hair and wool, the Bedouin make clothes, mats, ropes, rugs and carpets. These can also be exchanged at trading stations or oases for other necessities of life which the desert herdsmen cannot produce like dates, grain, beverages, medicines, firearms and other manufactured articles.

The Bedouin move in groups of about a hundred. They follow a regular pattern of routes, along which are scanty patches of pastures, wells or springs. In this manner, one group rarely clashes with the other in their search for new grounds to pitch their tents. Since they move so often, they always travel light and only the essentials are carried along.

3. **The caravan traders.** These were the travelling merchants of the desert. Their journeys across the wastes of the Sahara or Russian Turkestan (currently part of Kazakhstan, Kyrgyzstan, Tajikistan, Uzbekistan, and Turkmenistan) sometimes lasted months or even years. They travelled at night as a team and were well armed. They carried a wide range of goods into remote interiors where their merchandise was highly sought after. These goods were sold or exchanged for hides, rugs, carpets and other valuable products of the deserts. Though profits were high, the risks were equally great.

The pack-animal used by the caravans to carry their goods across the deserts was the camel, aptly described as the *ship of the desert.* Unlike horses which have sharp hooves that sink readily in the sandy desert, the camel has broad padded feet that will not slip in the sand. A pack-camel, adequately fed, can carry a load of 350 pounds (160 kg approx.) and travel 50 miles (80 km) a day. And a racing camel can do twice the distance when ridden! The camel has several other advantages, it provides milk and hair. It can store up water in its stomach, and fat in its hump, so that it can go for long periods without either food or water.

With the introduction of modern air, road and rail transport, the role of the caravan traders is greatly reduced. Goods can be conveyed much more cheaply and with greater security by desert jeeps, vans or trucks. But between the interior oases and scattered outposts beyond the reach of roads, the caravan routes remain the only form of available transport.

4. **The settled cultivators.** For crops to be cultivated in the desert, irrigation is indispensable. This is **obtained** either from oases, rivers or dams, through a network of canals. In Egypt, the Nile supports a population of 25 million, mainly concentrated in the Nile valley and delta. The life-giving waters of the Nile made it possible for the Egyptians to raise many crops as early as 5,000 years ago. When the Nile flooded in summer, the overflowed water was caught in basins with raised banks and led into the fields to irrigate the crops. This was basin irrigation, which was widely practised by the ancient Egyptian farmers and is still employed by the Egyptians today. Rice and cotton are cultivated in summer, followed by wheat, barley, beans and other minor crops in winter. Modern concrete dams constructed across the Nile, e.g. Aswan and Sennar Dams are even more effective for extensive irrigation works. The floodwater can be held back and controlled and then released at any part of the year to feed the fields that yield two, three or even more crops a year. In the same way, desert cultivators rely on the Indus in Pakistan, the Tigris-Euphrates in Iraq, and

the Colorado in the Imperial Valley of California, and are able to irrigate millions of acres of arid land for crop production.

In the deserts, wherever there are oases, some form of settled life is bound to follow. These are depressions of varying sizes, where underground, water reaches the surface. Some of them are abnormally large like the Tafilalet (also spelled Tafilalt) Oasis in Morocco which measures 5,000 square miles (12,950 sq. km), supporting many settlements, including large towns. Others may be so small that they are no bigger than the mining pools that we are so familiar with, e.g. the Ghadames Oasis of Libya is only one square mile in size. Life in an oasis is secure and well organized. A wall is usually constructed around the oasis to keep out the violent dust storms called simooms. The oasis people live in mud-brick houses with flat roofs, closely packed together. The streets are narrow and winding, and the heart of the settlement is dominated by the suq (central market place), the mosque, school and shopping blocks. *Suqs* may also be set up miles from anywhere and people come from a number of surrounding settlements on special days to trade.

The oasis in the Algerian Sahara. The dunes are gradually encroaching on the date palms.

Around the settlement are the agricultural lands. Water is led to the fields by irrigation channels or drawn up from wells by camels or mules. The most important tree is the date palm which is grown in dug-out hollows so that its roots can penetrate deep into the ground in search of water. The fruit is consumed locally and also exported. Other crops cultivated include maize, barley, wheat, cotton, sugar cane, fruits and vegetables. With the development of motor routes across the deserts, many sophisticated foreign goods can now reach the oases.

5. **The mining settlers.** The lure of mineral wealth has attracted many immigrants into the desert. Mining camps and isolated settlements have sprung up following the discovery of certain mineral deposits. It was gold that brought immigrants scrambling into the Great Australian Desert. Water and food supplies have to be brought 300 miles (482 km) from Perth to keep the mines going. Some of them like Kalgoorlie and Coolgardie have become towns of considerable size. In the Kalahari Desert, the discovery of diamonds and copper has brought many white men to the 'thirstland' as it is called. Even in the most arid Atacama, in northern Chile, large mining camps have been established for the mining of caliche (cemented gravels) from which *sodium nitrate,* a valuable fertilizer, is extracted and exported to all parts of the world. The mines are worked by local Indian labourers and supervised by foreign technicians. Besides nitrates, copper is also mined. These two products have directly or indirectly contributed to the growing size of the Chilean towns of Arica, Iquique, Antofagasta and Chuquicamata. The last named is the world's largest copper town. Similarly in the deserts of North America, *silver* is mined in Mexico, *uranium* in Utah and *copper* in Nevada. A host of other minerals and their by-products have, in fact, greatly altered the landscape and the economy of such arid regions.

In recent years, the discovery of oil, in many parts of the Saharan and Arabian Deserts has transformed this forgotten part of the globe. In Algeria, oil wells have been sunk two miles deep to tap oil. In the Middle East, pipelines over 1,000 miles (1,610 km) long have been laid to bring oil from the shores of the Persian Gulf across Saudi Arabia to Sidon (Lebanon) and Baniyas (Syria) on the Mediterranean coast. With still half of the world's reserves of oil untapped in this region, the deserts here will virtually be paved with gold! In Iraq, Kuwait, and Saudi Arabia the desert landscape is fast changing. New roads, huge palaces, ultra-modern hospitals, air-conditioned apartments and swimming pools, are examples of a thriving new era created entirely by oil – *liquid gold*.

QUESTIONS AND EXERCISES

1. Explain how the aridity of the desert is related to
   (a) offshore Trade Winds
   (b) the Sub-Tropical High Pressure Belts (the Horse Latitudes)
   (c) cold ocean currents
2. Bring out any distinct differences between the hot deserts and mid-latitude deserts in
   (a) climate
   (b) vegetation
   (c) way of life
3. With reference to actual examples, describe the activities and modes of living of the different groups of people that inhabit the deserts. Attempt to account for their differences.
4. Explain any *three* of the following.
   (a) The hot deserts of the world are located on the western coasts of continents.
   (b) Patagonia is a desert in the rain shadow of the Andes.
   (c) The annual range of temperature is much greater at Kashgar (Gobi) than at Iquique (Atacama).
   (d) Desert plants must adapt themselves to survive.
   (e) Camels are the 'ships of the desert'.
5. Write brief notes on any *three* of these topics.
   (a) The Bindibu of the Great Australian Desert.
   (b) Date palm cultivation in an oasis.
   (c) The role of oil in the development of desert economy.
   (d) The Bedouin – the wandering herdsmen.
   (e) Agricultural development of any selected desert region.

19 The Warm Temperate Western Margin (Mediterranean) Climate

Distribution

The Warm Temperate Western Margin Climate is found in relatively few areas in the world. They are entirely confined to the western portion of continental masses, between 30° and 45° north and south of the equator (Fig. 144). The basic cause of this type of climate is the shifting of the wind belts, explained in Chapter 13. Though the area around the Mediterranean Sea has the greatest extent of this type of 'winter rain climate', and gives rise to the more popular name Mediterranean Climate, the best developed form of this peculiar climatic type is, in fact, found in central Chile (Fig. 145 a). Valparaiso, a Chilean locale characterized by a Mediterranean climate, experiences the majority of its rainfall during the winter months (Fig. 145 b). Other Mediterranean regions include California (around San Francisco), the south-western tip of Africa (around Cape Town), southern Australia (in southern Victoria and around Adelaide, bordering the St. Vincent and Spencer Gulfs), and south-west Australia (Swanland).

Climate

The Mediterranean type of climate is characterized by very distinctive climatic features.

1. **A dry, warm summer with offshore trades.** As illustrated in Fig. 146 (a) and (b), the summer months have a relatively high temperature (77°F or 25°C in July in Rome and about 68°F or 20°C in February in Cape Town.) The highest temperatures are however experienced further away from the coast in the more continental eastern Mediterranean, in the interiors of the Balkan peninsula, the Anatolian Plateau and Mediterranean Middle East. For example, the July mean for Athens is 82°F or 28°C Larissa (Greece) 82°F or 28°C and Beirut

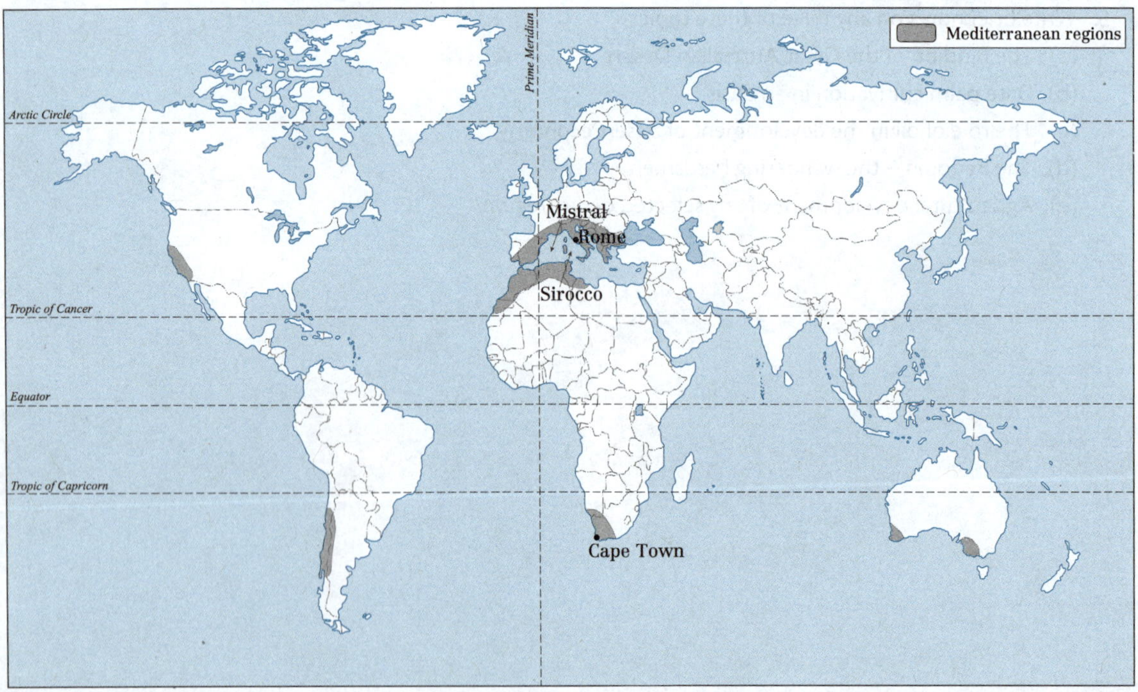

Fig. 144 Regions with a Mediterranean Climate

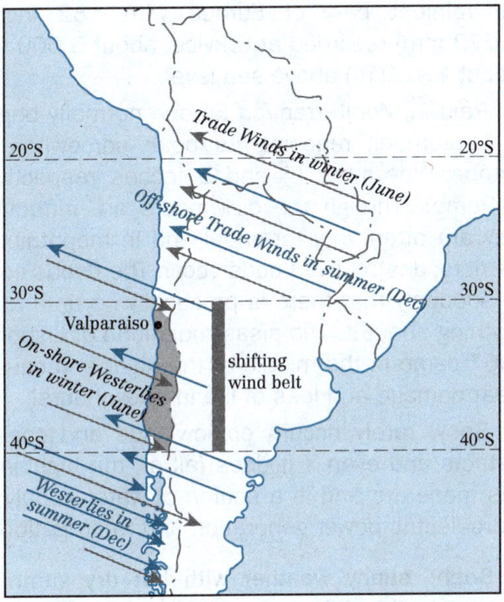

Fig. 145 (a) Central Chile—a region with a typical Mediterranean Climate—showing the shifting of the wind belt with most rain falling in winter

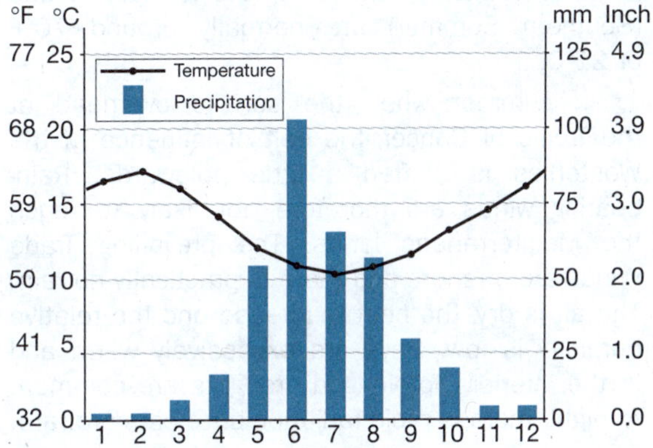

Fig. 145 (b) Valparaiso, Chile—known for its Mediterranean climate, receives the majority of its rainfall during the winter months.

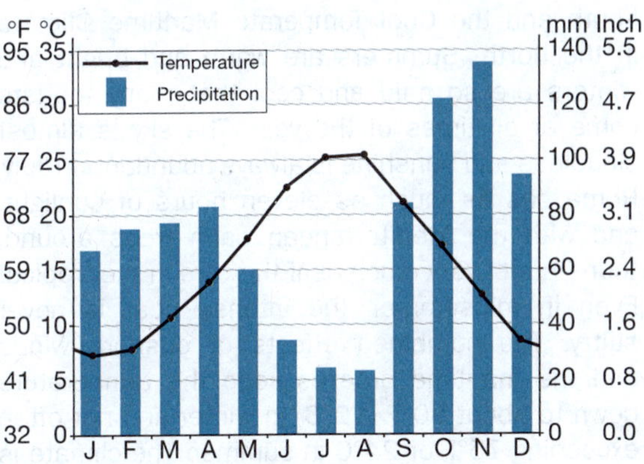

		J	F	M	A	M	J	J	A	S	O	N	D
Avg. Temp.	°C	7.2	7.8	10.6	13.8	17.9	22.5	25.2	25.4	21.1	17.1	12.6	8.5
	°F	45	46	51.1	56.9	64.2	72.5	77.3	77.7	70	62.8	54.7	47.3
Precip.	mm	67	75	77	83	60	34	24	23	84	122	135	94
	in	2	2	3	3	2	1	0	0	3	4	5	3

Data: 1991–2021

Place	Rome, Italy (42°N, 12°E)
Altitude	32 m or 105 feet
Annual precipitation	878 mm or 34.6 inches
Annual temperature range	32.7°F (77.7°F – 45.0°F) or 18.2°C (25.4°C – 7.2°C)

Fig. 146 (a) Mediterranean Climate in the northern hemisphere

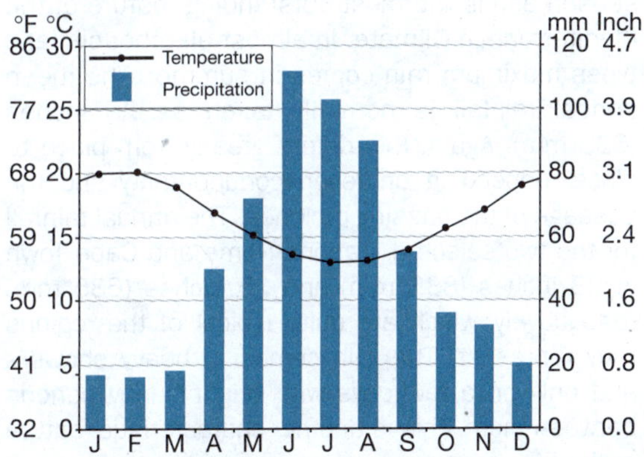

		J	F	M	A	M	J	J	A	S	O	N	D
Avg. Temp.	°C	20	20.1	18.9	16.9	15.1	13.6	13	13	14	15.7	17.1	19
	°F	67.9	68.1	66.1	62.3	59.2	56.4	55.5	55.5	57.1	60.2	62.7	66.2
Precip.	mm	17	16	18	50	72	112	103	90	55	36	32	20
	in	0	0	0	1	2	4	4	3	2	1	1	0

Data: 1991–2021

Place	Cape Town, South Africa (34°S, 18°E)
Altitude	27 m or 88 feet
Annual precipitation	621 mm or 24.4 inches
Annual temperature range	12.6°F (68.1°F – 55.5°F) or 7.0°C (20.1°C – 13.0°C)

(b) Mediterranean Climate in the southern hemisphere

(Lebanon) 79°F or 26°C. Elsewhere in central Chile, South Africa and Mediterranean Australia, due to their coastal position, the influence of the sea has modified the temperature and the January means (Southern Summer) are normally around 70°F or 21°C.

In summer when the sun is overhead at the Tropic of Cancer, the belt of influence of the Westerlies is shifted a little polewards. Rain-bearing winds are therefore not likely to reach the Mediterranean lands. The prevailing Trade Winds are offshore and there is practically no rain. The air is dry, the heat is intense and the relative humidity is low. Days are excessively warm and in the interiors, prolonged droughts are common. At night, there is rapid radiation but frosts are rare.

2. **A concentration of rainfall in winter with onshore Westerlies.** The Mediterranean lands receive most of their precipitation in winter when the Westerlies shift equatorwards. In the northern hemisphere, the prevailing onshore Westerlies bring much *cyclonic rain* from the Atlantic to the countries bordering the Mediterranean Sea. This is the rainy season and is the most outstanding feature of the Mediterranean Climate. In almost all other climatic types maximum rain comes in summer. The mean annual rainfall is normally taken as 25 inches (635 mm). Again, this differs greatly from place to place, depending on relief, continentality and the passage of the passing cyclones. The annual rainfall for the two selected stations Rome and Cape Town is 33 inches (838 mm) and 25 inches (635 mm) respectively, which are quite typical of the regions they represent. The rain comes in heavy showers and only on a few days with bright sunny periods between them. This is another characteristic feature of the Mediterranean winter rain.

With a little more caution in relating the relief of the Mediterranean lands to the rainfall distribution, you will notice that the Mediterranean regions are often backed by mountains of some kind. In Iberia, the central Meseta and other Sierras of the peninsula present an effective barrier to the oncoming Westerlies. As a result, the Portuguese coast is much wetter than eastern Spain. Lisbon has an annual rainfall of nearly 25 inches (635 mm) while Cartagena, along the eastern coast of Spain does not receive even half as much. Much heavier precipitation has been recorded in the highlands on windward slopes facing the Westerlies. The steep hills of the eastern Adriatic are the rainiest part of Europe with 182 inches (4,622 mm) recorded at Crkvice, about 3,600 feet (about 1,100 m) above sea level.

Rain in Mediterranean Europe normally begins in September, reaching its peak somewhere in October–November (4 and 5 inches respectively in Rome). Though the downpours are infrequent they are often very torrential and in mountainous districts, destructive floods occur. The floods come so suddenly that there is practically no time to do anything about it. The disastrous flood of Lisbon in 1967 came in the middle of the night and caused great damage and loss of life in a few hours!

Snow rarely occurs on lowlands and coastal districts and even if it does fall on the highlands, it is moderate and is a source of water supply for hydroelectric power generation and for irrigation.

3. **Bright, sunny weather with hot dry summers and wet, mild winters.** Considering its mid-latitude position, the Mediterranean regions have a very favourable climate, unrivalled by any other climatic regions. The climatic features are transitional between those of the Trade Wind Hot Desert in the south and the Cool Temperate Maritime Climate in the north. Summers are warm and bright and winters are so mild and cool that many tourists come at all times of the year. The sky is almost cloudless and sunshine is always abundant. In July, Rome has as much as eleven hours of sunlight, and with the Mediterranean palm trees around, tourists feel very much as if they are in the tropics! Even in midsummer, the intense heat is never sultry. The combined effects of onshore winds and the maritime breezes keep the temperature down to about 50°F (10°C) in winter and not often exceeding 75°F or 24°C in summer. The climate is so mild that many of the local people sleep in the open air. The annual temperature range is between 15° and 25°F (annual average air temperature of 16.3°C). The Mediterranean regions are famous for their health and pleasure resorts, frequented by millions all round the year.

4. **The prominence of local winds around the Mediterranean Sea.** Many local winds, some hot, others cold are common around the Mediterranean Sea. The causes are many and varied. The topography of the region with the high Alps in the north, the Sahara Desert in the south, continental interiors in the east and the open Atlantic on the west give rise to great differences in temperature,

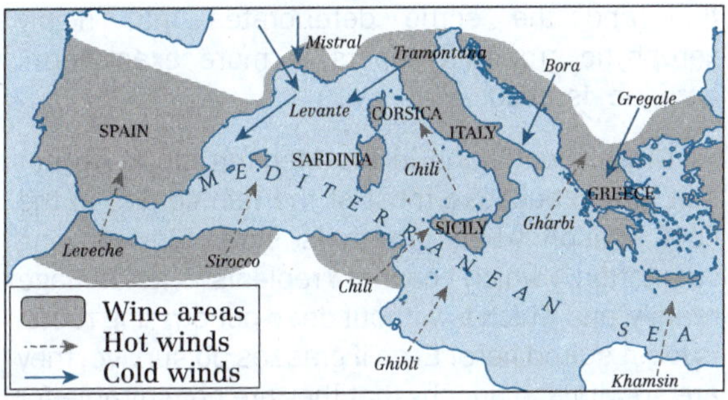

Fig. 147 Local Winds of the Mediterranean Sea

pressure and precipitation. The passing cyclones from the Atlantic, the anticyclones from the north, and the cold air masses from the continental interiors are often interrupted or channelled by relief features, resulting in the birth of local winds around the Mediterranean. These winds varying in *strength, direction and duration* affect the lives, crops and activities of the people there. Fig. 147 indicates the location and direction of some of these local winds and the more important ones are described below.

(a) **Sirocco.** This is a lot, dry dusty wind which originates in the Sahara Desert. Though it may occur at any time of the year, it is most frequent in spring and normally lasts for only a few days. The Sirocco blows outwards in a southerly direction from the desert interiors into the cooler Mediterranean Sea. It is usually associated with depressions from the Atlantic passing from the coast eastwards inland. After crossing the Mediterranean Sea, the Sirocco is slightly cooled by the absorption of the water vapour. Even then, it is still hot and dry with a temperature of over 105°F or 40°C. Its scorching breath withers vegetation and crops. The damage is particularly serious when it comes at the times during which vines and olives are in blossom. The Sirocco is so prominent that it is called by many other local names, such as Chili in Tunisia, Ghibli in Libya, Leveche in Spain, Khamsin in Egypt and Malta. In the Adriatic and Aegean Sea, this hot wind, better known as Gharbi, gathers much moisture causing fog, heavy dew and rain. This may be 'blood rain' because the wind is carrying the red dust of the Sahara Desert.

(b) **Mistral.** In contrast, the Mistral is a cold wind from the north, rushing down the Rhone valley in violent gusts between 40 and 80 miles per hour (64–128 km per hour). The velocity of the Mistral is intensified by the funnelling effect in the valley between the Alps and the Central Massif, and in extreme cases trains may be derailed and trees uprooted. In winter when the Mistral is most frequent the temperature of the wind may be below freezing-point, though the sky may be clear and cloudless. As a protective measure, many of the houses and orchards of the Rhone valley and the Riviera have thick rows of trees and hedges planted to shield them from the Mistral.

A similar type of cold north-easterly wind experienced along the Adriatic coast is called the Bora. Like the Mistral, it is caused by a difference in pressure between continental Europe and the Mediterranean. This usually occurs in winter, when the atmospheric pressure over continental Europe is higher than that of the Mediterranean Sea. The Bora thus blows outwards into the Mediterranean. This dry, icy wind is even more violent than the Mistral and speeds of over 100 m.p.h. (160 km.p.h.) have been recorded. During strong Boras, ships may be blown aground, and agricultural lands devastated. Tramontana and Gregale are similar cold winds of the Mediterranean Sea.

Natural Vegetation

In a land where half the year is dry, one cannot expect the natural vegetation to be luxuriant. Trees with small broad leaves are widely spaced and never very tall. Though there are many branches they are short and carry few leaves. The absence of shade is a distinct feature of Mediterranean lands. Growth is slow in the cooler and wetter season, even though more rain comes in winter. Growth is thus almost restricted to autumn and spring when the temperature is higher and moisture is just sufficient. The long summer drought checks the growth. One fact is clear, plants whether trees or shrubs, evergreen or deciduous, have to devise ways of adapting themselves to a climatic environment with such a marked rhythmic recurrence of rain and drought. In many ways, the vegetational responses to climatic demands in the Mediterranean are similar to those of the adjacent deserts and the savanna further south. Plants are in a continuous struggle against heat, dry air, excessive evaporation and prolonged droughts. They are, in short xerophytic, a word used to describe the drought-resistant plants in an environment deficient in moisture.

Types of Mediterranean vegetation. Various kinds of vegetation are found in the Mediterranean regions.

1. **Mediterranean evergreen forests.** These are open woodlands with evergreen oaks, of which the cork oaks of Spain and Portugal are the best known. They are found only in the climatically most favoured regions with a rainfall of well over 25 inches (635 mm). The trees are normally low, even stunted, with massive trunks, deeply fissured barks, small leathery leaves and a wide-spreading root system in search of water. The cork oaks are specially valued for their thick barks, used for making wine-bottle corks and for export around the world. In Australia, the eucalyptus forests replace the evergreen oak. The jarrah and karri trees are commercially the most important. The giant sequoia or redwood is typical of the Californian trees.

2. **Evergreen coniferous trees.** These include the various kinds of pines, firs, cedars and cypresses which have evergreen, needle-shaped leaves and tall, straight trunks. They appear more on the cooler highlands and where droughts are less severe. Deforestation has reduced their numbers considerably.

3. **Mediterranean bushes and shrubs.** This is perhaps the most predominant type of Mediterranean vegetation. Summers are so dry and hot that in places forests give place to short, evergreen shrubs and bushes. The low bushes grow in scattered clumps and are often thorny. The more common species are laurel, myrtle, lavender, arbutus and rosemary, of which a number are strongly scented or perfumed.

In many areas, due to people's interference in *forest depletion,* or to *overgrazing,* the original woodlands degenerate into a scrub vegetation with scattered, stunted trees and tall bushes. They are so different from the ordinary woodland or the true desert scrubland that special names have been given to them to distinguish their location in different parts of the Mediterranean lands. This type of vegetation is called maquis in southern France, and macchia in Italy. In California, the term chaparral is used and in Australia mallee scrub. In limestone uplands, where the soil is extremely thin and the scrub deteriorates into highly xerophytic ground creepers, a more exact term, garrigue, is used.

4. **Grass.** Conditions in the Mediterranean do not suit grass, because most of the rain comes in the cool season when growth is slow. Slow-growing vegetation, which cannot replenish its foliage readily, and which is without deep-penetrating roots, is least suited here. Even if grasses do survive, they are so wiry and bunchy that they are not suitable for animal farming. Cattle rearing is thus unimportant in the Mediterranean. The grass, which is replaced by certain drought-resistant varieties of shrubs and flowering herbs, can however support sheep or goats. Even this form of grazing has done more harm than good for it has promoted soil erosion and impoverished the hillslopes of the Mediterranean. Animal fats are not important here and the chief cooking oil is obtained from olives. Dairy products are net import items.

Economic Development of the Mediterranean Regions

Despite the semi-arid conditions over many parts of the Mediterranean lands, the climate as a whole is favourable. Its warm, bright summers and cool, moist winters enable a wide range of crops to be cultivated. One must not forget that the Mediterranean shore-lands were once the *cradle of world civilization.* Nowadays the area is important for fruit cultivation, cereal growing, winemaking and agricultural industries, as well as engineering and mining. We shall deal with some of them in greater detail below.

1. **Orchard farming.** The Mediterranean lands are also known as the world's orchard lands. A wide range of citrus fruits, such as oranges, lemons, limes, citrons and grapefruit, are grown. The fruit trees have long roots to draw water from considerable depths during the long summer drought. In exceptionally dry areas, *irrigation* helps to relieve the lack of moisture. In the Great Valley of California, the Vale of Chile, the Negev Desert of Israel and the northern shores of Mediterranean Europe, an elaborate system of irrigation canals enables both fruits and cereals to be successfully raised. The thick, leathery skin of the citrus fruits prevents excessive transpiration and the long, sunny summer enables the fruits to be

ripened and harvested. The various Mediterranean oranges are so distinctive in their shape, size, taste and quality that they are called by different names in their area of production. Of the Mediterranean oranges, perhaps, the best known are the Sunkist oranges from California, exported for table consumption and for making orange squash. The Seville oranges of Spain are small but very sweet and are particularly suitable for making marmalade. Those from Israel, the Jaffa oranges, are equally delicious and are specially grown for export. In Tangiers, the tangerine is of great local importance. In the temperate monsoon lands of China and Japan, which were, in fact, the native home of the orange, commercial cultivation of the fruit is less significant, and only in recent years has there been any serious effort made to popularize their export as mandarin oranges. The Mediterranean lands account for 70 per cent of the world's exports of citrus fruits.

The olive tree is probably the most typical of all Mediterranean cultivated vegetation. It is so hardy and long-rooted that it can survive even on very poor limestone soils with less than 10 inches of annual rainfall. Like our coconut palm, the olive tree is very 'versatile' and has many uses. The olive can be eaten fresh or pickled with spices. The fleshy part can be crushed and olive oil extracted, a valuable source of cooking oil in a region deficient in animal fat. Soap and margarine can also be made with the oil. Besides olives, many nut trees like chestnuts, walnuts, hazelnuts and almonds are grown and the nuts picked as fruits or for the chocolate industry. Other important fruits are peaches, apricots, pears, plums, cherries and figs.

2. **Crop cultivation.** Besides orchard fruits, the Mediterranean climate also supports many field crops. Cereals are by far the most important. Wheat is the leading food crop. Though conditions for extensive wheat cultivation are not as ideal as those of the cool temperate regions, the Mediterranean farmers have utilized the seasonal climatic rhythm to their best advantage. The wheat grown is mainly hard, winter wheat. It is suitable for both breadmaking and other food-products such as *macaroni, spaghetti* and *vermicelli.* The farmers

Olive cultivation in Andalusia, Spain. The small, gnarled trees are typical of the Mediterranean region.

usually sow the seeds in autumn, so that they germinate and grow steadily with the coming winter rain. By spring there is still sufficient moisture for the wheat to mature. The sunny weather of early summer ripens the grains and the wheat is harvested in almost guaranteed rainless weather. Barley is the next most popular cereal.

Summer crops are raised only where irrigation is possible. The water comes mainly from the melting snow that feeds the many rivers whose sources are in the highlands. Lowlands are intensively cultivated and the hill slopes are terraced. In Spain and Italy, the edges of the terraces are firmly piled with stones to prevent any soil from being washed away. Generally speaking, farms are small but there are also large holdings called *haciendas* in Spain which engage large numbers of paid labourers to work the farms. In a few localities, e.g. the Ebro basin in Spain, the Po Valley in Italy and in California, rice has been successfully cultivated and their yields are some of the highest in the world. In the more fertile plains, vegetables, especially beans, and flowers are grown for the local market. A little cotton and tobacco are also grown. The mountain pastures, with their cooler climate, support a few sheep, goats and sometimes cattle. Transhumance is widely practised.

3. **Wine production.** This is another speciality of the Mediterranean countries, because the best wine is essentially made from grapes. Some 85 per cent of grapes produced, go into wine. The long, sunny summer allows the grapes to ripen and then they are hand-picked. Viticulture is by tradition a Mediterranean occupation and the regions bordering the Mediterranean Sea account for three-quarters of the world's production of wine. In Spain, Portugal, France, and Italy, wine is the national drink. The average wine consumption of the Mediterranean countries is about 15 gallons per head per annum, whereas in USA it is not even one-twentieth as much!

Although grapes may be grown in many parts of the temperate lands, commercial viticulture is almost entirely confined to the Mediterranean regions. It has been estimated that 80 per cent

Grapes are grown in many Mediterranean countries. In Turkey, a portion of these grapes undergoes a unique and traditional process. Selected grapes are sun-dried to make sultanas, raisins and molasses.

of the world's total production of 70 million tons of grapes annually are being processed into wine. The quality of the fermented grape juice is decided by a number of factors including the types of *vines* grown, the quality of the *soil*, the *climate* of the region, the method and extent of *fermentation*. The fragrance, taste and quality of the final product is so varied that the price range is tremendous. Wine may be as cheap as any soft drink or as expensive as brandy. To differentiate the various kinds of wine, the principal wine areas of the world maintain their exclusive names. The wine from southern Spain is called *sherry*, from Portugal *port wine*. *Chianti*, *asti* and *marsala* come from different parts of Italy. In France the greatest wine regions are located further north, e.g. *Champagne* in the Paris basin, *Bordeaux* in the Garonne basin, *Burgundy* in the Rhone-Saone valley.

The world trade in fresh grapes is comparatively small, mainly from Mediterranean South Africa. Most of the inferior grapes are preserved as dried grapes and exported. They are known by several names, e.g. *currants* from the Levantine grapes, *raisins* from California, and *sultanas* from Asia Minor.

The other industries associated with Mediterranean agriculture are fruit canning, flour milling and food processing.

QUESTIONS AND EXERCISES

1. What is meant by the 'index plant' of a climatic type? In what ways are the following index plants representative of the type of climate indicated?
   (a) teak – Tropical Monsoon Climate
   (b) olive – Mediterranean Climate
   (c) cactus – Hot Desert Climate
   (d) spruce – Cool Temperate Continental Climate
2. The following statistics of the annual rainfall and annual temperature ranges of four Mediterranean lowland stations are taken from the Mediterranean shorelands. Attempt to explain their differences.

Station	Latitude	Longitude	rainfall	Annual temperature range
(a) Gibraltar	36°N	5°W	36"	20°F
(b) Marseilles	43°N	5°E	23"	28°F
(c) Athens	38°N	24°E	16"	32°F
(d) Alexandria	31°N	30°E	8"	23°F

3. Outline the various types of natural vegetation found in the Mediterranean regions. Relate this to climate, soil and human interference.
4. Give an explanatory account of the following statements about economic activities of the Mediterranean lands.
   (a) Orchard farming is the predominant occupation.
   (b) The chief cereal cultivated is hard, winter wheat.
   (c) Pastoral farming is of little importance.
5. Write geographical notes on any *three* of the following.
   (a) The Mediterranean Climate is typified by dry, sunny summers and wet, mild winters.
   (b) Hot, dusty Sirocco and cold stormy Mistral.
   (c) Mediterranean woodlands, shrubs and scrub.
   (d) Three-quarters of the world's wine comes from the Mediterranean regions of Europe.

20 The Temperate Continental (Steppe) Climate

Distribution

Bordering the deserts, away from the Mediterranean regions and in the interiors of continents are the temperate grasslands. Though they lie in the Westerly wind belt, they are so remote from maritime influence that the grasslands are practically treeless. These grasslands are so distinctive in their natural vegetation that, although those which occur in the southern hemisphere have a much more moderate climate, they are often dealt with together. In the northern hemisphere, the grasslands are far more extensive and are entirely continental. In Eurasia, they are called the Steppes, and stretch eastwards from the shores of the Black Sea across the great Russian plain to the foothills of the Altai Mountains, a distance of well over 2,000 miles (3,218 km). They are broken in a few places, being interrupted by the highlands. There are isolated sections in the Pustaz of Hungary and the plains of Manchuria (also called as Northeast China Plain). In North America, the grasslands are also quite extensive and are called Prairies. They lie between the foothills of the Rockies and the Great Lakes astride the American-Canadian border (Fig. 148).

In the southern hemisphere, due to the narrowness of the temperate portions of the southern continents, the grasslands are rather restricted and less continental. In the case of the Pampas of Argentina and Uruguay, the grasslands extend right to the sea and enjoy much maritime influence. In South Africa, the grasslands are sandwiched between the Drakensberg and the Kalahari Desert; and are further subdivided into the more tropical Bushveld in the north, and the more temperate Highveld in the south. The word 'veld' is a Dutch word given by the early pioneer Dutch farmers who came to settle here. It means 'field' and is pronounced as 'felt'. In Australia,

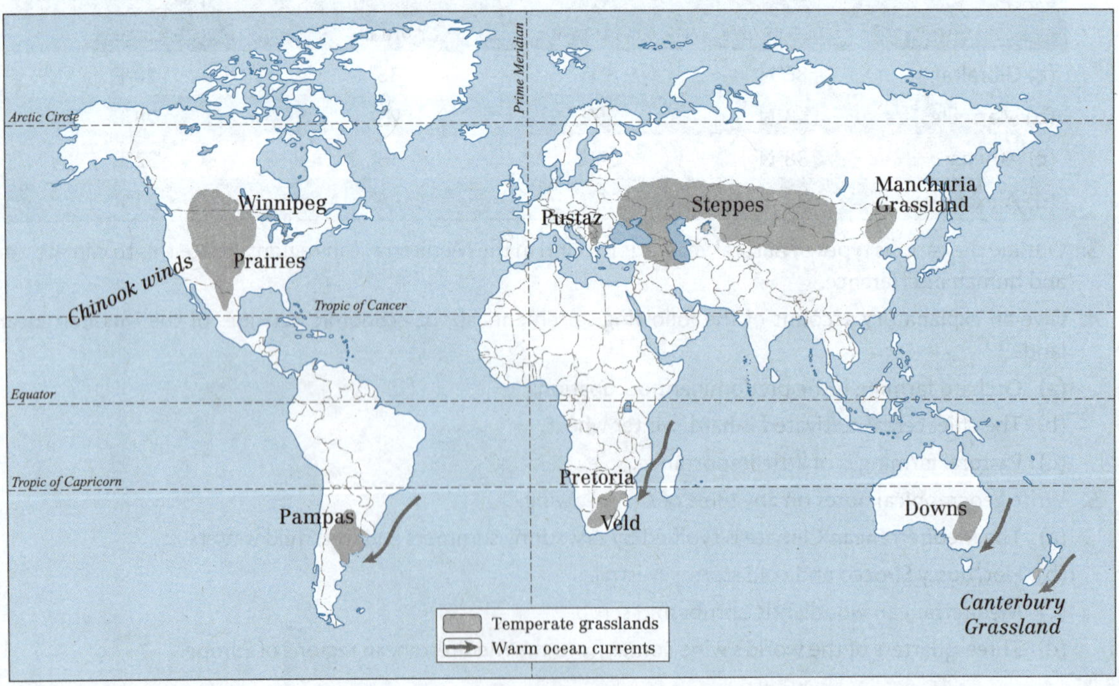

Fig. 148 The Temperate Grasslands

the grasslands are better known as Downs and are found in the Murray-Darling basin of southern Australia.

Climate

Temperature. Their location in the heart of continents means that they have little maritime influence. Their climate is thus continental with extremes of temperature. Summers are very warm, over 68°F (20°C) in Winnipeg for July, as illustrated in Fig. 149 (a) and 72°F (22°C) for January for Pretoria as shown in Fig. 149 (b). Winters are very cold in the continental steppes of Eurasia because of the enormous distances from the nearest sea. The winter months are well below freezing and in Winnipeg the January reading is 3.7°F (–15.7°C), 36° below freezing-point.

In contrast, the steppe type of climate in the southern hemisphere is never severe. The winters are so mild that the mean temperature for any of the winter months is usually between 35° and 55°F (2°–13°C). Temperatures below freezing point even in midwinter (July in the southern hemisphere) are exceptional. Pretoria, the station chosen to illustrate the steppe type of climate in the southern

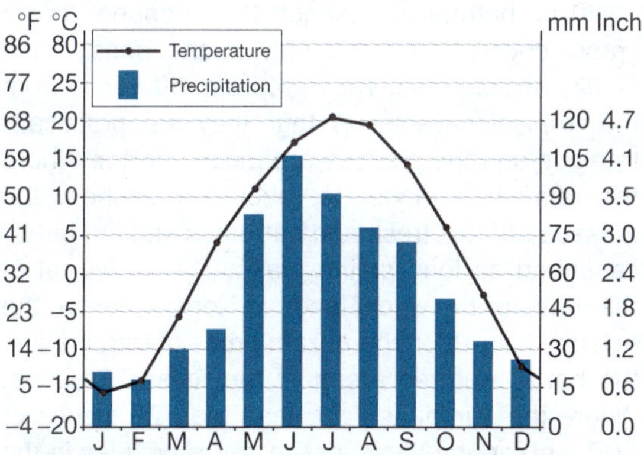

		J	F	M	A	M	J	J	A	S	O	N	D
Avg. Temp.	°C	–15.7	–14.1	–5.6	4.1	11.1	17.2	20.4	19.4	14.2	6	–2.8	–12.2
	°F	3.7	6.6	21.9	39.3	52.1	62.9	68.8	67	57.6	42.7	26.9	10.1
Precip.	mm	21	18	30	38	83	106	91	78	72	50	33	26
	in	0	0	1	1	3	4	3	3	2	1	1	1

Data: 1991–2021

Place	Winnipeg, Canadian Prairies (50°N, 97°W)
Altitude	234 m or 768 feet
Annual precipitation	646 mm or 25.4 inch
Annual temperature range	65.1°F (68.8°F–3.7°F) or 36.1°C (20.4°C– –15.7°C)

Fig. 149 (a) Steppe Climate in the northern hemisphere

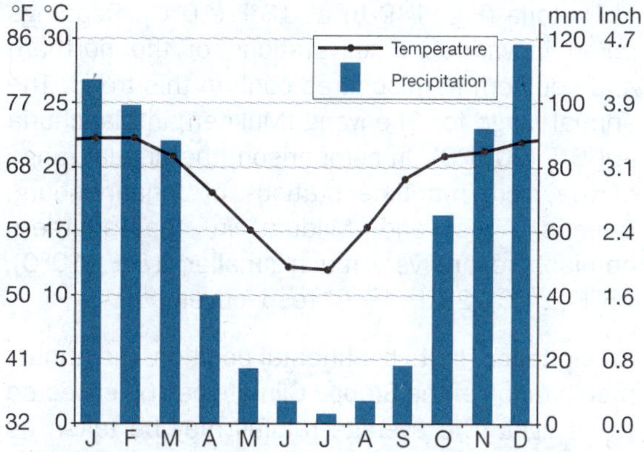

		J	F	M	A	M	J	J	A	S	O	N	D
Avg. Temp.	°C	22.3	22.3	20.8	18	15.1	12.2	12	15.3	19.1	20.9	21.3	22
	°F	72.1	72.1	69.5	64.4	59.1	54	53.6	59.5	66.3	69.6	70.3	71.6
Precip.	mm	107	99	88	40	17	7	3	7	18	65	92	118
	in	4	3	3	1	0	0	0	0	0	2	3	4

Data: 1991–2021

Place	Pretoria, Transvaal, Republic of South Africa (25°S, 28°E)
Altitude	1,280 m or 4,200 feet
Annual precipitation	661 mm or 26.0 inch
Annual temperature range	18.5°F (72.1°F–53.6°F) or 10.3°C (22.3°C–12.0°C)

Fig. 149 (b) Steppe Climate in the southern hemisphere

hemisphere has 53.6°F (12°C) in mid-winter (July), the coldest month of the year. Statistics from other parts of the southern continents also show a mild winter. For example, the July mean (mid-winter) for Johannesburg is 49°F (9.5°C), for Buenos Aires, 51°F (10.5°C), and for Mildura (Murray-Darling basin), 51°F (10.5°C) These statistics establish the moderating effects of oceans on the climates of the southern hemisphere.

The annual range of temperature is great, a direct result of continentality. Winters are so cold that parts of the Eurasian Steppes are snow-covered for several months. The snow melts with the return of spring and by mid-summer, temperatures soar to over 65°F (18°C). It is really hot for its latitude. For example, the mid-summer temperatures for Kyiv (Kiev) is 67°F (19°C). The stations in the southern hemisphere record even higher temperatures, e.g. 67°F (19°C) in Johannesburg, 74°F (23°C) in Buenos Aires and 77°F (25°C) in Mildura.

It is clear from the two selected stations given that there is a tremendous difference between the annual temperature range of the northern and southern hemispheres, again a factor of continentality. The range in Winnipeg (Fig. 149 a), is 65°F (36°C), over three times as great as that of Pretoria (Fig. 149 b) at 18°F (10°C). Readings taken in various other stations of the northern and southern hemispheres confirm this trend. The annual range for Shenyang (Mukden) in Manchuria is 69°F (20.5°C). In comparison, the annual range of the more maritime stations of Johannesburg, Buenos Aires and Mildura in the southern hemisphere are very much smaller, 18°F (10°C), 25°F (14°C), 28°F (17°C) respectively.

Precipitation. In its continental position, the annual precipitation of the Steppe Climate can be expected to be light. The average rainfall may be taken as about 20 inches (about 500 mm), but this again varies according to location from 10 inches to 30 inches (about 250–750 mm). Winnipeg, in Fig. 149 (a), has 25.4 inches (646 mm) with a distinct summer maximum from convectional sources, when the continental interiors are intensely heated. The heaviest rain comes in the middle of the year with 4.0 and 3.0 inches (106 and 91 mm) each in June and July. Most of the winter months have about an inch of precipitation, brought by the occasional depressions of the Westerlies and coming in the form of snow. In many other continental stations, the annual precipitation is even less, though the general pattern remains the same with most of the rain falling in the summer.

The maritime influence in the steppe type of climate of the southern hemisphere is even better brought out by the rainfall regime. Its annual precipitation is always more than the average 20 inches (or 500 mm) because of the warm ocean currents that wash the shores of the steppe-lands here. Pretoria, in Fig. 149 (b), has an annual precipitation of 26 inches (661 mm) with the wettest months in November, December, January and February, the summer season of the southern hemisphere. There are three months (June, July and August) without any rain. This is the period of drought that may have such a disastrous effect on the sheep rearing industry here. The dry season is particularly pronounced in temperate grasslands adjoining deserts, for example in Australia. Mildura, on the fringe of the mallee scrub of the Great Australian Desert, and also in the rain shadow area of the Great Dividing Range, has an annual rainfall of only 10.8 inches (274 mm). Irrigation is essential. The other southern hemisphere stations, have moderate rainfall, e.g. 30.9 inches (784 mm) in Johannesburg and 43.8 inches (1,112 mm) in Buenos Aires.

On the eastern slopes of the Rockies in Canada and USA a local wind, similar to the Fohn in Switzerland, called the Chinook, comes in a southwesterly direction to the Prairies and has a considerable effect on the local pastures. It actually comes with the depressions in winter or early spring from the Pacific coast ascending the Rockies and then descending to the Prairies. It is a hot wind and may raise the temperature by 40°F (about 4°–5°C) within a matter of 20 minutes. As it melts the snow cover in the pastures, animals can be driven out of doors to graze in the open fields. The agricultural year is thus accelerated. Local farmers welcome the Chinook for frequent Chinooks mean mild winters.

Natural Vegetation

Though the term 'steppe vegetation' geographically refers to the scanty vegetation of the sub-arid lands of continental Eurasia, many authors, including the late Professor Sir Dudley Stamp, have extended the term to include the temperate grassland all over the world. In this connection, our reference to steppe grassland is taken to mean the temperate grasslands of the mid-latitudes, the Steppes, Prairies, Pampas, Veld and Downs.

It is natural to expect the steppes to be grass- covered, differing only in the *density* and *quality* of the grass. Their greatest difference from the tropical savanna is that they are practically treeless and the grasses are much shorter. Where the rainfall is moderate, above 20 inches, the grasses are tall, fresh and nutritious and are better described as long prairie grass. This is typical of the grass of the wheat-lands in North America, the rich black earth or chernozem areas of Ukraine and the better watered areas of the Asiatic Steppes. Where the rainfall is light (less than 20 inches or 500 mm) or unreliable, or the soil is poor, as in the continental interiors of Asia the short steppe type of grass prevails (Fig. 150). The grasses are not only shorter but also wiry and sparse, often found in discontinuous clumps, with bare soil exposed between them. These areas are less suitable for arable farming and are used for some form of ranching as in the High Plains of USA.

The climatic requirements of grass are quite different from those of trees. They require less moisture than trees and an annual precipitation of 10 to 20 inches (about 250–500 mm) is adequate.

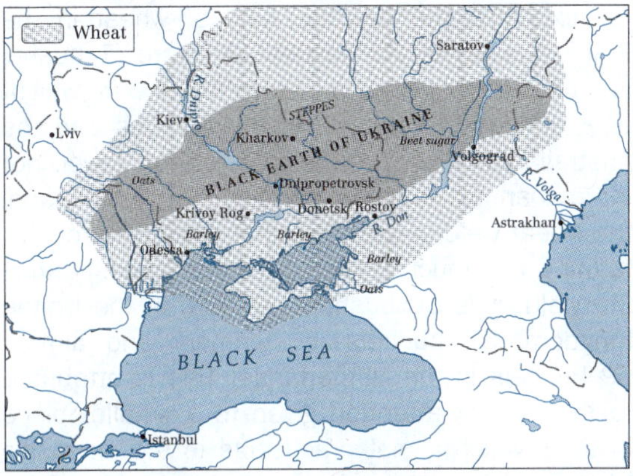

Fig. 150 The Black Earth region of Ukraine, part of the Eurasian Steppes

Their growth is not abruptly checked by summer droughts or winter cold. The steppe grass can lie dormant throughout the prolonged drought. They sprout and come to life as soon as the temperature is warm enough for plant growth (43°F or 6°C) and grow steadily with very little moisture.

The *appearance* of the temperate grasslands varies with seasons. In spring, the grass begins to appear, green, fresh and blooming with small, colourful flowers. The light rainfall that comes in late spring and early summer greatly stimulates their growth and there is plenty for the animals to graze. The herdsmen are busiest at this time. In summer, there is so much heat and evaporation that the grass is scorched. The carpet of bluish-green grass turns yellow and soon brown. Towards autumn, the grass withers and dies, but the roots remain alive and lie dormant throughout the cold winter. The winter is harsh and long, but the snow is never of great depth. Everything is quiet but with the next spring, the cycle is repeated and the steppe is alive again.

The prairies, Saskatchewan, Canada. Notice the grain elevators by the railway line

Trees are very scarce in the steppes, because of the scanty rainfall, long droughts and severe winters. The rolling plain is an endless stretch of grass, whether green or brown, except along the water courses where a few low willows, poplars or alders break the monotony. Polewards, an increase in precipitation gives rise to a transitional zone of wooded steppes where some conifers gradually appear. Even then, the trees are very scattered and few in number. Towards the equator, the steppe grass becomes shorter and sparser, till it merges into the desert with thorny scrub.

In the cultivated regions, such as the wheat farms of the Prairies, double rows of trees are planted around the house to shield the occupants from the strong winds which come unobstructed across miles of level ground. This provides the greatest contrast in a land which is essentially grass. There are no hedges and few fences and the rows of planted trees form an unusual landmark from the air!

Economic Development

The temperate grasslands were once the home of grazing animals; wild horses in the Asiatic Steppes, swift-footed bison in the Prairies and untamed buffaloes in the Pampas. Even as recently, as the last century, these grasslands were dominated by nomadic and semi-nomadic people like the *Kirghiz* of the Asiatic Steppes. They roamed far and wide with their herds and earned a precarious living from whatever pastures they could find. The *Red Indians* of North America were mostly hunters who moved around after the bison and other animals. Cultivation was unknown and the region was one of the most sparsely populated parts of the world. In recent years great changes have taken place in the grasslands and few areas, in fact; have managed to retain their original landscape. The grasslands have been ploughed up for extensive, mechanized wheat cultivation and are now the granaries of the world. Besides wheat, maize is increasingly cultivated in the warmer and wetter areas. The tufted grasses have been replaced by the more nutritious lucerne or alfalfa grass for cattle and sheep rearing. These temperate grasslands are now the leading ranching regions of the globe. We shall now describe more closely each of these economic activities.

1. **Nomadic herding.** This type of migratory animal grazing has almost disappeared from the major grasslands. The herders were wandering tribes, e.g. the Kirghiz, the Kazakhs, and the Kalmuks (also spelled Kalmyks). They used to travel over long distances like the Bedouin of the Arabian Desert, in search of grass and water for their animals-cattle, sheep, goats and horses. From these domesticated animals they obtained meat, milk, wool, hides, bones and horn. You would be surprised at the number of things they made out of these. The wool was woven into felt for tents and garments. The leather was used for making boots, saddles and belts, which were very essential in a country where the chief riding animal was the horse. The bones and horns were not wasted but made into tools, utensils and weapons. Many of their home-made products were exchanged at trading posts or with the caravans for guns, canned food, grains, tea, coffee, sugar, medicines and other essential goods.

The harsh environment of the nomads, with long droughts and unreliable showers made the Kirghiz a tough and fearless people, the Tartars and they long resisted subjugation by the Russians. Now, however, under the Communist regime they are being forced to settle down. The steppes which they used to wander have been made into huge collective farms and state farms for ranching or producing cereals.

2. **Extensive mechanized wheat cultivation.** The temperate grasslands are ideal for extensive wheat cultivation. The cool, moist spring stimulates early growth and the light showers in the ripening period help to swell the grains to ensure a good yield. The warm, sunny summer is not only advantageous for harvesting, but also enables the straw to be dried for farm use. In addition, the levelness of the Steppes and other temperate grasslands all over the world makes ploughing and harvesting a comparatively easy job. Mechanical ploughs loosen the soil and get the fields ready for sowing in the shortest possible time. In the Prairies, the Argentinian Pampas, the Ukrainian Steppes and the Downs of Australia *combine-harvesters,* reap, thresh, winnow and sack the grains almost as soon as the stalks are gathered.

One distinct drawback of this form of extensive mechanized farming is the consequent low yield. For example, the average yield of wheat in the Prairies is about 23 bushels per acre (1 bushel is approximately equivalent to 60 lb. in weight or 8 gallons in volume). In the Pampas and the Australian Downs, the yields are even lower, not more than 20 bushels per acre! In comparison, the wheat yield in countries that practise intensive farming are much higher, at times almost thrice the yield. It is 50 bushels per acre in the United Kingdom, 57 bushels in Denmark and almost 59 bushels in the Netherlands! This is attributed to the greater attention given to a smaller piece of land, which is not practicable in the extensive wheat-lands where a farmer owns anything from 600 to 40,000 acres as in the Prairies. But if we consider the yield per man, this is very much higher in the extensive farms. In this respect, the sparsely populated temperate grasslands of the mid-latitudes produce the greatest quantity of wheat per capita amongst the world's wheat-growing nations. They are, naturally the greatest wheat exporters. Three-quarters of Canada's 10 million tons of annual wheat production is exported, mainly to Europe which does not produce sufficient wheat to feed the very dense population, despite the high wheat yield. Europe's wheat needs are so great that shipments of wheat and flour arrive at the ports from almost every part of the temperate grasslands, from the USA, Argentina, Uruguay, Australia and Russia.

Three-quarters of the world's wheat is winter wheat, i.e. wheat sown in winter or late autumn. It is a hard wheat with a low moisture content, being ripened in the hot, sunny, continental summer. It is best for bread-making and is extensively traded. Polewards, where the winter temperatures are too cold for the wheat seedlings to survive, spring wheat is grown. It is the less important soft wheat, more suitable for making cakes, biscuits and pastes rather than bread. In North America, winter wheat is dominant south of the Great Lakes in USA, while spring wheat is sown mainly in the Canadian Prairie provinces of Alberta, Saskatchewan and Manitoba (Fig. 151). Scientific plant breeding has now devised cold resistant varieties that can mature within 110 days. This has resulted in the northward extension of the wheat cultivation into the Peace River region in Canada. In the warmer, wetter regions, maize is increasingly grown.

3. **Pastoral farming.** When pioneer settlers first moved into the temperate grasslands, there

A cargo ship loading grain for export at Port of Thunder Bay, Ontario

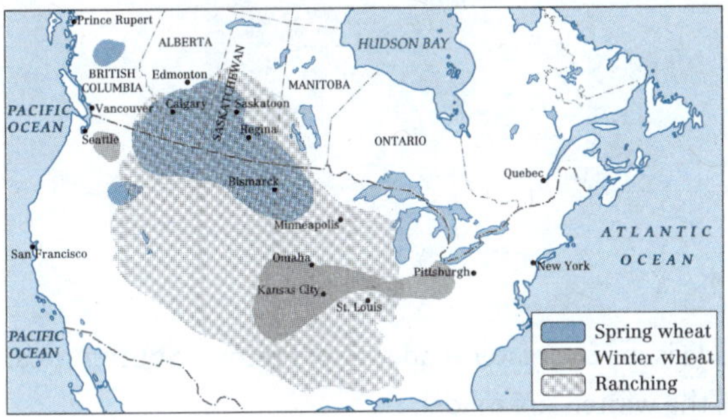

Fig. 151 Wheat production and ranching in the North American grasslands

were very few animals. The natural conditions suit animal farming. Subsequently, cattle, sheep, pigs and horses were introduced, and they proved very successful. With the development of refrigerated ships in the late nineteenth century, the temperate grasslands became major pastoral regions, exporting large quantities of beef, mutton, wool, hides. Milk, butter, cheese and other dairy products are also important in some parts of the North American grasslands. The development was particularly spectacular in the southern hemisphere, (Figs 152, 153 and 154) where the winters are milder and the rainfall is more evenly distributed. The original tuft-grass was ploughed up and replaced by sown alfalfa. The semi-wild cattle in the Pampas were either crossed with or replaced by the imported pedigree stock from Europe. Soon the Pampas became so involved with the pastoral industry that it took the lead in the world's export of beef. Large *estancias* (ranches) were established, linked to the *frigorificos* (meat-packing factories) in the coastal ports by a dense network of roads and railways. The growth was rapid and towns like Buenos

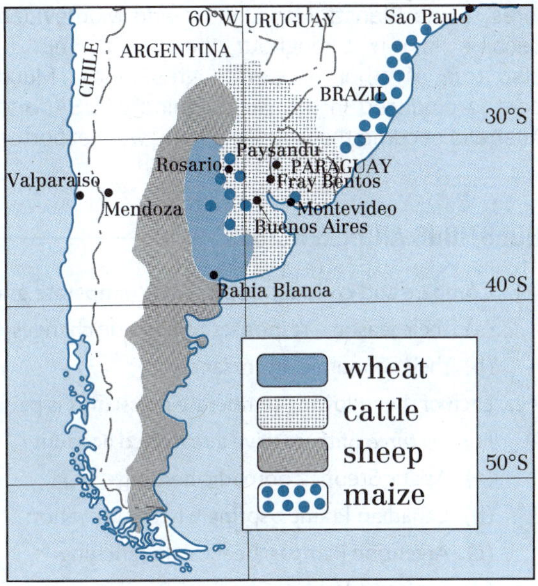

Fig. 152 Sheep, cattle, wheat and maize production in southern South America

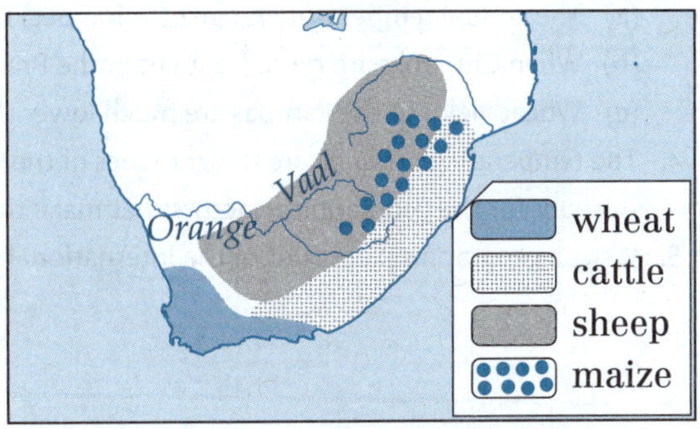

Fig. 153 Agriculture in the veld of southern Africa

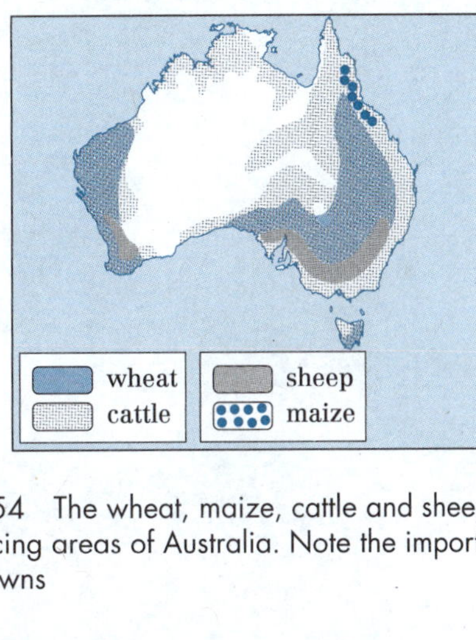

Fig. 154 The wheat, maize, cattle and sheep producing areas of Australia. Note the importance of the Downs

Aires, Bahia Blanca, Fray Bentos and Montevideo became known throughout the world. This is also true of other temperate grasslands. Much beef is produced in the Great Plains of USA, and Australia became the world's leading wool exporter, accounting for a third of its total production. In the Eurasian Steppes, too, increasing emphasis is being placed on the ranching of animals for meat production.

QUESTIONS AND EXERCISES

1. Compare and contrast tropical and temperate grasslands in respect of
   (a) their seasonal responses to climatic changes
   (b) their economic importance
2. Each of the following temperate grasslands is paired with an important aspect of its economic life. For any *three* of them, give a reasoned account
   (a) Asiatic Steppes: nomadic herding
   (b) Canadian Prairies: spring wheat cultivation
   (c) Argentine Pampas: beef cattle ranching
   (d) S. African Veld: maize growing
   (e) Australian Downs: sheep grazing
3. Explain why
   (a) The annual temperature range of Winnipeg, Canada is much greater than that of Pretoria, South Africa.
   (b) When Chinooks are more frequent in the Prairies, the winters are milder.
   (c) Wheat yields in the Pampas are much lower than those of Denmark.
4. The temperate grasslands are the granaries of the world. To what extent this is true? Account for the geographical factors that make this possible.
5. Write a geographical account of the international trade in wheat.

21 The Warm Temperate Eastern Margin (China Type) Climate

Distribution

This type of climate is found on the eastern margins of continents in warm temperate latitudes, just outside the tropics (Fig. 155). It has comparatively more rainfall than the Mediterranean climate in the same latitudes, coming mainly in the summer. It is, in fact, the climate of most parts of China – a modified form of monsoonal climate. It is thus also called the *Temperate Monsoon or China Type* of climate. In south-eastern USA, bordering the Gulf of Mexico, continental heating in summer induces an inflow of air from the cooler Atlantic Ocean. Though less pronounced, the overall climatic features resemble those of the China type. It is sometimes referred to as the Gulf type of climate.

In the southern hemisphere, this kind of climate is experienced along the warm temperate eastern coastlands of all the three continents: in New South Wales with its eucalyptus forests; in Natal where sugar cane thrives; and in the maize belt of the Parana-Paraguay-Uruguay basin. As the regions are influenced by the onshore Trade Winds all year round, without any monsoon variations, the climate cannot be described as temperate monsoon. It is sometimes referred to as the Natal type of climate.

Climate

The Warm Temperate Eastern Margin Climate is typified by a warm moist summer and a cool, dry winter. The mean monthly temperature varies between 40°F. and 82°F (5°C and 28°C). and is strongly modified by maritime influence. Occasionally, the penetration of cold air from the continental interiors may bring down the temperature to freezing point. Though frosts are rare they occasionally occur in the colder interiors. For most of the time, it is pleasantly warm. The relative humidity is a little high

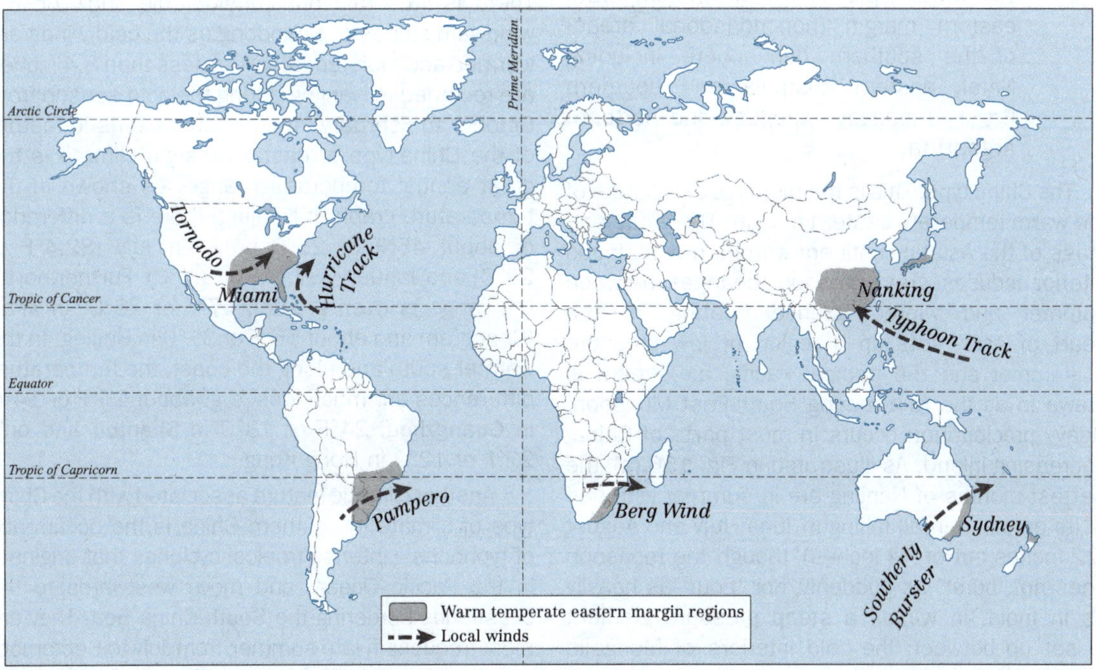

Fig. 155 Regions with a Warm Temperate Eastern Margin Climate

in midsummer when the heat becomes oppressive and can be very trying to the white settlers, e.g. in Natal.

Rainfall is more than moderate, anything from 25 inches to 60 inches (635 mm to 1525 mm). This is adequate for all agricultural purposes and the Warm Temperate Eastern Margin Climate supports a wide range of crops. Areas which experience this climate are very densely populated. Another important feature is the fairly uniform distribution of rainfall throughout the year. There is rain every month, except in the interior of central China, where there is a distinct dry season. Rain comes either from convectional sources or as orographic rain in summer, or from depressions in prolonged showers in winter. Local storms, e.g. typhoons, and hurricanes, also occur.

There is a good deal of variation in detail within the eastern margins and it is essential to examine them by reference to specific areas, where the local factors affect the climates. We shall subdivide them into three main types.

1. **The China type:** central and north China, including southern Japan (temperate monsoonal)
2. **The Gulf type:** south-eastern United States, (slight-monsoonal)
3. **The Natal type:** all the warm temperate eastern margin (non-monsoonal areas) of the southern hemisphere including Natal, eastern Australia and southern Brazil – Paraguay – Uruguay and northern Argentina.

1. **The China type.** This is the most typical climate of the warm temperate eastern margin. The great land mass of the Asiatic continent with its mountainous interior induces great pressure changes between summer and winter. Intense heating in 'the heart of Asia' sets up a region of low pressure in summer and the tropical Pacific air stream is drawn in as the rain-bearing South-East Monsoon. Heavy precipitation occurs in most parts of China, decreasing inland. As illustrated in Fig. 156 (a), the wettest months of Nanjing are in summer with half of its annual rainfall falling in June, July and August (22 inches out of 44 inches), though the monsoon does not 'burst' as suddenly, nor 'pour' as heavily as in India. In *winter,* a steep pressure gradient is set up between the cold interiors of Mongolia and Siberia, and the warmer Pacific coastlands.

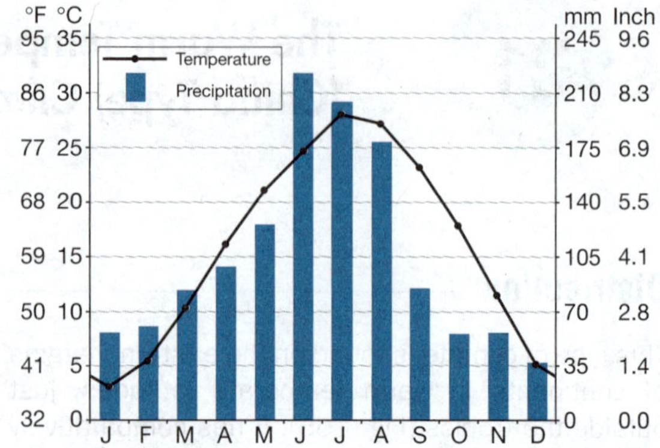

		J	F	M	A	M	J	J	A	S	O	N	D	Range/ Total
Temp.	°C	3.1	5.4	10.3	16.1	21.1	24.6	28.0	27.2	23.2	17.8	11.5	5.0	7
	°F	37.5	41.7	50.6	61.0	69.9	76.3	82.4	81.0	73.8	64.1	52.6	41.0	45
Precip.	mm	56	60	83	98	125	222	203	178	84	55	56	36	1256
	in	2	2	3	3	4	8	7	7	3	2	2	1	44

Data: 1991–2021

Place	Nanjing, China (32°N, 119°E)
Altitude	12 metre or 39 feet
Annual temperature range	45°F or 7°C
Annual precipitation	49 inches or 1256 mm

Fig. 156 (a) Warm Temperate Eastern Margin Climate in the northern hemisphere (China type)

The continental polar air stream flows outwards as the North-West Monsoon, bitterly cold and very dry. There is little rain but considerable snow on the windward slopes of Shandong as the cold winds are warmed and moistened. In fact, less than 8.4 inches are recorded in Nanjing during the cold season from October to February. Another characteristic feature of the China-type of eastern margin climate is the great annual temperature range. As shown in the temperature graph of Nanjing, there is a difference of about 45°F or 25°C between July (82.4°F or 28°C) and January (37.5°F or 3.1°C). Further north, the range is even greater, 47°F or 26°C. in Xi'an (Chang'an) and about 56°F or 31°C in Beijing. In the warmer south and along the coast, the temperature differences are much less, e.g. about 25°F or 14°C in **Guangzhou**, 24°F or 13°C in **Shantou** and only 22°F or 12°C in Hong Kong.

Another climatic feature associated with the China type of climate in southern China is the occurrence of typhoons – intense tropical cyclones that originate in the Pacific Ocean, and move westwards to the coastlands bordering the South China Sea. They are most frequent in late summer, from July to September and can be very disastrous. The winds blow with tremendous strength, the sky is overcast and there are torrential downpours. As much as 24 inches (610 mm) in a day have been recorded and flooding is widespread. Millions of people across large parts of eastern China were affected by Typhoon Muifa, which hit the area in September 2022.

2. **The Gulf type.** The Gulf-Atlantic regions of the United States experience a type of climate similar to that of central China except that the monsoonal characteristics are less well established. There is no complete seasonal wind reversal, for the pressure gradient between mainland America and the Atlantic Ocean is less marked. As can be seen from the graph in Fig. 156 (b) for Miami, Florida, the difference in temperature between mid-summer (July, 82°F or 28°C) and mid-winter (January, 68°F or 20°C) is only 14°F or 8°C. The warm Gulf Stream and the onshore Trade Winds help to bring about this narrow range of temperature.

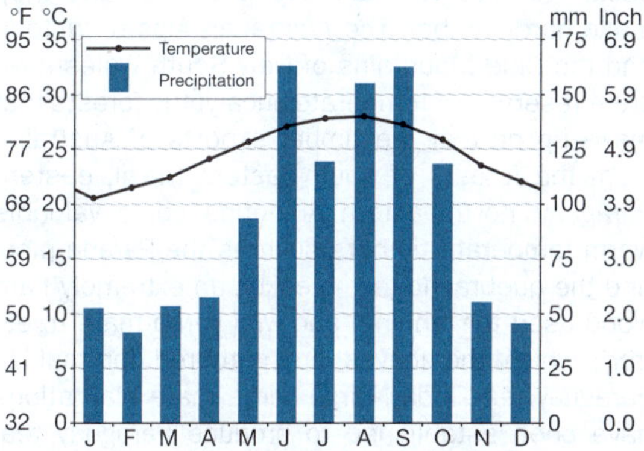

		J	F	M	A	M	J	J	A	S	O	N	D	Range/ Total
Temp.	°C	20.5	21.4	22.3	24.0	25.6	27.0	27.8	28.0	27.2	25.8	23.4	22.0	7.5
	°F	68.8	70.5	72.2	75.3	78.1	80.7	82.0	82.3	81.0	78.4	74.2	71.6	13.5
Precip.	mm	52	41	53	57	93	163	119	155	162	118	55	45	1113
	in	2	1	2	2	3	6	4	6	6	4	2	1	44

Data: 1991–2021

Place	Miami, Florida, USA (26°N, 80°W)
Altitude	11 m or 36 feet
Annual temperature range	13.5°F or 7.5°C
Annual precipitation	44 inches or 1113 mm

Fig. 156 (b) Warm Temperate Eastern Margin Climate in the northern hemisphere (Gulf type)

Summers are warm and pleasant, Miami, being an important holiday resort, and it rarely snows in winter.

The annual rainfall is heavy with 44 inches or 1113 mm in Miami, 54 inches or 1183 mm in New Orleans; 45.6 inches or 1159 mm in Montgomery and 48 inches or 1219 mm in Charleston. There is no distinct dry period as in monsoon lands, and the abundant moisture has stimulated extensive cultivation of cotton and maize, in the Cotton and Corn Belts both of which are the world's leading areas for these crops. From the rainfall pattern in Fig. 156 (b), it is clear that there is a tendency towards a summer maximum, brought by the onshore Trade Winds which swing landwards from the Atlantic. The amount of rain is increased by the frequent thunderstorms in summer and by hurricanes in September and October.

Some stations, e.g. Montgomery in Alabama, also show a secondary maximum in late winter when cyclonic activities are greatest. Sometimes, violent tornadoes occur, due to intense local heating on land. Though these whirling storms follow only a narrow path in the central plain (Mississippi basin), they leave behind a trail of destruction.

3. **The Natal type.** There are three distinct areas on the eastern coasts of the southern continents, lying just south of the Tropic of Capricorn which experience this type of climate. The narrowness of the continents and the dominance of maritime influence eliminate the monsoonal elements which characterize the corresponding climates of the northern hemisphere. The South-East Trade Winds bring about a more even distribution of rainfall throughout the year as illustrated by the climatic graph for Sydney, Australia. It has a mean monthly precipitation of 4 inches, which is adequate for most agricultural activities. The annual amount of 48 inches is fairly representative of this climatic type in the southern hemisphere. The annual precipitation of Durban in Natal is 35 inches or 890 mm and that of Asunción in Paraguay is 64 inches or 1630 mm. The passage of depressions across the southern edges of the warm temperate eastern margins results in a slight autumn or winter maximum, typified by Sydney (Fig. 156 c) which has its wettest months in March, April, May, June and July (the autumn-winter part of the year). The rain comes in prolonged showers. Much of the water seeps into the ground and there is little run-off, so the regions are well suited to agriculture and are some of the best settled parts of the southern continents.

Another feature to note is the small annual temperature range, without any really cold month. The annual range for Sydney is 18°F (10°C) and the

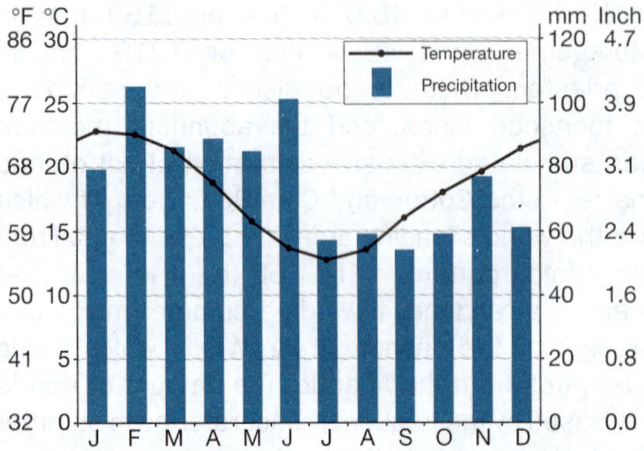

		J	F	M	A	M	J	J	A	S	O	N	D	Range/ Total
Temp.	°C	22.8	22.6	21.3	18.8	15.8	13.6	12.7	13.5	16.0	18.0	19.7	21.4	10.1
	°F	73.1	72.6	70.4	65.9	60.4	56.5	54.9	56.4	60.8	64.5	67.4	70.6	18.2
Precip.	mm	79	105	86	89	85	101	57	59	54	59	77	61	912
	in	3	4	3	3	3	3	2	2	2	2	3	2	36

Data: 1991–2021

Place	Sydney, New South Wales, Australia (34°S, 151°E)
Altitude	27 m or 89 feet
Annual temperature range	18.2°F or 10.1°C
Annual precipitation	35.9 inches or 912 mm

Fig. 156 (c) Warm Temperate Eastern Margin Climate in the southern hemisphere (Natal type)

coldest month is 23°F above freezing (about 55°F or 12.7°C in July). The range is smaller for Durban, only 13°F (7°C), with July, the coldest month at 63°F (17°C). In Asunción, the range is 19.3°F (10.7°C), and the climate is pleasantly warm all the time.

However, the southern continents also have violent local storms, which, though not as severe as the typhoon, hurricane or tornado, are nevertheless, quite significant. The Southerly Burster, a violent cold wind blowing along the coast of New South Wales, leads to a sudden fall in temperature. It is most frequent in spring and summer. The corresponding cold wind in Argentina and Uruguay is the Pampero, which is often accompanied by thunder and lightning besides the rain and dust. In southeastern Africa, a hot, dry wind called the Berg Wind comes down from the interior plateau. It is comparable to the Fohn or Chinook, and brings unpleasantly high temperatures and oppressive weather.

Natural Vegetation

The eastern margins of warm temperate latitudes have a much heavier rainfall than either the western margins or the continental interiors and thus have a luxuriant vegetation. The lowlands carry both evergreen broad-leaved forests and deciduous trees quite similar to those of the tropical monsoon forests. On the highlands, are various species of conifers such as pines and cypresses which are important softwoods. As the perennial plant growth is not checked by either a dry season as in the Mediterranean, or a cold season as in the cool temperate regions, conditions are well suited to a rich variety of plant life including grass, ferns, lianas, bamboos, palms and forests. The well distributed rainfall all the year round makes the regions look green at all times.

It is interesting to note that the warm temperate eastern margins are the homes of a number of valuable timber species. In eastern Australia, the most important are eucalyptus trees with scanty foliage and thick fern undergrowth. Some of the eucalyptus are very tall, over 250 feet and they, make hardy timber. The Australian Alps of Victoria and the Blue Mountains of New South Wales have great reserves of temperate eucalyptus forests that make up part of the timber exports of Australia. From the forests of south-eastern Brazil, eastern Paraguay, north-eastern Argentina come valuable warm temperate timbers such as the Parana pine, and the quebracho (axe-breaker, an extremely hard wood used for tanning) and wild yerba mate trees, from which the leaves are gathered for making Paraguay tea. Today, large yerba mate plantations have been established to produce Paraguay tea, an increasingly important export item of Paraguay. In Natal, the warm Mozambique current encourages heavy precipitation along the coast and many species of palm trees thrive. The highlands yield extensive forests of chestnuts, ironwood and blackwoods. An unusual occupation is the commercial cultivation of wattle trees in plantations for tanning extracts and for use in Natal's coal mines as pit-props.

The forests of China and southern Japan also have considerable economic value and include oak, camphor, camelia and magnolia. Unfortunately, the tremendous population pressure in the two countries has caused much of the original forest to be cleared for fuel or crop cultivation. Deforestation has resulted in many barren hill-slopes that are still feeling the impact of soil erosion. The Gulf states of USA have lowland deciduous forests. The trees grow close together with thick undergrowth and leafy branches. Walnut, oak, hickory and maple are some of the more common species, while in the more sandy regions grow pines. Much of the forest cover has given way to the cultivation of sub-tropical crops like cotton, maize and fruits.

Economic Development

The warm temperate eastern margins are the most productive parts of the middle latitudes. There is adequate rainfall, no prolonged drought, and the cold season is warm enough for most crops to survive. Thus the growing season is almost continuous, though summer is the busiest part of the farming year. Monsoon China together with southern Japan and other parts of the eastern margin climatic zone accounts for almost a third of the world population. Food has to be raised to feed the teeming population. The hills are terraced, fields are irrigated, and agriculture is extended to the limits of production. It is no exaggeration to say that the temperate monsoon lands are the most intensively tilled parts of the earth. Besides the widespread cultivation of maize and cotton in the Corn and Cotton Belts of USA, fruit and tobacco are also grown. Rice, tea and mulberries are extensively grown in monsoon China. Elsewhere are found other products of economic importance, e.g. cane sugar in Natal, coffee and maize in South America and dairying in New South Wales and Victoria. Let us now examine some of the regions more closely.

1. **Farming in monsoon China.** Undoubtedly this is the world's greatest rice growing area. About a third of the world's rice is grown in China, though the huge population of 1,410 million leaves very little for export. In fact, in normal years, imports of rice and other food grains are essential. The Chinese peasants raise wet padi or *swamp rice* in flooded fields that call for endless hard labour for the greater part of the year. It is said that nowhere else is there so much manual labour devoted to raise a food crop that gives so little economic return. Farming is usually on a subsistence basis. Despite increasing mechanization in padi-cultivation, very few farmers actually make use of new machines because they are expensive and may be impractical in some areas. The only progress that has been made is towards double or treble cropping, which has increased the annual total rice production.

Terraced land for rice farming in Japan

When compared with the rapid population growth of the rice-eating nations, the increased production has in no way relieved the critical food problem of Monsoon Asia. Furthermore, milled rice which forms the stable food of the Orient is a seriously deficient diet; the people are therefore not only inadequately fed also physically undernourished.

Monsoon China has all the ideal conditions for padi cultivation; a warm climate, moderately wet throughout the year, and extensive lowlands with fertile moisture-retentive alluvial soil, which if necessary, can be easily irrigated. The land has been tilled from generation to generation, and yet there is little deterioration in soil fertility. The muddy irrigation water from the river basins is silty and constantly brings new soil to the fields. The water is greatly enriched during floods, though these are far less frequent now, with the improvement made in flood control by the Communist regime. In practice, the Chinese peasants add all kinds of organic wastes to enrich their fields. Rice straw, ashes, clippings, animal dung, refuse, and last but not least, human manure.

The most intensively farmed areas are the basins of the Si-kiang, Yang-tze Kiang and Hwang Ho, which are also the most densely peopled areas. The eastern coastlands are equally important. As the flat lands are insufficient for rice cultivation, farmers move up the hill-slopes and grow padi on terraced uplands. The artificial terraces retain the excess water as it flows down the slope. Besides rice the other important crops are *tea,* grown for home consumption and *mulberry leaves* gathered for feeding silk worms, though sericulture is declining.

2. **Agriculture in the Gulf states.** Agriculture in the Gulf states of America differs from that of monsoon China, though they have a similar climate.

Lack of population pressure and the urge to export, make rice cultivation a relatively unimportant occupation. It is grown only in a few areas in the southern coastlands of the Mississippi delta. Americans are breadeaters and one can well imagine how insignificant is rice in the economy of the Gulf states. The most important crops are corn, cotton and tobacco.

a. **Corn.** The chief food crop raised is, in fact corn or maize. The humid air, the sunny summer and the heavy showers suit the crop well. It is grown right from the Gulf coast to the Mid-west south of the Great Lakes, with the greatest concentration in the Corn Belt of Nebraska, Iowa, Indiana and Ohio. The region accounts for more than half the world's production of corn, but only 3 per cent of the world's export. This is because most of the corn is used for fattening animals, mostly farm animals. The fattened animals are then sold to the meat plants in Chicago and Cincinnati. Very little corn is consumed as a staple food in America, though the cereal originated in America as the food crop of the native Indian people. Apart from its ease of cultivation, in respect of soil, climatic and labour requirements, corn's most outstanding feature is its prolific *yield*. It gives almost twice as much food (mainly starch) per acre as wheat or other cereals. This explains why it is so widely cultivated in both the warm temperate and the tropical latitudes.

b. **Cotton.** Of the cash crops grown in the Gulf states, none is comparable with cotton. In the Deep South, the fibre is so vital to the economic well-being of the southerners that 'cotton is king'! It shapes the destiny of the southern states, being directly responsible for their trade, prosperity and politics. In the early days of America millions of black people were brought from Africa as slave labour for the cotton plantations, because the climate was too hot for the white settlers to harvest the cotton themselves. Although slavery was abolished in the nineteenth century, a large number of the black people are still poor and underprivileged.

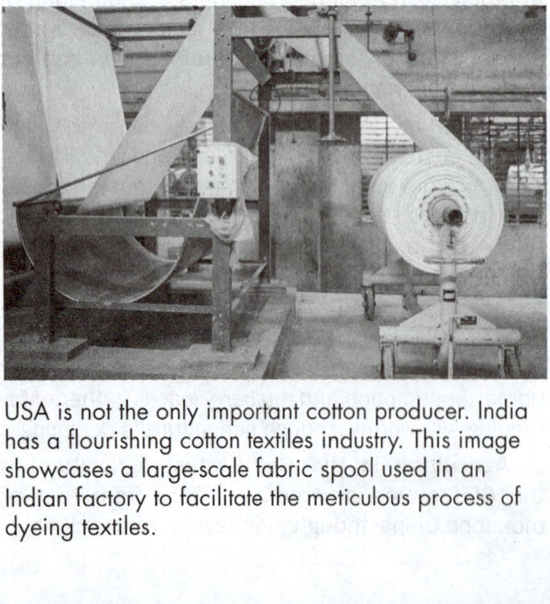

USA is not the only important cotton producer. India has a flourishing cotton textiles industry. This image showcases a large-scale fabric spool used in an Indian factory to facilitate the meticulous process of dyeing textiles.

The Gulf type of climate is undoubtedly the best for cotton growing. Its long, hot growing season with 200 days frost free and a moderately high temperature of about 75°F (24°C) permits the crop to grow slowly and mature within six months. Like most fibres, cotton likes ample rain and an annual precipitation of around 40 inches or 1016 mm is essential. In fact, an adequate moisture supply coming from frequent light showers with bright sunshine between them gives the highest yield. Fine quality cotton also comes from irrigated fields in the drier west provided sufficient water is supplied during the growing season. The Cotton Belt is thus limited by the 20-inch isohyet on the west and 77°F or 25°C isotherm in the north, within which there are at least 200 days without frost. In the very south, in the Gulf-lands, the heavy rainfall damages the lint. This area is therefore less suitable for cotton and is devoted to citrus fruits, cane sugar and market gardening, as in Florida. The commercial cultivation of cotton is now concentrated only in the most favourable areas which are the Mississippi flood plains, the clayey Atlantic coastlands of Georgia and South Carolina, the Black Prairies of Texas and the Red Prairies of Oklahoma. Fig. 157 shows the chief cotton areas of the USA.

Generally speaking, the best cotton comes from the maritime districts where the sea breezes and the warming effect of the ocean are most strongly felt. The *Sea Island Cotton* grown in the islands off the coast of Georgia and South Carolina is long-stapled (the fibres are between 1–5 and 2–3 inches in length) and is the best in the world. Further inland, the staples are shorter (about an inch long). This is typical of the bulk of the 'American' cotton. Besides the problem of soil exhaustion and erosion caused by prolonged cotton cultivation, the most dreaded enemy of the Cotton Belt is the boll-weevil.

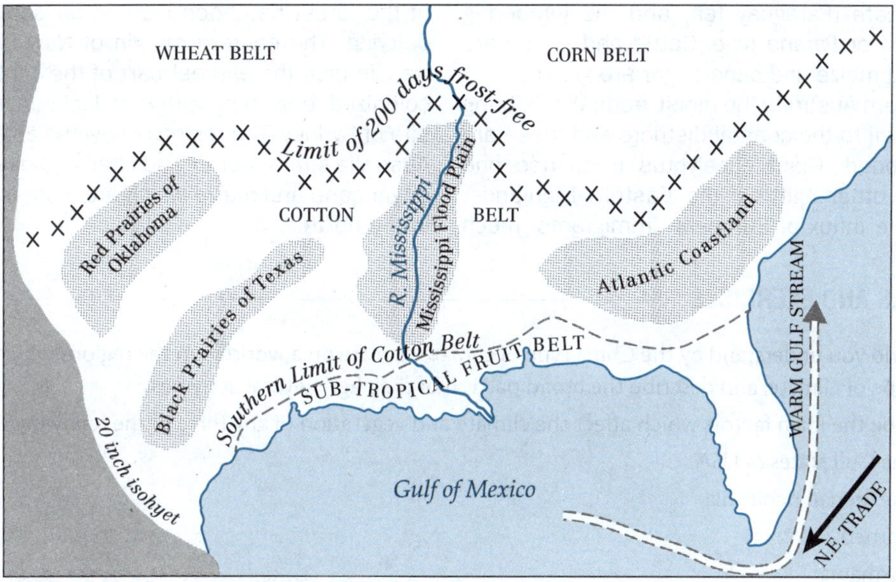

Fig. 157 The Cotton Belt of the USA

The pest multiplies so rapidly that a pair of boll-weevils, if left unchecked, will breed over 10 million grubs within a single season! The pest is responsible for the westward migration of the Cotton Belt. When it first appeared in 1892 in the eastern USA, it attacked the Sea Island Cotton. Aerial spraying with insecticides and the thorough burning of old cotton stalks, have been found effective in eliminating the boll-weevil.

c. **Tobacco.** Another interesting crop closely associated with the Gulf type of climate is tobacco, which incidentally is also a native crop of America. Though it is cultivated in many parts of the world, and the finished products range from Turkish tobacco to Havana cigars and Malaysian cheroots, there is none so universally known as the *Virginia tobacco.* It is the raw material from which most of the world's cigarettes are blended to suit the smokers' taste. The humid atmosphere, the warmth and the well-drained soils of the Gulf states, enable tobacco to be successfully cultivated in many of the eastern states of USA, e.g. Virginia, Maryland, Georgia, North and South Carolina, Kentucky and Tennessee. No less than half the tobacco that enters international trade comes from these states.

3. **Crop cultivation in the eastern margins of the southern hemisphere.** A close look at the economic map of the southern hemisphere will at once reveal the agricultural importance of its eastern margins which experience a Natal type of climate. The warm moist summers and frost-free winters not only support many crops but also animals. In the coastlands of Natal, sugar cane is the dominant crop, followed by *cotton and tobacco* in the interior. Recent expansion of these crops has come about with improved *irrigation.* Maize is extensively cultivated for use both as 'mealie' an important food item for Africans and 'silage', an animal fodder for cattle rearing. But in comparison with the maize yield of the Corn Belt of USA, the African yield is rather low, often only half. Improvements can be made, if farmers attempt some form of crop rotation to arrest the rapid rate of soil exhaustion in regions of maize monoculture. Scientific manuring and better methods of cultivation would raise yields.

In South America where rainfall is less than 40 inches there is much grassland on which many cattle and sheep are kept for meat, wool and hides. It is the continuation of the Argentinian Pampas. The mild winters mean that the animals can be kept out-of-doors all the time. The extensive natural pastures provide valuable forage for both cattle and sheep. The products from these two kinds of domesticated animals account for over three-quarters of the annual exports of Uruguay. The remaining exports come mainly from wheat and flax. Further north in southern Brazil, the rainfall increases to more than 40 inches (1016 mm) and forest gradually replaces grass. Here the important occupations are the cultivation of *yerba mate* (Paraguay tea) and the lumbering of *araucaria* or *Parana pine.* Cattle and sheep are reared, and maize and cane sugar are grown.

In eastern Australia the moist Trade Winds bring heavy rainfall to the coastal districts and these are thickly wooded. Giant eucalyptus trees rise one above the other right up the Eastern Highlands. But with the influx of European immigrants, much of the forest has been cleared for settlement and dairying. The eastern margin of New South Wales was, in fact, the earliest part of the continent to be colonized, beginning with Port Jackson, the present site of Sydney. The region is now the chief source of Australia's *milk, butter* and *cheese,* besides cotton, sugar cane and maize which are increasingly grown in the north.

QUESTIONS AND EXERCISES

1. What do you understand by the China type of climate? Locate on a world map the regions which experience this type of climate, and describe the broad pattern of their agricultural activities.
2. Describe the main factors which affect the climate and vegetation of any *three* of the following regions.
   (a) the Gulf states of USA
   (b) the Iberian peninsula
   (c) Borneo
   (d) Tasmania
   (e) Ceylon
3. Give a reasoned account of any *two* of the following
   (a) Cotton cultivation in the United States of America
   (b) Padi growing in monsoon China
   (c) Dairying in eastern Australia
   (d) Lumbering in Canada
4. Analyse, in relation to latitude and other geographical factors, the following climatic figures.

Station	Location	Altitude	Mean January Temp.	Mean July Temp.	*Annual Temp. Range*	Annual Rainfall
Singapore	1°N, 104°E	50 feet	78.4°F	80.6°F	2.2°F	93.1 inches
Santiago	33°S, 71°W	1,700 feet	71.9°F	48.1°F	23.8°F	204 inches
Shanghai	31°N, 121°E	20 feet	40.7°F	82.5°F	41.8°F	52.2 inches

5. Give an explanatory account of any *three* of the following.
   (a) Local storms (e.g. typhoon, hurricane, pampero) are often associated with the Warm Temperate Eastern Margin Climate.
   (b) The predominant forest trees of eastern Australia are eucalyptus.
   (c) The USA is the world's largest corn producer and exporter, contributing 31 per cent of the world's total corn production and nearly 38 per cent of the world's total corn exports.
   (d) Farming in monsoon China is usually on a subsistence basis, and the peasants are permanently 'land-hungry'.

22 The Cool Temperate Western Margin (British Type) Climate

Distribution

The cool temperate western margins are under the permanent influence of the Westerlies all round the year. They are also regions of much cyclonic activity, typical of Britain, and are thus said to experience the British type of climate. From Britain, the climatic belt stretches far inland into the lowlands of North-West Europe, including such regions as northern and western France, Belgium, the Netherlands, Denmark, western Norway and also north-western Iberia. There is so much oceanic influence on both the temperature and the precipitation that the climate is also referred to as the North-West European Maritime Climate. In North America, the high Rockies prevent the onshore Westerlies from penetrating far inland and the British type of climate is confined mainly to the coastlands of British Columbia.

In the southern hemisphere, the climate is experienced in southern Chile, Tasmania and most parts of New Zealand, particularly in South Island. The surrounding large expanses of water have increased the maritime nature of the climate here (Fig. 158).

Climate

Temperature. The mean annual temperatures are usually between 40°F and 60°F (4.4°C and 15.6°C) The warmest month in London as illustrated in the temperature graph of London Fig. 159 (a) is 64°F (17.8°C) and the coldest month is just around 40°F (4.8°C), thus giving an annual temperature range of only 23.4°F (13°C), which is comparatively small for its latitude (51°N) Summers are, in fact, never very warm. Monthly temperatures of over 65°F (18.3°C) even in mid-summer are rare. 'Heat waves', as they are popularly called (that is a short spell of warm summer days) are a welcome feature in such cool temperate latitudes, where people do not often see enough of the sun. The climate is

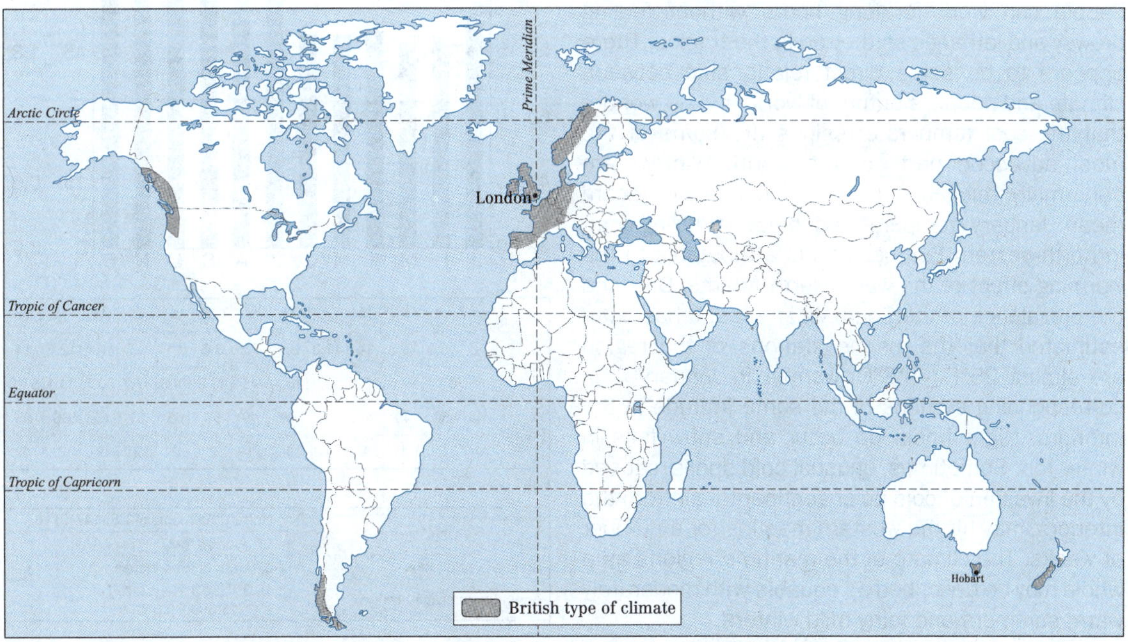

Fig. 158 Regions with Cool Temperate Western Margin Climate (British type)

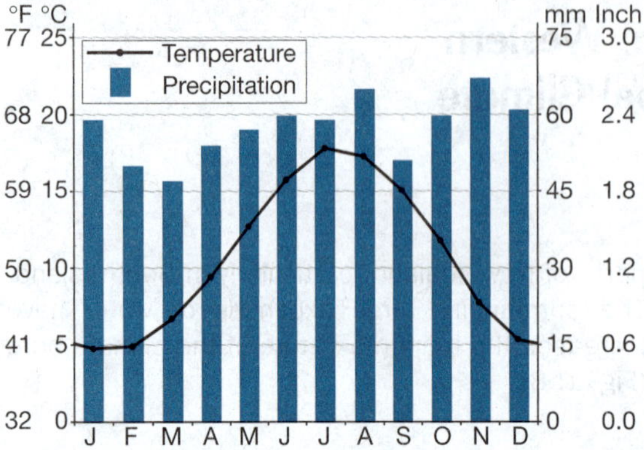

		J	F	M	A	M	J	J	A	S	O	N	D
Temp.	°C	4.8	4.9	6.7	9.4	12.7	15.7	17.8	17.3	15	11.8	7.8	5.3
	°F	40.6	40.8	44	48.9	54.8	60.3	64	63.1	59.1	53.2	46	41.6
Precip.	mm	59	50	47	54	57	60	59	65	51	60	67	61
	in	2	1	1	2	2	2	2	2	2	2	2	2

Data: 1991–2021

Place	London, British Isles (51°N, 0°W)
Altitude	5.4 m or 18 feet
Annual precipitation	670 mm or 26.4 inches
Annual temperature range	23.4°F (64°F – 40.6°F) or 13°C (17.8°C – 4.8°C)

Fig. 159 (a) British type of climate in the northern hemisphere

ideal for maximum comfort and *mental alertness*. People can work for long hours without feeling drowsy and lethargic as they do in the tropics. There appears to be some direct relationship between climate and people's output of work. It is no wonder that the cool temperate regions are some of the most advanced parts of the world. Winters are abnormally mild, and no stations actually record mean January temperatures below freezing-point in north-western Europe. This is attributable to the warming effect of the warm North Atlantic Drift and the prevalence of the South-Westerlies. It has been estimated that the marine stations of the region are almost 25°F (–3.8°C) warmer in January than corresponding stations of the same latitude in the interiors. Night frosts do occur and snow falls in winter too. Sometimes, unusual cold spells, caused by the invasion of cold polar continental air from the interiors, may hit the western margins for a number of weeks. The climate of the maritime regions as a whole may be described as equable with moderately warm summers and fairly mild winters.

It is quite apparent from Fig. 159 (b) of Hobart, Tasmania that the British type of climate in the southern hemisphere is even more equable. Lack of continental land masses in Tasmania, New Zealand and southern Chile means that extremes of temperature are not likely at all. Hobart has mid-summer temperatures of not more than 61°F (16°C). while its coldest month in July (winter in the southern hemisphere) is barely below 44°F (6.6°C). The annual temperature range is reduced to only 16.3°F (9°C), which is unusual for the middle latitudes. This is in fact, the average figure for all the maritime stations in the southern continents where insularity overrides all other factors. The annual ranges of other southerly stations are Dunedin 15.8°F (8.9°C), Christchurch 19.7°F (11°C), Valdivia 16°F (9°C). and Punta Arenas 14°F (7.6°C). The last two stations, Valdivia and Punta Arenas, are in southern Chile. The oceanic influences not only keep the winters very mild but also keep the summers cool. Some geographers have described these southerly islands as 'the favoured isles' which has much truth in it.

Precipitation. The British type of climate has adequate rainfall throughout the year with a

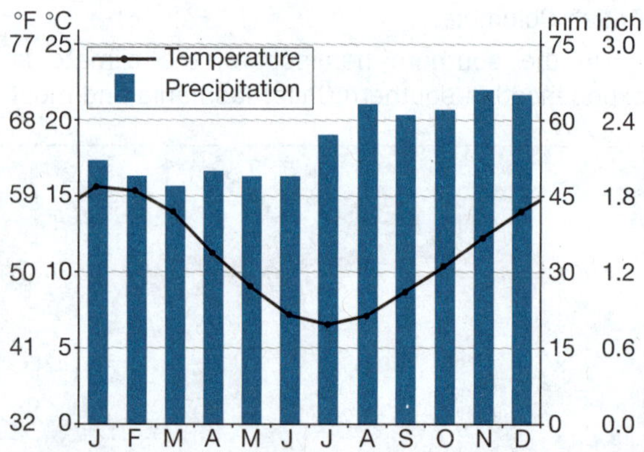

		J	F	M	A	M	J	J	A	S	O	N	D
Temp.	°C	15.6	15.3	14	11.3	9.1	7.2	6.6	7.1	8.7	10.4	12.3	14
	°F	60.1	59.6	57.1	52.3	48.3	45	43.8	44.8	47.7	50.7	54.1	57.2
Precip.	mm	52	49	47	50	49	49	57	63	61	62	66	65
	in	2	1	1	1	1	1	2	2	2	2	2	2

Data: 1991–2021

Place	Hobart, Tasmania (43°S, 147°E)
Altitude	17 m or 56 feet
Annual precipitation	670 mm or 26.4 inches
Annual temperature range	16.3°F (60.1°F – 43.8°F) or 9°C (15.6°C – 6.6°C)

Fig. 159 (b) British type of climate in the southern hemisphere

tendency towards a slight winter or autumn maximum from cyclonic sources. Since the rain-bearing winds come from the west, the western margins have the heaviest rainfall. The amount decreases eastwards with increasing distance from the sea. Though both the quoted stations London and Hobart have 26 inches (670 mm) of precipitation a year, the actual amount varies quite considerably from place to place. Relief can make great differences in the annual amount. For example, the western slopes of the Southern Alps of South Island, New Zealand have as much as 200 inches (5,080 mm) of rainfall (mainly orographic rain) while the Canterbury Plain, in the rain-shadow area has as little as 25 inches (635 mm). Similarly, the Lake District of Britain has well over 100 inches (2,540 mm) in contrast to only 24 inches (609 mm) in East Anglia. It is therefore difficult to say how much annual rainfall is typical of the British type of climate. Perhaps, a useful guide would be to confine ourselves to lowland regions which normally have 20 to 40 inches (500 to 1,000 mm) a year, e.g. 28 inches (710 mm) in Paris, 36 inches (914 mm) in Dublin, 54 inches (1,370 mm) in Seattle and 31.7 inches (806 mm) in Dunedin. Generally, western coastal stations are wetter. Vancouver has 92.6 inches (2,351 mm) of rain, Valdivia 77.6 inches (1,972 mm) and Bergen 97 inches (2,464 mm). They are exceeded in the annual amount only by the highland stations as mentioned earlier.

The seasons. As in other temperate regions there are four distinct *seasons* in the British climate type. Light snowfalls can be expected in the winter months normally only of short duration because of the comparatively mild weather. But over the highlands such as the Scandinavian Mountains and the American Rockies, snowfall is heavy and feeds the mountain glaciers that move down the valleys. Winter is the season of cloudy skies, foggy and misty mornings, and many rainy days from the passing depressions. Out at sea, gales are frequent and can be dangerous to shipping. Spring is the driest and the most refreshing season when people emerge from the depressing winter to see everything becoming green again. This is followed by the long, sunny summer. Sun-bathers, picnickers and sightseers are out in the open to enjoy themselves. With the roar of gusty winds and the fall of 'golden' leaves, autumn is ushered in, and the cycle repeats itself. This type of climate with its four distinct seasons is something that is conspicuously absent in the tropics.

Natural Vegetation

The natural vegetation of this climatic type is deciduous forest. The trees shed their leaves in the cold season. This is an adaptation for protecting themselves against the winter snow and frost. Shedding begins in autumn, the 'fall' season, during which the leaves fall and are scattered by the winds. The golden-brown leaves and the 'naked' branches present a very interesting scene. When they are in leaf the deciduous trees have typical rounded outlines with thick trunks and out-spreading branches that yield valuable temperate hardwood. Some of the more common species include oak, elm, ash, birch, beech, poplar, and hornbeam. In the wetter areas grow willows, alder and aspen. Elsewhere are found other species, e.g. chestnut, sycamore, maple, and lime.

Some deciduous trees

Unlike the equatorial forests, the deciduous trees occur in pure stands and have greater lumbering value from the commercial point of view. The open nature of the forests with sparse undergrowth is useful in logging operations. Easy penetration means much cost can be saved in the movement of the logs. The deciduous hardwoods are excellent for both fuel and industrial purposes. In Tasmania, the temperate eucalypts are also extensively felled for the lumbering industry. Higher up the mountains in the Scandinavian highlands, the Rockies, southern Andes and the Southern Alps of New Zealand, the deciduous trees are generally replaced by the conifers which can survive a higher altitude, a lower temperature and poorer soils.

Economic Development

A very large part of the deciduous woodlands have been cleared for fuel, timber or agriculture. The dense population necessitates the removal of the lowland forests, particularly for the plough. In Britain there is only 13 per cent of the original forest left. A large range of cereals, fruits and root crops are raised, mainly for home consumption rather than for export. North-West Europe, which includes some of the most crowded parts of the globe, has little surplus for export. It is, in fact, a net importer of food-crops, especially wheat from almost all parts of the wheatlands for bread-making and other food items. The region differs from many others in its unprecedented industrial advancement. The countries are concerned in the production of machinery, chemicals, textiles and other manufactured articles rather than agriculture, fishing or lumbering, though these activities are well represented in some of the countries. Fishing is particularly important in Britain, Norway and British Columbia. Since the manufacturing aspect of industrial geography will be dealt with in much greater detail in Chapter 23, we shall deal here with the agricultural development of the region.

1. **Market gardening.** Though market gardening is practised throughout the world wherever there is a large urban population, nowhere else is it so highly specialized as in North-West Europe. Several factors account for this. All the north-western European countries (Britain, France, Germany, Benelux and Denmark) are highly industrialized and have high population densities. There are more towns and cities than in other continents despite its small size. It is understandable that the demand for fresh vegetables, green salads, eggs, meat, milk and fruits will be tremendous. The city dwellers, the factory workers and the civil servants who make up the bulk of the urban population consume large quantities of fresh provisions daily and these must be provided by local farmers if *freshness* of the produce is to be ensured.

In north-western Europe *intensive market gardening* is carried out in many specialized areas, e.g. the Vales of York and Evesham in the UK where climatic, soil and other factors best suit this form of agriculture. Farms are normally small, located near large cities or industrial areas. Soils, whether silty, loamy or podzolic, are carefully maintained at a high degree of fertility. Very selective fertilizers are applied depending on the type of crops in cultivation. Farming is carried out intensively, aiming at high yield and maximum cash returns. As the crops are perishable, a good network of transport is indispensable. The produce such as lettuces, cabbages, cauliflowers, tomatoes, onions, peas and fruits are seldom shipped but conveyed by high-speed conveyances such as trucks or vans. Perhaps a more appropriate term to use is truck farming, which is commonly used in the United States.

In a few instances warmer weather or better soils, as in south-west England (Devon and Cornwall), can also induce farmers to take to market gardening despite their remoteness from the more populated districts. Early vegetables, early potatoes and tomatoes reach London from the Canary Islands, the Channel Islands, and from Brittany, in north-west France. Similarly, bulbs and flowers from the polderlands of the Netherlands and eggs, bacon and other dairy products from Denmark are sent to most of the major industrial centres of Europe in almost perfect condition for household consumption. The horticultural industry in the Netherlands is so highly specialized that Dutch tulips and bulbs are flown by the K.L.M. (Royal Dutch Airlines) to Rome, Paris, Zurich, and London. In Australia, high-speed boats ply across the Bass Strait daily from Tasmania to rush vegetables, tomatoes, apples and beans to most of the large cities in mainland Australia. It is no wonder the Australians nicknamed Tasmania the 'garden state'.

2. **Mixed farming.** Throughout Britain and north-western Europe, farmers practise both arable farming (cultivation of crops on ploughed land) and pastoral farming (keeping animals on grass meadows). Crops may be raised for cash sales or as fodder for cattle or sheep. The proportion of crops and animals in the farm at any time depends to a great extent on the type of *soil*, the *price* of the, cereals and the *demand* for animals and animal products. The farmers also plant a few fruit trees (apples, pears, plums), rear animals for meat, keep poultry, mainly for eggs, and even have bees for honey. There is such a great variety in the farms that the term mixed farming is most aptly applied.

Amongst the cereals, wheat is the most extensively grown, almost entirely for home consumption because of the very dense population in north-western Europe. At one time, some of the European countries (France, Denmark and the Netherlands) used to be wheat exporters, but the keen competition from the new wheat-lands of the New World forced most of the farmers to divert their interest to other more profitable uses of their land such as market gardening, dairying or an intensive form of mixed farming. With the rise of industry, more arable farms are being devoured by factories and wheat is now a net import item in Europe.

The next most important cereal raised in the mixed farm is barley. The better quality barley is sold to the breweries for beer-making or whisky distilling and is raised preferably in the drier areas. *Malting barley* is thus grown in south-eastern Britain near the hop-growing area (hops are also used for beer) where rainfall is less than 30 inches (762 mm). On heavy soils or wetter regions, barley is grown mainly as an animal fodder, sometimes mixed with oats as 'dredge corn'. Both are raised in crop rotations with a leguminous crop (beans or clover) and a root crop (turnips or beet sugar).

The most important animals kept in the mixed farm are cattle. North-western Europe was originally the home of many world renowned cattle breeds, e.g. Guernsey, Ayrshire and Friesian, which are first class dairy cattle for milk production. The countries bordering the North Sea (Britain, Denmark, the Netherlands) are some of the most advanced dairying countries where cattle are kept on a scientific and intensive basis. Europeans drink more milk than anybody else except the New Zealanders. In the UK, a person drinks almost a pint of milk a day! From milk, other important

An English farm. Notice the well-wooded countryside

dairy products are derived. These are *butter, cheese, cream,* and *skimmed milk* or *casein,* a raw material for making plastics, paper and drugs. The temperate western margin type of climate is almost ideal for intensive dairying. Cheese is a specialized product of the Netherlands, from Edam and Gouda. From Denmark comes high-quality butter, of which Denmark ranks with New Zealand as one of the world's greatest exporters. In Devon and Cornwall clotted cream is made, which is less perishable than fresh milk. It can be sent over longer journeys without being contaminated. The Swiss have also made excellent use of their alpine pastures for keeping dairy cattle. Fresh milk is converted into various forms of condensed or evaporated milk, and exported around the world for baby-feeding, confectionery, ice-cream and chocolate making.

Besides dairying, some cattle are kept as beef cattle, e.g. the Hereford and Aberdeen Angus, but their numbers are very small in comparison with those of Argentina or Australia, where meat production is the primary concern. The high rate of per capita meat consumption in Europe (about 68 kilo grams per year) necessitates large imports of frozen and chilled meat. In the mixed farms in Europe, farmers keep cattle also with a view of enriching their fields with the *animal dung*. The pigs and poultry act as scavengers that feed on the leftovers from root-crops and dairy processes. In this way, Denmark is able to export large quantities of *bacon* from pigs that are fed on the *skimmed milk,* a by-product of butter-making. Fresh chickens' eggs from the farms and more recently, from large poultry yards also form part of the export products of Denmark. Sheep are kept both for wool and mutton. In British Columbia, mixed farming is restricted only to the most favoured parts of the Western lowlands, the region being so mountainous and thickly forested.

3. **Sheep rearing.** This is well developed in some parts of the British type of climate. Britain is the home of some of the best known sheep breeds, e.g. Leicesters, Lincolns and Southdowns which are dual-purpose, noted for mutton as well as wool. With the greater pressure exerted on land by increased urbanization, industrialization and agriculture, sheep rearing is being pushed further and further into the less favoured areas. The principal sheep areas are on foothills, well-drained uplands, chalk and limestone scarplands,

and the light, sandy coasts. In the UK, the major sheep areas are the Pennines, (Swaledale breeds) Scottish Highlands (the Blackface), the Southern Uplands (Cheviot), the Wales Mountains (Black Welsh) and the scarplands of south-eastern England (Romney Marsh). In 2020, UK was the fourth largest exporter of wool in the world.

In the southern hemisphere, sheep rearing is a major occupation of New Zealand, with its greatest concentration in the Canterbury Plain. However, the sheep population in the country has declined significantly in the last few decades. The 2020 estimates showed that for every New Zealander there were only five sheep whereas in 1982, there were about 22 sheep for every New Zealander. Many factors were responsible for the growth of the sheep population during the past century including extensive meadows, a mild temperate climate, well-drained level ground, scientific animal breeding, and last, but most vital, the development of refrigeration, which enabled frozen or chilled Canterbury lamb and Corriedale mutton to reach every corner of the globe. Today New Zealand has about 2 per cent of the world's sheep population. In Tasmania and southern Chile, sheep rearing has always been a predominant occupation with surplus sheep products for the international trade.

4. **Other agricultural activities.** Apart from market gardening and mixed farming which have been singled out for greater individual treatment, the British type of climate also supports a number of other important crops. Amongst the food crops, potatoes feature prominently in the domestic economy of the cool temperate regions. It is the staple food in supplementing wheat or bread for millions of people. In terms of starch, it yields far more food than any cereals and can be cultivated over a wide range of climatic and soil types. But normally a cooler and more northerly latitude is preferred because the crop will be less prone to the attack of 'blight', a virus disease that is particularly infectious in warm and humid countries. Since the introduction of the crop by the Spanish conquerors from the Andean states of Peru and Bolivia in the sixteenth century, potato-growing has spread far and wide in Europe. Today almost one-fourth of the world's annual production of potatoes comes from Europe, of which Ukrain, Germany, France, Poland and the Netherlands are the major producers. Besides its principal use as a substitute for bread, large quantities of potatoes are also consumed as animal fodder and as a source of industrial alcohol. Potato is also as an important source of chips and pancakes in these countries.

A sheep station near Hawkes Bay, New Zealand

Another interesting crop that is found almost exclusively in north-western Europe (including European Russia) and parts of the USA is sugar beet. The need for such a crop was greatly felt during the Napoleonic Wars around 1800 when military blockades caused a scarcity of sugar. High prices of imported tropical sugar (from sugar cane) drove many governments of the temperate lands to think seriously about the vital importance of securing a certain amount of self-sufficiency in their sugar requirements. The first sugar beet factory in Europe was established in 1801. Farmers were given subsidies (aids or allowances) to induce them to devote at least part of their farm to the crop. Since then sugar beet has become an integral part of many European farms. It is grown either on special beet farms for cash sales or in conjunction with cereals in crop rotation. The beet is crushed for sugar and the green tops are used as animal fodder. The crop thrives best in the warmer and drier east of the UK and in mainland Europe. The highest sugar yield is obtained when the autumn is both dry and sunny.

The European Union (EU) is the world's largest producer of sugar beet, with about half of the total output. However, sugar beet contributes only about a fourth of the world's sugar production; over three-fourths of the sugar output comes from sugar cane.

The major sugar beet growing areas of the EU lie in northern France, Germany, the Netherlands, Belgium and Poland. The EU also has an important refining industry that processes imported raw sugar cane.

QUESTIONS AND EXERCISES

1. The following statements attempt to describe a type of climate.

   '...... Westerlies come all the year round ...... there is a tendency towards an autumn or winter maximum of rainfall ...... light snow falls in winter ...... ports are never frozen ...... but frosts do occur on cold nights ...... the seasons are very distinct ...... and the climate is very favourable for maximum human output ....

   (a) Name the type of climate that it describes.

   (b) Locate with the aid of a sketch map a region where such a type of climate is best represented.

   (c) Explain why such a type of climate is ideal for human habitation.

2. Describe and explain with the aid of sketch maps the essential differences between the various climatic types found within the cool temperate zone.

3. (a) What are the characteristic features of temperate deciduous forests?

   (b) Name the various species of deciduous forests and account for some of their industrial uses.

   (c) Explain why there is comparatively little of the original forest left.

4. Write a geographical account of any *three* of the following economic activities.

   (a) mixed farming

   (b) sugar beet cultivation

   (c) cool temperate orchard farming

   (d) sheep rearing

   (e) woollen textile industry

5. Give an explanatory account of any *two* of the following.

   (a) The Netherlands is a major exporter of butter and cheese.

   (b) Sheep outnumber the population of New Zealand by 5 : 1.

   (c) No country produces and exports more wool than Australia.

   (d) Market-gardening is a product of urbanization.

23 The Cool Temperate Continental (Siberian) Climate

Distribution

The Cool Temperate Continental (Siberian) Climate is experienced only in the northern hemisphere where the continents within the high latitudes have a broad east-west spread (Fig. 160). On its poleward side, it merges into the Arctic tundra of Canada and Eurasia at around the Arctic Circle. Southwards, the climate becomes less severe and fades into the temperate Steppe climate dealt within Chapter 19.

The predominant vegetation of this Siberian or 'sub-Arctic' type of climate is evergreen coniferous forest. It stretches in a great, continuous belt across North America, Europe and Asia. The greatest single band of the coniferous forest is the taiga (a Russian word for coniferous forest) in Siberia. In Europe, the countries that have a similar type of climate, forest are mainly found in northern Europe, Sweden and Finland. There are small amounts of natural coniferous forest, due to high altitude, in Germany, Poland, Switzerland, Austria and other parts of Europe. In North America, this sub-Arctic belt stretches from Alaska across Canada into Labrador, and is found on the high Rocky Mountains farther south.

The Siberian Climate is conspicuously absent in the southern hemisphere because of the narrowness of the southern continents in the high latitudes. The strong oceanic influence reduces the severity of the winter and coniferous forests are found only on the mountainous uplands of southern Chile, New Zealand, Tasmania and south-east Australia.

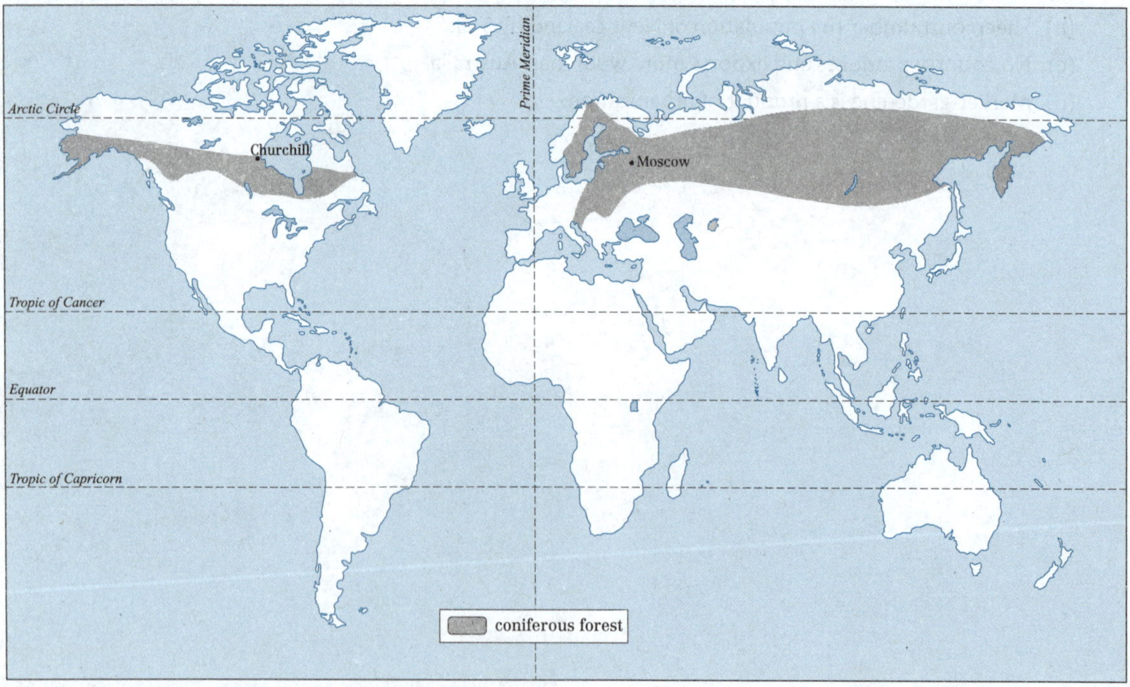

Fig. 160 The cool temperate coniferous forest

Climate

Temperature. The climate of the Siberian type is characterized by a bitterly cold winter of long duration, and a cool brief summer. Spring and autumn are merely brief transitional periods. The isotherm of 50°F or (10°C) for the warmest month forms the poleward boundary of the Siberian climate and the winter months are always below freezing. The stations chosen to illustrate this type of climate are Moscow, in continental Europe and Churchill, in northern Canada, bordering Hudson Bay. The coldest month in Moscow is January with 18°F (14° below freezing point) or –10°C. The warmest month (July) is as high as 68°F (20°C); thus there is an annual range of 50°F (30°C), which is common in the Siberian type of climate. In comparison, the annual temperature range for Churchill is even higher, reaching 67°F or 19°C (–13°F or –25°C in January, and 54°F or 12°C in July). This is due to the more northerly position of Churchill. The extremes of temperature are so great in Siberia that it is often referred to as the 'cold pole of the earth'. Some of the lowest temperatures in the world are recorded in Verkhoyansk (68°N 113°E and only 415 feet in altitude) where –90°F (–67.8°C) was once recorded. This is, in fact, 170°F (–76°C) colder than Kuala Lumpur! It is almost unimaginable. In North America, the extremes are less severe, because of the continent's lesser east-west stretch. The lowest mid-winter means in the cold Mackenzie Valley are not lower than –70°F (–57°C).

With such low temperatures in the cold season, heavy snowfall can be expected. Frosts occur as early as August and by September lakes and ponds are already ice-bound. All over Russia, nearly all the rivers are frozen. The number of days in which the rivers are frozen increases from south to north. In normal years, the Volga is ice-covered for about 150 days, while those further north (e.g. the lower courses of the Ob, Lena and Yenisey) are ice-covered for more than 210 days or 7 months! Occasionally cold, northerly polar winds such as the blizzards of Canada and buran of Eurasia blow violently at 50 m.p.h. (80 km per hour) or more and at a temperature of 50°F (10°C) below freezing-point. The powdery snowflakes are blown around in the lower atmosphere and visibility is greatly reduced. Conditions are so unbearable that Siberia is very sparsely populated but it is gradually being developed.

Precipitation. The interiors of the Eurasian continent are so remote from maritime influence that annual precipitation cannot be high. Generally speaking, a total of 15 to 25 inches (380 to 500 mm) is typical of the annual precipitation of this sub-Arctic type of climate. It is quite well distributed throughout the year, with a summer maximum from convectional rain when the continental interiors are greatly heated (mid-summer temperatures of 60° to 75°F (15°–25°C) are quite usual and the maximum recorded in Siberia is a real surprise – 102°F (39°C). In winter the precipitation is in the form of snow, as mean temperatures are well below freezing all the time.

The precipitation rhythm can best be grasped from the two representative stations chosen, in Fig. 161 (a) and 161 (b). Moscow with an annual precipitation of 26 inches (660 mm) has most of the rainfall concentrated in the warmer months (May–October). There is no month without some form of moisture. In a region where overall temperature is low, evaporation is not rapid and the relative humidity is high, this small amount of precipitation is adequate for tree growth. The conifers, which require little moisture, and

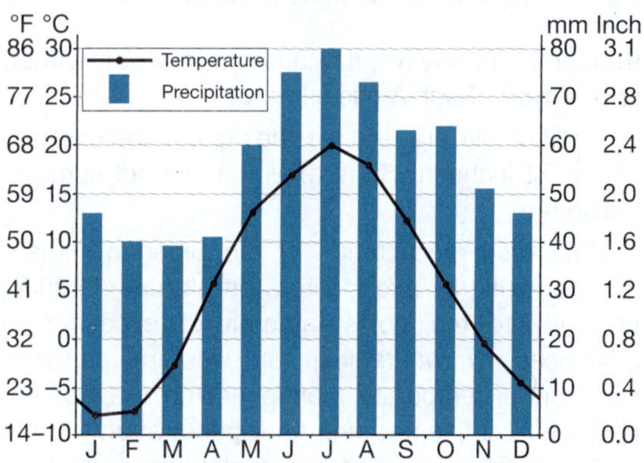

		J	F	M	A	M	J	J	A	S	O	N	D
Avg. Temp.	°C	–7.9	–7.6	–2.8	5.7	13.2	17	20	18	12.3	5.7	–0.5	–4.5
	°F	17.7	18.4	27	42.2	55.7	62.5	68	64.4	54.1	42.2	31.2	23.8
Precip.	mm	46	40	39	41	60	75	80	73	63	64	51	46
	in	1	1	1	1	2	2	3	2	2	2	2	2

Data: 1991–2021

Place	Moscow, Russia (56°N, 37°E)
Altitude	150 m or 480 feet
Annual precipitation	660 mm or 26 inches
Annual temperature range	50°F (68°F–18°F) or 28°C (20°C– –8°C)

Fig. 161 (a) Siberian Climate in Eurasia

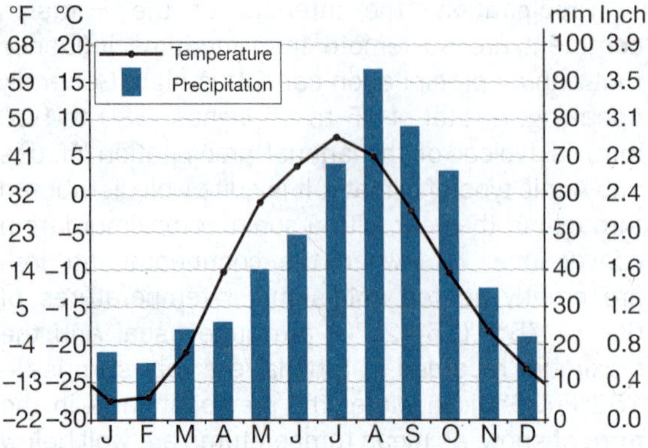

		J	F	M	A	M	J	J	A	S	O	N	D
Avg. Temp.	°C	–25.3	–24.2	–17.5	–8.6	–0.7	6.9	12.3	12.2	7.4	–0.1	–11.3	–21.2
	°F	–13.5	–11.6	0.5	16.6	30.7	44.4	54.1	53.9	45.3	31.9	11.6	–6.1
Precip.	mm	18	15	24	26	40	49	68	93	78	66	35	22
	in	0	0	0	1	1	1	2	3	3	2	1	2

Data: 1991–2021

Place	Churchill, Manitoba, Canada (58°N, 94°W)
Altitude	10 m or 33 feet
Annual precipitation	534 mm or 21 inches
Annual temperature range	67.5°F (54°F– –13.5°F) or 13°C (12.3°C– –25.3°C)

Fig. 161 (b) Siberian Climate in Canada.

transpire an equally small amount, are best suited to this type of sub-Arctic climate.

In Churchill, Fig. 161 (b), the annual precipitation is just 21 inches (534 mm) with a distinct summer maximum.

The total precipitation of the Siberian climate is determined by such factors as altitude, latitude, proximity to the poles, amount of exposure to influences by Westerlies, (on western parts of continents), temperate monsoons (on the eastern parts of continents) and the penetration of the cyclones. European Russia usually has more than 20 inches (500 mm) of annual precipitation because of some oncoming Westerlies and the periodic penetration of cyclones. Eastern Siberia also has over 20 inches (500 mm), being moistened by the S.E. Monsoon from the Pacific Ocean. Central Siberia and Canada have about 15 inches (380 mm), due to their continentality and lack of sea influence. Polewards and southwards, the amount again decreases to only 12 inches (300 mm) or less. The cold, dry air of the north is incapable of holding moisture, and in the south are the semi-arid steppes.

Snow falls nearly everywhere in Russia in the long, cold winter. The amount varies from place to place. It is heaviest in the northern tundra and in the Siberian taiga, where a thickness of several feet is common. Permanent snowfields like those of the Alps or the Himalayas are absent, because any accumulation of snow is melted with the return of spring and the warm summer. Frozen rivers are thawed, causing a rise in the water level and extensive floods occur. The lower courses of the Ob, Lena and Yenisey are marshy and ill-drained. On the other hand, the presence of a thick mantle of snow is not without its blessings. Snow is a poor conductor of heat and protects the ground from the severe cold above, which may be as much as 30°–50°F (–1°C–10°C). colder! It also provides moisture for the vegetation when the snow melts in spring. When the ground is ploughed and the leached, acidic podzolic soil is improved, the continental interiors of the coniferous forest belt are capable of supporting some agriculture.

Natural Vegetation

No other trees are so well adapted as the conifers to withstand such an inhospitable environment as the Siberian type of climate. The coniferous forest belts of Eurasia and North America are the richest sources of softwood for use in building construction, furniture, matches, paper and pulp, rayon and other branches of the chemical industry. The world's greatest softwood producers are Russia, USA, Canada and the Fennoscandian countries (Finland, Norway and Sweden). In the production of wood pulp (by both chemical and mechanical methods), the USA is second largest leader after China. But in the field of newsprint, Canada has outstripped all other producers, accounting for almost one-third of the world's total annual production. The more accessible coniferous forests have reached the limit of production but the relatively inaccessible taiga of Siberia will remain the richest reserve of temperate softwood.

There are four major *species* in the coniferous forests.

1. Pine, e.g. white pine, red pine, Scots pine, Jack pine, lodgepole pine
2. Fir, e.g. Douglas fir and balsam fir
3. Spruce
4. Larch

Their presence in pure stands and the existence of only a few species are a great advantage in commercial forest exploitation.

Coniferous forests on the Rockies of Canada

Coniferous Forests

1. **Coniferous forests are of moderate density.** Unlike the equatorial rainforests which are luxuriant and contain trees of various heights, the coniferous forests are more uniform and grow straight and tall, up to a height of about 100 feet. Where the poleward limit of tree growth is approached the trees are widely spaced, and give way to tundra vegetation (Fig. 162).

2. **Almost all conifers are evergreen.** The low annual temperature with more than half the year below the growing-point temperature of 43°F (about 6°C), means that evergreens are at an advantage. Growth can begin as soon as growing-point is reached in spring. The conifer has a two-year fructification cycle. The seeds are pollinated in one year and dispersed in the following year. There is no annual replacement of new leaves as in deciduous trees. The same leaf remains on the

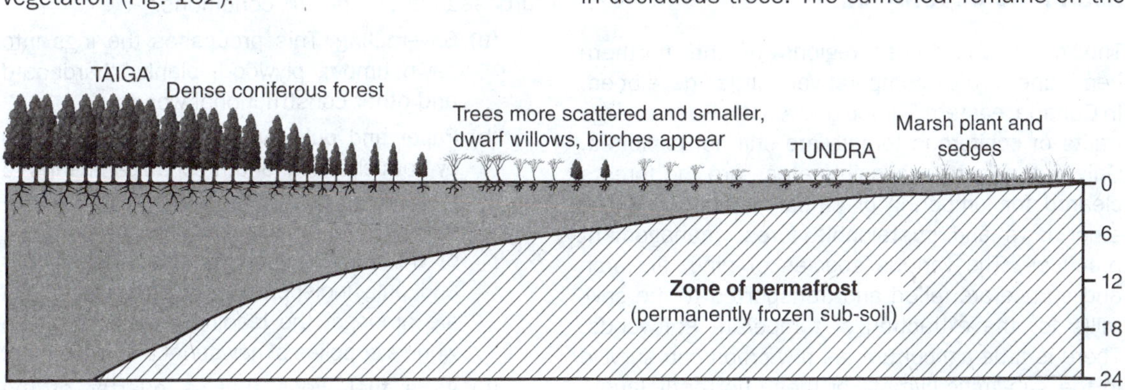

Fig. 162 Diagram to show changes in vegetation in journey polewards from the Taiga Zone

tree for as long as five years. Food is stored in the *trunks,* and the bark is thick to protect the trunk from excessive cold.

3. **Conifers are conical in shape.** This is another adaption to survive the sub-Arctic climate. The sloping branches prevent snow accumulation which may snap the branches. It also offers little grip to the winds.

4. **Leaves are small, thick, leathery and needle-shaped.** This is to check excessive transpiration. The leaf surface is reduced to the minimum, as transpiration can be quite rapid in the warm summer due to intense continental heating.

5. **There is little undergrowth.** The podzolized soils of the coniferous forests are poor. They are excessively leached and very *acidic.* The evergreen leaves provide little leaf-fall for humus formation, and the rate of decomposition of the leathery 'needles' in a region of such low temperature is slow. All these factors are deterrents to the growth of much undergrowth. Absence of direct sunlight and the short duration of summer are other contributary factors to a sparse undergrowth, but where trees are widely spaced near the treeline, heath and tundra plants cover the intervening ground.

Besides the continental interiors of the higher latitudes, coniferous forests are also found in other climatic regions wherever altitude reduces the temperature. The conifers are, in fact, the dominant trees of the mountainous districts in both the temperate and tropical countries. But on very steep slopes where soils are immature or non-existent, even the conifer cannot survive.

Economic Development

The coniferous forest regions of the northern hemisphere are comparatively little developed. In Canada, eastern Europe and Asiatic Russia, large tracts of coniferous forests are still not exploited. Only in the more accessible areas are the forests cleared for lumbering or timber harvesting under strict laws and sustainable forest management practices. The various species of pine, fir, larch and spruce are felled and transported to the saw-mills for the extraction of temperate softwoods. There is little agriculture, as few crops can survive in the sub-Arctic climate of these northerly lands. The long, cold winter, the frozen soils and the low mean annual temperature throughout the year exclude all but the hardiest crops. Only in the more sheltered valleys and the lands bordering the steppes are some cereals (barley, oats, rye) and root crops (potatoes) raised for local needs. Many of the Samoyeds and Yakuts of Siberia, and some Canadians are engaged in hunting, trapping and fishing. We shall deal with two of the major activities in greater detail.

1. **Trapping.** Many fur-bearing animals inhabit the northerly lands of Canada and Eurasia. Wherever the cold is keenest, the quality and thickness of the fur also increases. Consequently, the most severe winters produce the finest furs which fetch the highest prices. Nowadays the trapping of fur-bearing animals in Canada is licensed and regulated by provincial and territorial governments whose wildlife experts have framed regional management plans to ensure healthy furbearer populations. Trapping activities are generally consistent with international agreements such as CITES (Convention on International Trade in Endangered Species), the Convention on Biological Diversity (CBD) and the IUCN (International Union for Conservation of Nature).

Beaver, badger, muskrat, bobcat, fox, lynx, wolverine, etc. are the most important fur-bearing animals sought after in Canada. In the past, the Hudson Bay Company had many stations scattered in the northern regions to trade in furs with the Canadian trappers and hunters.

2. **Lumbering and timber harvesting.** This is probably the most important occupation of the Siberian type of climate. The vast reserves of coniferous forests provide the basis for the lumbering industry. The trees are felled for many purposes but on specific conditions.

(a) **Saw-milling.** This processes the logs into sawn timber, plywood, planks, hardboard and other constructional woods.

(b) **Paper and pulp industry.** Timber is pulped by both chemical and mechanical means to make wood pulp the raw material for paper-making and newsprint. The development of the printing industry has made paper and pulp indispensable. Canada and USA are amongst the leading producers of the world's supplies of newsprint and wood pulp.

(c) **As a fuel.** Less than a quarter of the world's softwood is burnt as fuel, because

A lumberjack cuting a log at the Grouse Mountain, North Vancouver, British Columbia, Canada

its industrial uses are far more significant. In contrast, almost three-quarters of the world's hardwoods are burnt as fuel, particularly tropical hardwoods where the trees occur in mixed stands.

(d) **As an industrial raw material.** Timber has a wide range of uses. In Sweden, matches form a major export item. In other temperate countries, timber is used for making furniture, woodcarvings, toys, crates and packing cases. From the by-products of the timber, many chemically processed articles are derived such as rayon turpentine, varnishes, paints, dyes, liquid resins, wood-alcohols, disinfectants and cosmetics.

The coniferous forests are characterized by the following features.

1. The conifers are limited in species. Pine, spruce and fir are the most important in the northern forests, while larch is more predominant in the warmer south. They occur in homogeneous groups and not mixed as in the tropical forests. This not only saves time and costs, but also enhances the commercial value of the felled timber.

2. In these northerly latitudes, agriculture is almost impossible and lumbering or timber harvesting replaces farming in the continental interiors. Even where crops are cultivated, farmers are idle in the winter months and can supplement their

Loading of logs on wagons in Canada.

income by doing part-time lumbering in the forests, as they do in most parts of Europe.

3. Lumbering is normally carried out in the *winter* when the sap ceases to flow. This makes felling much simpler. The snow-covered ground also makes logging and haulage a relatively easy job. Earlier, the logs were dragged to the rivers and floated to the sawmills downstream when the rivers thawed in spring. However, the use of modern techniques and transportation methods have helped to load and transport timber to the sawmills easily. This has greatly assisted the development of the lumbering industry in eastern Canada and Sweden. Unfortunately, over the greater part of Siberia, all the rivers drain polewards into the Arctic Ocean which is frozen for three-quarters of the year, and there are few sawmills there. With the use of the Northern Sea Route, which links Murmansk and Vladivostok via the Arctic Ocean, development is increasing. Many sawmill operators are now venturing into Siberia Cheap hydroelectricity for driving the sawmills is harnessed in the mountainous uplands of North America and Europe and has greatly assisted the lumbering industry.

QUESTIONS AND EXERCISES

1. Compare and contrast deciduous forests and coniferous forests in respect of the following.
   (a) distribution
   (b) vegetational characteristics
   (c) climatic influence
   (d) economic development
2. Distinguish between hardwoods and softwoods. What industrial uses are made of them? Account for their large scale production for export in any one country.
3. Give a reasoned account of any three of the following.
   (a) The annual temperature range of Moscow is 50°F or 12°C.
   (b) The annual precipitation of St Petersburg is not more than 28 inches or 710 mm.
   (c) The lower courses of the Siberian rivers are frozen for as long as seven months.
   (d) One of the coldest spots on the globe is Verkhoyansk with a record lowest temperature of –90°F (–67.8°C).
4. What is meant by
   (a) the taiga
   (b) the veld
   (c) the selvas

   Account for the distribution and characteristics of any *two* of them.
5. Describe the role played by forest products in the economy of *either* Canada *or* Sweden.
6. Describe the modern-day trapping methods and policies associated in this regard in Canada.

24 The Cool Temperate Eastern Margin (Laurentian)

Distribution

The Cool Temperate Eastern Margin (Laurentian) Climate is an intermediate type of climate between the British and the Siberian type of climate. It has features of both the maritime and the continental climates. It is apparent from Fig. 163 that the Laurentian type of climate is found only in two regions. One is north-eastern North America, including eastern Canada, north-east USA, (i.e. Maritime Provinces and the New England states), and Newfoundland. This may be referred to as the North American region. The other region is the eastern coastlands of Asia, including eastern Siberia, North China, Manchuria, Korea and northern Japan. It may be referred to as the Asiatic region.

In the southern hemisphere, this climatic type is absent because only a small section of the southern continents extends south of the latitude of 40°S. The only possible location is in eastern Patagonia, south of Bahia Blanca (lat. 39°S) to Tierra del Fuego (lat. 54°S). But the climatic barrier of the southern Andes is so complete, that the Westerlies hardly ever reach Patagonia. The region is subjected to aridity rather than continentality. Its annual precipitation is not more than 10 inches (250 mm), so that it is a rain-shadow desert. Elsewhere in the southern hemisphere, the climate is so equable and the oceanic influence is so profound that neither the continental nor the eastern margin type of climate exists.

Climate

The Laurentian type of climate has cold, dry winters and warm, wet summers. Winter temperatures may be well blow freezing-point and snow falls to quite

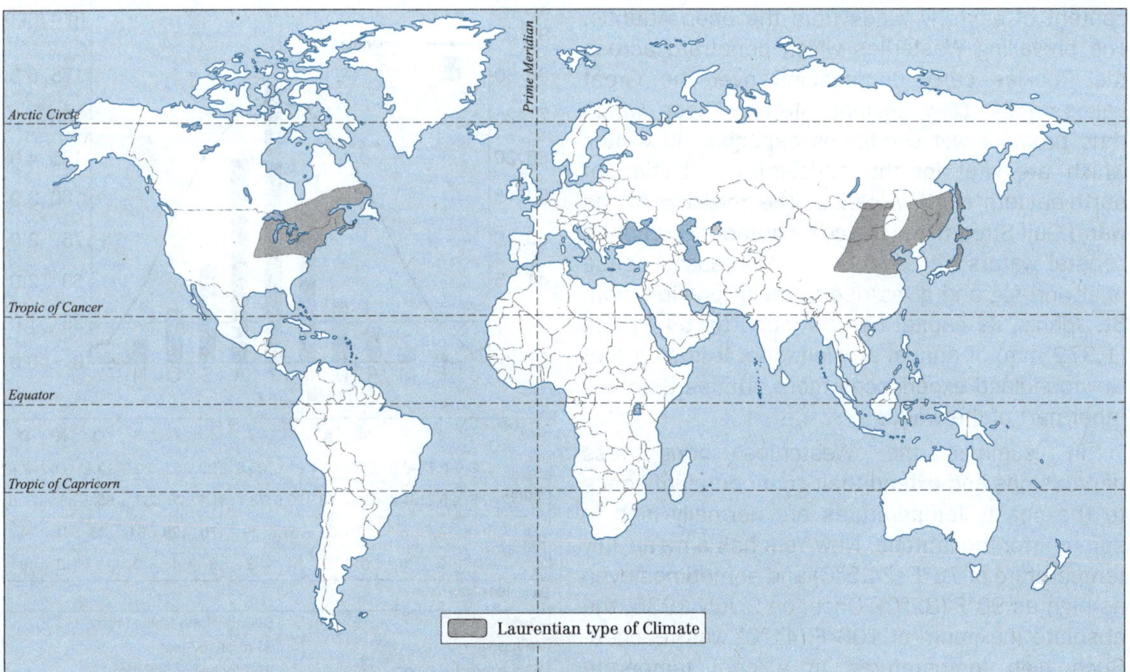

Fig. 163 Regions with a Cool Temperate Eastern Margin Climate (Laurentian type)

a depth. Summers are as warm as the tropics (70° – 80°F or 21° – 27°C) and if it were not for the cooling effects of the offshore cold currents from the Arctic, the summer might be even hotter. Though rain falls throughout the year, there is a distinct summer maximum from the easterly winds from the oceans. Of the annual precipitation of 30 to 60 inches (762–1,524 mm), two-thirds come in the summer. Winter is dry and cold, because the winds are dry Westerlies that blow out from the continental interiors. We shall now examine in closer detail the variations of the Laurentian type of climate between the North American region and the Asiatic region.

The North American region. The most remarkable characteristic of the Laurentian climate of the North American region is its uniformity in precipitation (about 3 to 4 inches or 75 to 100 mm monthly) with a late summer maximum. New York in Fig. 164 (a) has an annual precipitation of about 45 inches (1,140 mm) with the wettest months in June, July and August (4.0 inches each). No month is really dry, and the driest month, November, has 2.0 inches (76 mm) of rain. This uniformity of precipitation is largely due to the Atlantic influence and that of the Great Lakes. The warm Gulf Stream increases the moisture content of easterly winds from the open Atlantic. The prevailing Westerlies which penetrate across the Rockies carry depressions over the Great Lakes to the New England states. These winds thus promote wet conditions especially in winter, which are vital for the agricultural activities of north-eastern North America. The meeting of the warm Gulf Stream and the cold Labrador Current on coastal waters off Newfoundland produces dense mist and fog and gives rise to much precipitation. St. John's, its capital has as much as 54 inches (1,372 mm) of annual precipitation. It is said that Newfoundland experiences more drizzles than any other part of the world.

In summer the Westerlies bring less depressions and extend their continental influence to the coast. Temperatures are normally high in summer for the latitude. New York has a mean July temperature of 76°F (24.5°C) and sometimes even as high as 90°F (32°C). Once, on 9 July 1936, the absolute maximum of 106°F (41°C) was reached. Such high temperatures in a cool temperate maritime region, where the relative humidity is high, can be very trying. Prolonged heatwaves cause discomfort and frustration in crowded cities.

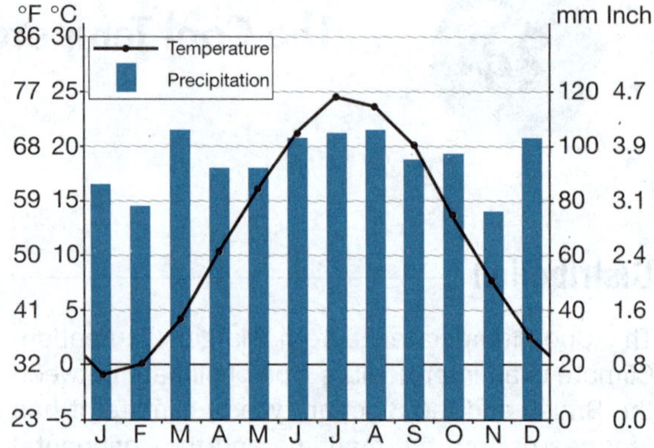

		J	F	M	A	M	J	J	A	S	O	N	D
Avg. Temp.	°C	–1	0	4.1	10.4	16	21.3	24.5	23.6	20.1	13.7	7.7	2.5
	°F	30.3	32	39.4	50.8	60.9	70.3	76	74.5	68.1	56.6	45.8	36.5
Precip.	mm	86	78	106	92	92	103	105	106	95	97	76	103
	in	3	3	4	3	3	4	4	4	3	3	2	4

Data: 1991–2021

Place	New York, USA (41°N, 74°W)
Altitude	20 m or 66 feet
Annual precipitation	44.8 inches or 1139 mm
Annual temperature range	45.8°F (76.0°F – 30.2°F) or 25.4°C (24.5°C – –1.1°C)

Fig. 164 (a) Laurentian type of Climate in North America

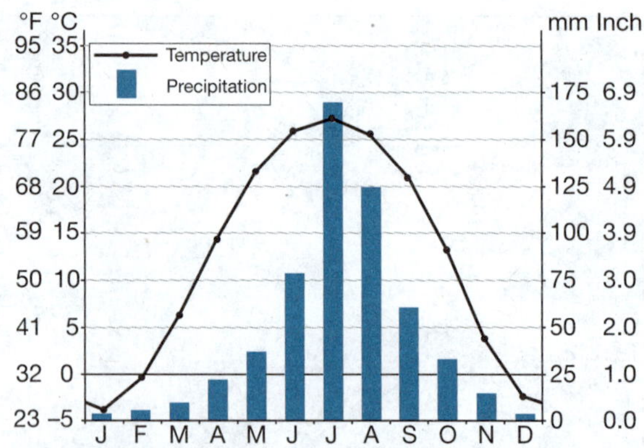

		J	F	M	A	M	J	J	A	S	O	N	D
Avg. Temp.	°C	–3.7	–0.3	6.3	14.4	21.6	25.9	27.3	25.5	20.9	13.2	3.8	–2.4
	°F	25.3	31.4	43.4	58	70.9	78.7	81.1	78	69.6	55.8	38.9	27.8
Precip.	mm	4	6	10	22	37	79	170	125	61	33	15	4
	in	0	0	0	0	1	3	6	4	2	1	0	0

Data: 1991–2021

Place	Beijing, North China (40°N, 116°E)
Altitude	51 m or 167 feet
Annual precipitation	22.3 inches or 566 mm
Annual temperature range	55.8°F (81.1°F–25.3°F) or 31.0°C (27.3°C– –3.7°C)

Fig. 164 (b) Laurentian type of climate in Asia

In winter, the temperature drops and snow falls. New York has two months below freezing-point, and an annual temperature range of 45.8°F (25.4°C). Away from the maritime influence, the cold increases. The mean January temperatures for Quebec, Ottawa and Montreal are about 12°F (–11°C), 15°F (–9°C) and 15°F (–9°C) respectively. The temperature ranges widen accordingly.

The Asiatic region. In contrast, the rainfall distribution of the Asiatic region is far less uniform. Winters are cold and very dry while summers are very warm and exceptionally wet. Beijing, a typical station of the Laurentian Climate in northern China, as shown in Fig. 164 (b), will bring out these facts very clearly. It has eight dry months from October to May with a total rainfall of about 2.0 inches (50 mm), which is only one-eleventh of the annual total of 22 inches (566 mm). The remaining four months receive more than two inches a month, with 6.0 inches (170 mm) in July alone. The rainfall regime, is, in fact, similar to that of the tropical monsoon type in India, where the whole year's rainfall is concentrated in the three summer months. The mountainous interior of China has such pronounced continental effects that the intense heating in summer creates a region of extreme low pressure, and moisture-laden winds from the Pacific Ocean and the Sea of Japan blow in as the South-East Monsoon. The Laurentian type of climate here is often described as the Cool Temperate Monsoon Climate. It has a very long, cold winter, and a big annual range of temperature. The July mean for Beijing is 81°F (27°C) while that of January is only 25°F (–3.5°C). The temperature range is therefore more than 55°F (31°C). The dry, cold wind that blows out from the heart of Asia in winter carries fine, yellowish dust and deposits it as a thick mantle of loess in Shansi, Shensi and other neighbouring provinces at the bend of the Hwang Ho. Much of the winter precipitation in northern China, Korea and Hokkaido (Japan) is in the form of snow. In the mountainous districts, the snow piles to a depth of 5 to 10 feet (1.5 – 3.0 m).

The climate of Japan is modified by its insularity, and also by the meeting of warm and cold ocean currents. It receives adequate rainfall from both the South-East Monsoon in summer and the North-West Monsoon in winter. The latter is the dry, cold wind from mainland Asia, but after crossing the Sea of Japan it has gathered sufficient moisture to give heavy relief rain or snow on the western coasts of Japan. The rainfall is more evenly distributed, as in Tokyo, with two maxima, one in June, the Plum Rain (6.3 inches or 161 mm), and the other in September–October, the Typhoon Rain (7.7–8 inches or 195–207 mm). On the windward slopes of the Japanese Alps on the west, some stations, e.g. Kanazawa, have more than 92 inches (2,338 mm) of rain, much of it falling as snow. The maritime influence also effectively moderates the temperature range. Tokyo has a range of 40°F or 22°C (79°F in August and 39°F in January) with none of the months below freezing-point. The warm Kuroshio has played an important part in making the climate of Japan less extreme. In meeting the cold Oyashio from the north, it also produces fog and mist, making north Japan a 'second Newfoundland'. Fishing replaces agriculture as the main occupation in many of the idented coastlands.

Natural Vegetation

The predominant vegetation of the Laurentian type of climate is cool temperate forest. The heavy rainfall, the warm summers and the damp air from fogs, all favour the growth of trees. Generally speaking, the forest tend to be coniferous north of the 50°N parallel of latitude. The increase in the length and severity of the winter excludes forests that are not adaptable to cold conditions. In the Asiatic region (eastern Siberia and Korea), the coniferous forests are, in fact, a continuation of the great coniferous belt of the taiga. Lumbering has always been a major occupation of this sparsely populated part of eastern Asia and timber is a leading export item. Much of the original coniferous forests of fir, spruce and larch have been cleared as a result of lumbering rather than agriculture. Eastern Canada, along the banks of the St. Lawrence River is the heart of the Canadian timber and wood pulp industry.

South of latitude 50°N, the coniferous forests give way to deciduous forests. Oak, beech, maple and birch are the principal trees. Like their counterparts on the western margins, the deciduous forests are fairly open. A long growing season of over six months and an adequate supply of moisture from maritime sources encourage rapid growth of ferns and other temperate undergrowth. The occurrence of trees in almost pure stands, and the predominance of only a handful of species greatly enhance the commercial value of these forests. As a result, they have been extensively felled for the extraction of temperate hardwood. In many parts of Manchuria, Korea and Japan, the forests have made way for the plough. Both food and cash crops are raised. In Canada, due to the greater reserves of coniferous softwoods and their overriding importance in industrial uses, the annual production of deciduous hardwood is much less significant.

Economic Development

Lumbering and its associated timber, paper and pulp industries are the most important economic undertaking. (Details of lumbering have already been dealt within Chapter 22.)

Agriculture is less important in view of the severity of the winter and its long duration. Fortunately the maritime influence and the heavy rainfall enable some hardy crops to be raised for local needs. Potatoes thrive over large areas of the podzolized soils, while hardy cereals like oats and barley can be sown and successfully harvested before the onset of the cold winter. A number of other interesting crops are produced in the Asiatic region such as soya beans (northern China, Manchuria and Korea are amongst the world's leading producers), groundnuts, sesame, rape seeds, tung oil and mulberry. In the North American region, arable farming is not carried out on a sizable scale, except in the more favoured localities. Farmers are engaged in *dairy farming, hay cultivation* and, in mild maritime areas, *fruit growing*. The fertile Annapolis valley in Nova Scotia is the world's most renowned region for apples. Fishing is, however, the most outstanding economic activity of the Laurentian climatic regions.

Fishing

Fishing off Newfoundland, the Maritime Provinces and New England

This is one of the world's largest fishing grounds particularly on the Grand Banks of Newfoundland (Fig. 165). The reasons for its importance are geographical. Fish feed on minute marine organisms, collectively called plankton, which is present in abundance only in shallow waters adjacent to land masses, where sunlight can penetrate through. The gently sloping continental shelves (less than 600 feet or 183 metres deep) which stretch for over 200 miles (about 322 km) south-east of Newfoundland, and off the coasts of the Maritime Provinces and New England contain a rich collection of microscopic plankton. Fish of all types and sizes feed and breed here and support a thriving fishing industry not only in Canada and USA, but also in countries like Norway, France, Britain, Portugal, Denmark, Russia and Japan, who send fishing fleets to the Grand Banks.

As less than 1 per cent of Newfoundland is cultivated, fishing provides employment for almost the entire population. It is not only the chief source of wealth to Newfoundland, but also a major export item of all the Maritime Provinces. Both pelagic fish which live near the surface and demersal fish which live near the bottom of shallow seas are caught. The chief fish caught is *cod* which is consumed fresh or dried, salted, smoked, canned or packed in ice for export to mainland America, Central and South America and southern Europe. Cod liver oil is exported too. Other fishes caught are haddock, halibut, hake, herring, plaice, and mackerel. Various kinds of fishing craft and techniques are employed to obtain maximum harvests from the sea. Modern trawlers, dragging large conical-shaped nets, and drifters, carrying curtain-like rectangular nets, operate extensively off the Atlantic coasts. They are equipped with radio and radar devices to navigate through the dense fog, avoid collision with icebergs and also maintain contact with their headquarters on land. Offshore fishermen also use traps, lines and nets to catch crabs, lobsters and shrimps for home consumption and increasingly for export. Further inland, in lakes and rivers, such as the St. Lawrence and the Great Lakes, freshwater fish, e.g. salmon, trout, eels and sturgeons are caught.

In Newfoundland and along the Atlantic coasts are many fishing ports. St. John's, chief port of Newfoundland with a population of nearing 100,000, is the headquarters of the Grand Banks fishing industries. It also had interests in sealing and whaling but these have declined. In the fishing ports of Halifax and Yarmouth in Nova Scotia and in the New England ports are processing plants that cut, clean, salt, pack or preserve fish for disposal by refrigerated boats, trains or trucks to all parts of the continent. They are bases for large fleets of trawlers. A modern trawler may well cost anything around a million dollars and have men stay on board in floating factories far out at sea for days and even weeks. Fishing in this part of the world is highly specialized and very efficient.

Fig. 165 Fishing: the North American region

In fact overfishing is a growing problem. The United States government and international fishing bodies are now contemplating strict measures in fish conservation if this major source of protein food is to be sustained for regular supply in the years to come.

Fishing off Japan. In the north-west Pacific, surrounding the islands of Japan, is another major fishing area of the world. Nowhere else in the world are there so many people engaged in fishing as in this part of the north-west Pacific. The mountainous nature of Japan and parts of mainland eastern Asia have driven many to seek a livelihood from the sea. The scarcity of meat (there is little pasture in Japan for livestock farming of any kind) and *religious reasons* have popularized fish as the principal item of diet and the chief protein food of the Japanese and the Chinese as well. Large quantities of fish and fish products are either canned or preserved for export to neighbouring countries. The Japanese also make use of fish wastes, fish meal and seaweeds as fertilizers in their farms. Japan is one of the few countries that has taken to seaweed cultivation. Coastal farms that are submerged in water grow weeds for sale as fertilizers, chemical ingredient and even as food.

Another interesting aspect of Japanese fishing is pearl culture. The divers of southern Japan dive down into the coastal waters and bring to the surface shellfish called pearl oysters and extract the highly prized *pearls* for sale as ornaments. The lining of the oyster shells, called *mother-of-pearl,* is used for the

A fishing settlement in Newfoundland – much of the fish is dried for export

manufacture of pearl buttons, and other decorative articles. As natural pearls in oysters are difficult to obtain in large numbers, the Japanese have begun to breed the young oysters. By injecting tiny 'seeds' into them, the oysters are made to secrete the pearl material, which accumulates to form 'cultured pearls. These are collected and exported.

The Japanese interest in fishing is not confined to their own territorial waters, they venture far and wide into the Arctic, Antarctic and the Atlantic waters. Large whaling fleets complete with processing plants and experienced crews stay out in the open seas and return only occasionally for refuelling or replenishment of fresh provisions. As a nation, Japan accounts for eighth of the world's total annual catch. Japan is one of the world's greatest fishing nations today with about 8 per cent of the global captures. Its active participation in international fishing enterprises and advanced fishing techniques, speak well of Japan's relentless drive to make good from the seas what it lacks on land.

Let us find out why this is possible.

1. Japan is not well endowed with natural resources, for as much as 80 per cent of the land is classed non-agricultural. It has to take the help of the sea if it wants to survive. This has compelled the people to develop the seas, and fishing has for centuries been the traditional occupation of many coastal Japanese.

2. The continental shelves around the islands of Japan are rich in plankton, due to the meeting of the warm Kuroshio and the cold Oyashio currents and provide excellent breeding grounds for all kinds of fish including herring, cod, mackerel, bonito, salmon, sardine and tuna, as well as crabs and lobsters.

3. The indented coastline of Japan, provides sheltered fishing ports, calm waters and safe landing places, ideal for the fishing industry. In Hokkaido, where the Laurentian type of climate is too cold for active agriculture, fishing takes first place. Hakodate and Kushiro are large fishing ports, complete with refrigeration facilities.

4. Lack of lowlands and pastures means that only a few animals can be kept to supply meat and other protein food. *Fish,* in all its varied forms, fresh, canned, dried, frozen, and in the form of fish pastes, fish sauce and spiced condiments takes the place of meat as Japan's primary source of protein food. There is a great demand for it locally, and for export to other east Asiatic neighbours which lack the techniques of large scale commercial fishing.

A cultured pearl farm in Japan

5. The Japanese fishermen began with small fishing boats, using nets, traps and lines. With the progress made in industries, fishing has also become more scientific, aiming at heavy hauls, high returns and economy of *time, effort and money.* Though three-quarters of the fishermen practise offshore pelagic fishing either full-time or part-time, in small boats, most of the commercial deep-sea demersal fishing is now highly mechanized. Powered trawlers and modern refrigeration plants backed by sound financial organizations have greatly increased the annual fish yield. Japan is now not only a major producer and exporter of fish and marine products, but also a centre for marine and fishing research.

QUESTIONS AND EXERCISES

1. (a) Locate on a world map the extent of the Cool Temperate Eastern Margin (Laurentian) Climate.
   (b) Explain why this type of climate is confined to the northern hemisphere
   (c) Describe its climate.
2. Compare and contrast the climate of any *two* of the following pairs of areas.
   (a) Laurentian Climate in the North American region and the Asiatic region.
   (b) Tropical monsoon Climate of India and the Warm Temperate Eastern Margin (China type) Climate in S. China.
   (c) The Steppe type of climate in Eurasia and the Siberian type of climate in northern Canada.
   (d) The Tundra Climate of Greenland and Trade Wind Desert Climate of central Australia.
3. (a) Name the major fishing areas of the world.
   (b) What types of fishing can normally be distinguished in such major fishing grounds?
   (c) Name a few methods used to catch the fish.
   (d) For any *one* major fishing area you have selected, explain the geographical factors which have contributed to its importance.
4. Write brief notes on any *three* of the following.
   (a) The economy of the forests of the Laurentian regions.
   (b) Fishing in Japan.
   (c) Soya bean cultivation in Manchuria.
   (d) Fruit growing in the Maritime Provinces of Canada.
5. The following statistics are a guide to four different types of climate in the northern hemisphere.
   (a) Name the type of climate that each of them represents.
   (b) Locate a probable station for each.
   (c) For any *two* of them describe their climatic characteristics.

Stations	July temp.	January temp.	Annual temp. range	Annual *Rainfall*	Month of max. rainfall
A	81°F	78°F	3°F	96″	April and October
B	55°F	12°F	43°F	8″	June, July, August
C	91°F	56°F	35°F	3″	irregular
D	74°F	30°F	44°F	41″	July, August, September

25 The Arctic or Polar Climate

Distribution

The polar type of climate and vegetation is found mainly north of the Arctic Circle in the northern hemisphere. The ice-caps are confined to Greenland and to the highlands of these high-latitude regions, where the ground is permanently snow-covered. The lowlands, with a few months ice-free, have tundra vegetation. They include the coastal strip of Greenland, the barren grounds of northern Canada and Alaska and the Arctic seaboard of Eurasia. (Fig. 166). In the southern hemisphere, the virtually uninhabited continent of Antarctica is the greatest single stretch of ice-cap where the layers of permanent ice are as thick as 10,000 feet.

Climate

Temperature. The polar climate is characterized by a very low mean annual temperature and its warmest month in June seldom rises to more than 50°F (10°C). In mid-winter (January) temperatures are as low as −22°F to −13°F (−30°C to −25°C) and much colder in the interior. Normally not more than four months have temperatures above freezing point! Winters are long and very severe; summers are cool and brief. Within the Arctic and Antarctic Circles, there are weeks of continuous darkness. At the North Pole, there are six months without light in winter. Despite the long duration of sunshine in summer, when the sun does not set, temperatures remain low because the sun is low in the sky and much of the warmth of its

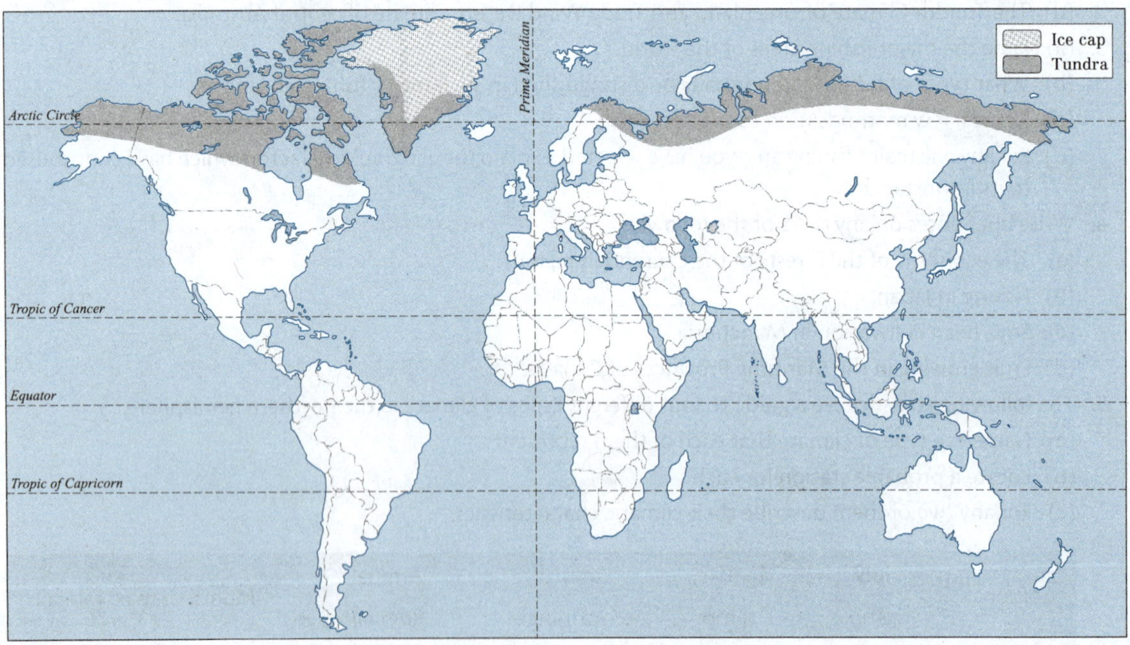

Fig. 166 Ice Cap and Tundra

faint rays is either reflected by the ground snow, or used up in melting the ice. It has little power left to raise the air temperature. Water in the soil is frozen to great depths and the summer heat can only thaw the upper six inches of the soil. The ground remains solidly frozen for all but four months, inaccessible to plants. Frost occurs at any time and blizzards, reaching a velocity of 130 miles an hour (about 210 kmph) is not infrequent. They can be very hazardous for the polar inhabitants. In coastal districts, where warmer water meets cold land thick fogs may develop. They last for days, and in many instances it is not possible to see for more than a few feet.

Precipitation. Precipitation is mainly in the form of snow, falling in winter and being drifted about during blizzards. Snowfall varies with locality; it may fall either as ice crystals or large, amalgamated snowflakes. As it takes 10–12 inches of snow to make 1 inch of rain, precipitation in polar regions can be expected to be light, not more than 12 inches (305 mm) in a year. Convectional rainfall is generally absent because of the low rate of evaporation and the lack of moisture in the cold polar air. There is normally a summer maximum, and the precipitation is then in the form of rain or sleet.

In regions where winds blowing out from the large anticyclones developed over the ice-caps are prevalent, rain comes in summer, when more evaporation is possible. But in coastal areas, where cyclones are more strongly felt, the tendency is towards a winter maximum, for that is when cyclonic activity is greatest. In such regions the annual rainfall of 10 to 12 inches (about 250–305 mm) for the tundra may be exceeded. Much heavier rainfall has been recorded, especially in areas where the cyclones are most frequent e.g. Jan Mayen (71°N, 8°W) has 15 inches (380 mm), Vardo (70°N, 31°E) has 26 inches (660 mm) and Tasiilaq, formerly Angmagssalik (66°N, 38°W), has over 37 inches (940 mm)!

Fig. 167 shows the rhythm of temperature and precipitation of a tundra region taken at Upernavik, Greenland (72°N, 56°W). Its winter temperature is –10°F (23°C) while its warmest month in July is only about 43°F (6°C), giving an annual range of about 54°F (30°C). Precipitation is low, only 15.4 inches (390 mm), falling mainly in the second half of the year, both as rain and snow.

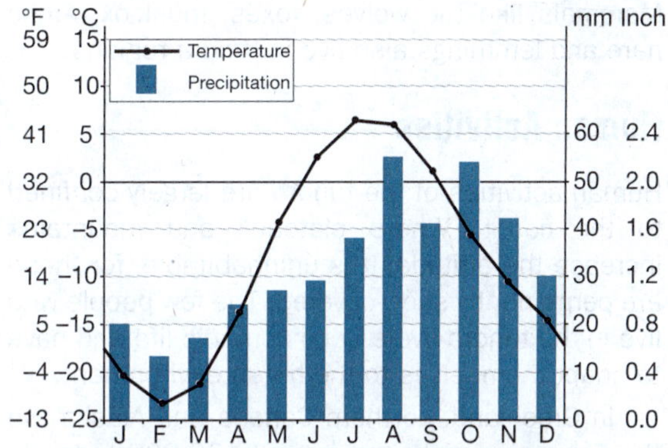

		J	F	M	A	M	J	J	A	S	O	N	D	Range/ Total
Avg. Temp.	°C	–20.2	–23.4	–21.3	–13.7	–4.3	2.6	6.4	6	1.2	–5.7	–10.8	–14.6	29.8
	°F	–4.4	–10.2	–6.3	7.4	24.3	36.6	43.6	42.8	34.1	21.8	12.6	5.8	53.7
Precip.	mm	20	13	17	24	27	29	38	55	41	54	42	30	390
	in	0	0	0	0	1	1	1	2	1	2	1	1	15.4

Data: 1991–2021

Place	Upernavik, Greenland (72°N, 56°W)
Altitude	1 m or 3.2 feet
Annual precipitation	15.4 inches or 390 mm
Annual temperature range	53.7°F (43.6°F – –10.2°F) or 29.8°C (6.4°C – –23.4°C)

Fig. 167 Tundra Climate

Tundra Vegetation

In such an adverse environment as the tundra, few plants survive. The greatest inhibiting factor is the region's deficiency in heat. With a growing season of less than three months and the warmest month not exceeding 50°F (the tree-survival line), there are no trees in the tundra. Such an environment can support only the lowest form of vegetation, mosses, lichens and sedges. Drainage in the tundra is usually poor as the sub-soil is permanently frozen. Ponds and marshes and waterlogged areas are found in hollows.

In the more sheltered spots, stunted birches, dwarf willows and undersized alders struggle for a meagre existence. Climatic conditions along the coastal lowlands are a little more favourable. Here are found some hardy grasses and the *reindeer moss* which provide the only pasturage for the herbivorous animals like reindeer. In the brief summer, when the snows melt and the days are warmer and longer, berry-bearing bushes and Arctic flowers bloom. Though short-lived, they brighten the monotonous tundra landscape into Arctic prairies. In the summer, the tundra is full of activities. Birds migrate north to prey on the numerous insects which emerge when the snow thaws.

Mammals like the wolves, foxes, musk-ox, Arctic hare and lemmings also live in tundra regions.

Human Activities

Human activities of the tundra are largely confined to the coast. Where plateaux and mountains increase the altitude, it is uninhabitable, for these are permanently snow-covered. The few people who live in the tundra live a semi-nomadic life and have to adapt themselves to the harsh environment.

In Greenland, northern Canada and Alaska live the Eskimos, numbering around 160,000 today. In the past, they used to live as hunters, fishermen, food-gatherers. However, in recent times, more of them have been making permanent huts for settling. Their economy now relies somewhat less on traditional activities and more on gathering plant products. Whales, seals, caribou, various kinds of fish, and many animals with fur, along with birds, provide them with everything they need for food and clothing. These resources also play a significant role in supplying materials for tools, weapons, and everyday items or utensils. The Polar Eskimos, living around Thule in north-west Greenland still lead an uncertain life, not very much different from their forefathers. The seasonal changes in climate necessitate a nomadic way of life. During winter they live in compact igloos and in summer when they move out to hunt they pitch portable tents of skins by the side of streams. Their food is derived from fish, seals, walruses and polar bears. Other Eskimos hunt caribou (the name given to reindeer in America) and other animals to secure a steady supply of their daily meat, milk, fat, skins and bones.

In the last sixty years through their contact with the Europeans, the way of life of the Eskimos has undergone tremendous changes. Coastal villages have permanent wooden houses complete with modern facilities; speedboats are replacing frail *kayaks*. Deadly rifles instead of traditional harpoons are used to track down animals and seals. Furbearing animals are being reared on a commercial scale and fishing, too, is being commercialized. In some more accessible parts of Canada and Alaska, schools have been established and the Eskimo children are being taught the skills which will allow them to fit into the modern way of life.

In the Eurasian tundra are other nomadic tribes such as the Lapps of northern Finland and Scandinavia, the Samoyeds of Siberia (from the Ural Mountains and the Yenisey basin), the Yakuts from the Lena basin, and the Koryaks and Chuckchi of north-eastern Asia. They wander with their herds of reindeer across the Eurasian tundra where there are pastures. Many of them have taken to a more settled life. In Russia large farms have been established for raising reindeer and for breeding fur-bearing animals.

The Importance and Recent Development of the Arctic Region

The Arctic region, once regarded as completely useless, is now of some economic importance. Apart from the efforts of the various governments in assisting the advancement of the Arctic inhabitants the Eskimos, Lapps, Samoyeds, etc., new settlements have sprung up because of the discovery of minerals. Gold is mined in Alaska, nickel near Petsamo, Russia, petroleum in the Kenai Peninsula, Alaska; and copper at the Rankin Inlet, Canada. Coal has been mined in Spitsbergen for a long time and also in Alaska. With the declining reserves of iron ore around Lake Superior, the Great Lakes industrial concerns are using more and more iron from large iron ore deposits in Labrador. New railway lines have been constructed to bring the ores to the St. Lawrence River for subsequent shipment to the major industrial districts. Rich deposits of iron ores at Kiruna and Gallivare in Sweden have made it possible for Sweden to enjoy a prosperous export trade in iron and steel and other metallurgical products.

With the establishment of ports on the Arctic seaboard of Eurasia, it is now possible to ship timber and fur from Siberia. Though the ports, such as Igarka at the mouth of the Yenisey, are not ice-free, modern ice-breakers keep the passage open most of the time. On the Arctic lowlands where the growing season is lengthened by warm currents or higher temperatures, experiments have been

The borderlands between the Taiga and the tundra

carried out to devise varieties of hardy cereals for local needs. It may not be long before the tundra is brought under greater agricultural, especially pastoral, use. The healthy air and its preservative qualities (it is practically germ-free) are factors worth consideration for future colonization. Scientists, meteorologists and explorers have lived in the Arctic and Antarctica, making studies of their geology, weather conditions, plant and animal life, that will be of great significance in years to come.

QUESTIONS AND EXERCISES

1. Draw separate sketch maps to show the area covered by each of the following:
   (a) tundra in Eurasia
   (b) savanna in South America
   (c) hot desert in Australia
   (d) equatorial forest in Africa

   For any *three* of them describe their characteristic features of natural vegetation and for any one of them explain how the features are related to the climate of the area.
2. The following are representative of plants found in different climatic zones:
   spruce, olive, teak, reindeer moss, date, oak, eucalyptus and bamboo.
   For any *six* of them:
   (a) Name the type of climate in which each of them thrives.
   (b) State the sort of natural vegetation with which they are associated.
   (c) Describe very briefly the role each of them plays in the economy of a named country in which they are found in abundance.
3. Explain briefly any *four* of the following terms connected with the Arctic climate and the tundra vegetation: blizzards, permafrost, midnight sun, icecap, snow-blindness, kayaks, international deep-freeze.
4. Make a comparative study of the Polar Eskimos of Greenland and the Orang Asli (e.g. Senois or Sengois) under the following headings.
   (a) How they obtain their food
   (b) How they shelter themselves
   (c) What significant changes have taken place in their environment and their way of life?
5. Statistics of rainfall and temperature for three towns are given below. For any *two* of them.
   (a) State their season of maximum rainfall
   (b) Name the type of climate
   (c) Suggest a possible location of the town
   (d) Describe their climatic rhythm

	J	F	M	A	M	J	J	A	S	O	N	D	Range/ Total
Town A	Altitude: 207 feet												
Temp. (°F)	47	49	51	57	64	71	76	76	70	62	53	46	30
Precip. (inches)	3.2	2.7	2.9	2.6	2.2	1.6	0.7	1.0	2.5	5.0	4.4	3.9	32.7
Town B	Altitude: 65 feet												
Temp. (°F)	−8	−9	−6	25	35	41	41	34	34	25	14	10	49
Precip. (inches)	0.4	0.5	0.7	0.6	0.6	0.5	0.9	0.1	1.1	1.1	1.1	0.5	9.1
Town C	Altitude: 9,350 feet												
Temp. (°F)	55	55	55	55	55	55	55	55	55	55	55	54	1.0
Precip. (inches)	3.2	3.9	4.8	7.0	4.6	1.5	1.1	2.2	2.6	3.9	4.0	3.6	42.3

6. (a) With the aid of sketch maps to show *one* major region where each type is found, describe the main features of vegetation of tropical grassland (savanna) and coniferous forest.
   (b) For *either* tropical grassland (savanna) *or* coniferous forest, show how the main features of the vegetation are influenced by climate.

Index

I

J

K

L

M